Leonard C. Burson, MD.

THE HARVEY LECTURES

From the engraving by Jacobus Houbraken

WILLIAM HARVEY

BORN APRIL 1, 1578 - DIED JUNE 3, 1657

THE HARVEY LECTURES

DELIVERED UNDER THE AUSPICES OF

The HARVEY SOCIETY of NEW YORK

1978–1979

———

BY

D. BENNETT
STANLEY N. COHEN
HOWARD GREEN

ALAN F. HOFMANN
A. KLUG
PHILIP LEDER

GEORGE D. SNELL

SERIES 74

1980
ACADEMIC PRESS
A Subsidiary of Harcourt Brace Jovanovich, Publishers
New York   London   Toronto   Sydney   San Francisco

ACADEMIC PRESS, INC.
111 Fifth Avenue, New York, New York 10003

United Kingdom Edition published by
ACADEMIC PRESS, INC. (LONDON) LTD.
24/28 Oval Road, London NW1 7DX

LIBRARY OF CONGRESS CATALOG CARD NUMBER: 7–2726

ISBN 0–12–312074–8

PRINTED IN THE UNITED STATES OF AMERICA

80 81 82 83   9 8 7 6 5 4 3 2 1

CONTENTS

CONSTITUTION OF THE HARVEY SOCIETY vii

BY-LAWS OF THE HARVEY SOCIETY, INC. ix

OFFICERS OF THE HARVEY SOCIETY xv

HARVEY LECTURES 1978–1979

THE *T* COMPLEX IN THE MOUSE: AN ASSESSMENT AFTER 50
YEARS OF STUDY 1
D. Bennett, Memorial Sloan-Kettering Cancer Center, New York,
New York 10021

THE MEDICAL TREATMENT OF GALLSTONES: A CLINICAL
APPLICATION OF THE NEW BIOLOGY OF BILE ACIDS 23
Alan F. Hofmann, Division of Gastroenterology, Department of
Medicine (H-811D), University of California at San Diego Medi-
cal Center, San Diego, California 92103

THE MAJOR HISTOCOMPATIBILITY COMPLEX: ITS EVOLUTION AND
INVOLVEMENT IN CELLULAR IMMUNITY 49
George D. Snell, The Jackson Laboratory, Bar Harbor, Maine
04609

THE ORGANIZATION AND EXPRESSION OF CLONED GLOBIN
GENES 81
Philip Leder, Laboratory of Molecular Genetics, National Institute
of Child Health and Human Development, National Institutes of
Health, Bethesda, Maryland 20205

THE KERATINOCYTE AS DIFFERENTIATED CELL TYPE 101
Howard Green, Department of Biology, Massachusetts Institute of
Technology, Cambridge, Massachusetts 02139

AN ORGANIZING PRINCIPLE FOR CEREBRAL FUNCTION: THE
NEOCORTEX AND DIRECTED ATTENTION*
Vernon B. Mountcastle, Jr., Department of Physiology, Johns
Hopkins University School of Medicine, Baltimore, Maryland
21205

THE ASSEMBLY OF TOBACCO MOSAIC VIRUS: STRUCTURE AND
SPECIFICITY 141
A. Klug, MRC Laboratory of Molecular Biology, Cambridge CB2
2QH, England

THE TRANSPLANTATION AND MANIPULATION OF GENES IN
MICROORGANISMS 173
Stanley N. Cohen, Departments of Genetics and Medicine, Stanford
University, Stanford, California 94305

FORMER OFFICERS OF THE HARVEY SOCIETY 205

CUMULATIVE AUTHOR INDEX 217

ACTIVE MEMBERS 227

DECEASED MEMBERS, FORMERLY ACTIVE AND ASSOCIATE ... 247

*Manuscript not received.

THE HARVEY SOCIETY*

A SOCIETY FOR THE DIFFUSION OF KNOWLEDGE OF THE MEDICAL SCIENCES

CONSTITUTION

I

This Society shall be named the Harvey Society.

II

The object of this Society shall be the diffusion of scientific knowledge in selected chapters in anatomy, physiology, pathology, bacteriology, pharmacology, and physiological and pathological chemistry, through the medium of public lectures by men who are workers in the subjects presented.

III

The members of the Society shall constitute two classes: Active and Honorary members. Active members shall be workers in the medical or biological sciences, residing in the metropolitan New York area, who have personally contributed to the advancement of these sciences. Active members who leave New York to reside elsewhere may retain their membership. Honorary members shall be those who have delivered lectures before the Society and who are not Active members. Honorary members shall not be eligible to office, nor shall they be entitled to a vote.

Active members shall be elected by ballot. They shall be nominated to the Executive Committee and the names of the nominees shall accompany the notice of the meeting at which the vote for their election will be taken.

IV

The management of the Society shall be vested in an Executive Committee to consist of a President, a Vice-President, a Secretary, a Treasurer, and

*The Constitution is reprinted here for historical interest only; its essential features have been included in the Articles of Incorporation and By-Laws.

three other members, these officers to be elected by ballot at each annual meeting of the Society to serve one year.

V

The Annual Meeting of the Society shall be held at a stated date in January of each year at a time and place to be determined by the Executive Committee. Special meetings may be held at such times and places as the Executive Committee may determine. At all meetings ten members shall constitute a quorum.

VI

Changes in the Constitution may be made at any meeting of the Society by a majority vote of those present after previous notification to the members in writing.

THE HARVEY SOCIETY, INC.

A SOCIETY FOR THE DIFFUSION OF KNOWLEDGE
OF THE MEDICAL SCIENCES

BY-LAWS

ARTICLE I

Name and Purposes of the Society

SECTION 1. The name of the Society as recorded in the Constitution at the time of its founding in 1905 was the Harvey Society. In 1955, it was incorporated in the State of New York as The Harvey Society, Inc.

SECTION 2. The purposes for which this Society is formed are those set forth in its original Constitution and modified in its Certificate of Incorporation as from time to time amended. The purposes of the Society shall be to foster the diffusion of scientific knowledge in selected chapters of the biological sciences and related areas of knowledge through the medium of public delivery and printed publication of lectures by men and women who are workers in the subjects presented, and to promote the development of these sciences.

It is not organized for pecuniary profit, and no part of the net earnings, contributions, or other corporate funds of the Society shall inure to the benefit of any private member or individual, and no substantial part of its activities shall be carrying on propaganda, or otherwise attempting, to influence legislation.

ARTICLE II

Offices of the Society

SECTION 1. The main office and place of business of the Society shall be in the City and County of New York. The Board of Directors may designate additional offices.

ARTICLE III

Members

SECTION 1. The members of the Society shall consist of the incorporators, members of the hitherto unincorporated Harvey Society, and

ix

persons elected from time to time. The members of the Society shall constitute two classes: Active and Honorary Members. Active members shall be individuals with either the Ph.D. or the M.D. degree or its equivalent, residing or carrying on a major part of their work in the New York metropolitan area at the time of their election, who are personally making original contributions to the literature of the medical or biological sciences. Honorary members shall be those who have delivered a lecture before the Society and who are not Active members. Honorary members shall be exempted from the payment of dues. Active members who have remained in good standing for 35 years or who have reached the age of 65 and have remained in good standing for 25 years shall be designated Life members. They shall retain all the privileges of their class of membership without further payment of dues. Honorary members shall not be eligible to office, nor shall they be entitled to participate by voting in the affairs of the Society. Volumes of The Harvey Lectures will be circulated only to Active and Life members. Honorary members will receive only the volume containing their lecture. New Active members shall be nominated in writing to the Board of Directors by an Active member and seconded by another Active member. They shall be elected at the Annual Meeting of the Society by a vote of the majority of the Active members present at the meeting. Members who leave New York to reside elsewhere may retain their membership. Active members who have given a Harvey Lecture and who have moved out of the New York metropolitan area may, if they wish, become Honorary members. Membership in the Society shall terminate on the death, resignation, or removal of the member.

SECTION 2. Members may be suspended or expelled from the Society by the vote of a majority of the members present at any meeting of members at which a quorum is present, for refusing or failing to comply with the By-Laws, or for other good and sufficient cause.

SECTION 3. Members may resign from the Society by written declaration, which shall take effect upon the filing thereof with the Secretary.

ARTICLE IV

Meetings of the Members of the Society

SECTION 1. The Society shall hold its annual meeting of Active members for the election of officers and directors, and for the transaction of such other business as may come before the meeting in the month of January or

February in each year, at a place within the City of New York, and on a date and at an hour to be specified in the notice of such meeting.
SECTION 2. Special meetings of members shall be called by the Secretary upon the request of the President or Vice-President or of the Board of Directors, or on written request of twenty-five of the Active members.
SECTION 3. Notice of all meetings of Active members shall be mailed or delivered personally to each member not less than ten nor more than sixty days before the meeting. Like notice shall be given with respect to lectures.
SECTION 4. At all meetings of Active members of the Society ten Active members, present in person, shall constitute a quorum, but less than a quorum shall have power to adjourn from time to time until a quorum be present.

ARTICLE V

Board of Directors

SECTION 1. The number of directors constituting The Board of Directors shall be seven: the President, the Vice-President, the Secretary, and the Treasurer of the Society, and the three members of the Council. The number of directors may be increased or reduced by amendments of the By-Laws as hereinafter provided, within the maximum and minimum numbers fixed in the Certificate of Incorporation or any amendment thereto.
SECTION 2. The Board of Directors shall hold an annual meeting shortly before the annual meeting of the Society.
Special meetings of the Board of Directors shall be called at any time by the Secretary upon the request of the President or Vice-President or of one-fourth of the directors then in office.
SECTION 3. Notice of all regular annual meetings of the Board shall be given to each director at least seven days before the meeting and notice of special meetings, at least one day before. Meetings may be held at any place within the City of New York designated in the notice of the meeting.
SECTION 4. The Board of Directors shall have the immediate charge, management, and control of the activities and affairs of the Society, and it shall have full power, in the intervals between the annual meetings of the Active members, to do any and all things in relation to the affairs of the Society.

SECTION 5. Council members shall be elected by the members of the Society at the Annual Meeting. One Council member is elected each year to serve for three years, there being three Council members at all times. Vacancies occurring on the Council for any cause may be filled for the unexpired term by the majority vote of the directors present at any meeting at which a quorum is present. Only Active members of the Society shall be eligible for membership on the Council.

SECTION 6. A majority of the Board as from time to time constituted shall be necessary to constitute a quorum, but less than a quorum shall have power to adjourn from time to time until a quorum be present.

SECTION 7. The Board shall have power to appoint individual or corporate trustees and their successors of any or all of the property of the Society, and to confer upon them such of the powers, duties, or obligations of the directors in relation to the care, custody, or management of such property as may be deemed advisable.

SECTION 8. The directors shall present at the Annual Meeting a report, verified by the President and Treasurer, or by a majority of the directors, showing the whole amount of real and personal property owned by the Society, where located, and where and how invested, the amount and nature of the property acquired during the year immediately preceding the date of the report and the manner of the acquisition; the amount applied, appropriated, or expended during the year immediately preceding such date, and the purposes, objects, or persons to or for which such applications, appropriations, or expenditures have been made; and the names of the persons who have been admitted to membership in the Society during such year, which report shall be filed with the records of the Society and an abstract thereof entered in the minutes of the proceedings of the Annual Meeting.

ARTICLE VI

Committees

SECTION 1. The Board of Directors may appoint from time to time such committees as it deems advisable, and each such committee shall exercise such powers and perform such duties as may be conferred upon it by the Board of Directors subject to its continuing direction and control.

ARTICLE VII

Officers

SECTION 1. The officers of the Society shall consist of a President, a Vice-President, a Secretary, and a Treasurer, and such other officers as the Board of Directors may from time to time determine. All of the officers of the Society shall be members of the Board of Directors.

SECTION 2. The President shall be the chief executive officer of the Society and shall be in charge of the direction of its affairs, acting with the advice of the Board of Directors. The other officers of the Society shall have the powers and perform the duties that usually pertain to their respective offices, or as may from time to time be prescribed by the Board of Directors.

SECTION 3. The officers and the directors shall not receive, directly or indirectly, any salary or other compensation from the Society, unless authorized by the concurring vote of two-thirds of all the directors.

SECTION 4. The officers shall be elected at the Annual Meeting of the Active members. All officers shall hold office until the next Annual Meeting and until their successors are elected or until removed by vote of a majority vote of the directors. Vacancies occurring among the officers for any cause may be filled for the unexpired term by the majority vote of the directors present at any meeting at which a quorum is present. Officers must be Active members of the Society.

ARTICLE VIII

Fiscal Year—Seal

SECTION 1. The fiscal year of the Society shall be the calendar year.

SECTION 2. The seal of the Society shall be circular in form and shall bear the words "The Harvey Society, Inc., New York, New York, Corporate Seal."

ARTICLE IX

Amendments

SECTION 1. These By-Laws may be added to, amended, or repealed, in whole or in part, by the Active members or by the Board of Directors, in each case by a majority vote at any meeting at which a quorum is present, provided that notice of the proposed addition, amendment, or repeal has been given to each member or director, as the case may be, in the notice of such meeting.

THE *T* COMPLEX IN THE MOUSE: AN ASSESSMENT AFTER 50 YEARS OF STUDY*

D. BENNETT

Memorial Sloan-Kettering
Cancer Center,
New York, New York

THE study of mutant genes at the *T* locus in the mouse had an inauspicious beginning more than 50 years ago, when Nelly Dobrovolskaia-Zavadskaia, a Russian cancer researcher interested in radiation biology, made an unwanted discovery. A mouse she had treated with X-rays produced some progeny with short tails, and although she looked on this as a diversion from more important things, Dobrovolskaia-Zavadskaia nevertheless felt obligated to define the abnormality she had produced. First she demonstrated by breeding tests that the short-tailed animals carried a dominant mutation that she named Brachyury but was later symbolized by *T*, for tail, in English. In further experiments she found it impossible to obtain a true-breeding line of short-tailed mice, and so she came to the correct conclusion that homozygotes for the new mutation died before birth (Dobrovolskaia-Zavadskaia, 1927). Eventually, she made the mistake of outcrossing short-tailed animals to two unrelated lines of apparently normal mice; one was a French strain of uncertain origin, and one was derived from a wild mouse trapped by Dobrovolskaia (who was by this time apparently a dedicated mouse fancier) while she was on vacation near the Spanish border. To her surprise, some offspring of both these crosses had a sharply different abnormality; they had no tails at all. The logical next step was to inbreed the tailless offspring from each cross; this was done, and the results were completely perplexing to the cancer researcher because this time the abnormal phenotype clearly bred true, and two tailless parents produced only tailless offspring (Dobrovolskaia-Zavadskaia and Kobozieff, 1932). At this point, Dobrovolskaia threw

*Lecture delivered September 21, 1978.

1

in the sponge. She visited the laboratory of L. C. Dunn at Columbia University and apparently pleaded with him to take over her animals, so that she could, according to Dunn's quotation, "Give up the confusing tails and return to my proper field which is cancer research." It is an interesting sidelight that now, so many years later, a group of us at the Sloan-Kettering Institute are convinced that the study of these mutations can have significant implications for cancer biology.

In any case, Dunn was excited to have this material fall into his hands, because he was convinced that a combined study of genetics and development should be capable of uncovering rules that apply both to mechanisms of development and to their genetic regulation. The main hypothesis behind this conviction is equally valid today: it is basically that a mutation that disrupts development presumably does so by interfering initially with a single essential process, and therefore can be used as an analytical tool to dissect development. Actually, the general concept here was perhaps phrased first, and much more elegantly, by the man for whom this society was named. In 1657 Sir William Harvey wrote in a letter to another physician that "Nature is nowhere accustomed more openly to display her secret mysteries than when she shows traces of her working apart from the beaten path. . . . For it has been found in almost all things that what they contain of useful or of applicable is hardly perceived unless we are deprived of them, or they become deranged in some way." Thus, the hope is that studying the effects of a developmental mutation will permit the definition, isolation, and biochemical characterization of the process gone wrong. I should be quick to point out that these expectations have never been fully realized with respect to any such mutation that I know of; certainly not with T/t mutations, although we think just now that we are beginning to come close.

I should like now to begin to summarize the results of work that Dunn began on the T locus, first with the essential help of his colleagues Paul Chesley and Salome Gluecksohn-Waelsch, and later continued by others too numerous to mention.

The tailless mice that were originally described proved not only to present an easily solved puzzle, but to be uniquely important because they reflected a genetic system that was crucial in identifying and describing further genetic variance in the T locus. The essential point is that tailless mice of the same line were quickly shown by Chesley and

Dunn (1936) and by Dunn and Glueckshon-Schoenheimer (1939) to constitute a "balanced lethal" system, so called because both homozygous classes die and heterozygotes therefore breed true. The situation is illustrated in Fig. 1, which was prepared by Glueckshon-Waelsch and used in a Harvey Lecture by Dunn almost 40 years ago (Dunn, 1940). The mutation involved here (t^0) that interacts with *T* to produce the tailless phenotype behaves as a true genetic allele to *T* and is itself a recessive, without any detectable effects on the morphology of embryonic development in heterozygotes. It is obvious that recessive mutations like this, that kill in homozygous condition as early as at 6 days of development, would have virtually no chance of detection were it not for the dominant gene acting as a kind of diagnostic tool.

The situation is actually more complicated, and more informative. Crosses between tailless mice whose lethal recessive mutations were of

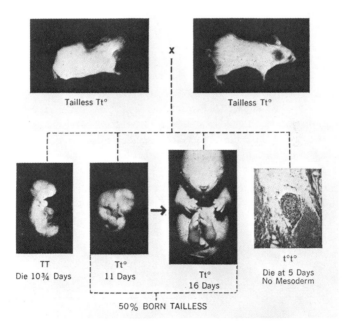

FIG. 1. A pictorial representation of the T/t^0 balanced lethal system in the mouse. Taken from Dunn (1940).

different origin, as was the case of Dobrovolskaia's original two out-
crosses, often did not behave as simple balanced lethal systems, but
gave an additional class of progeny with normal tails. The interpretation
was made that the two recessive mutations were sufficiently different to
show genetic complementation, and it was predicted and quickly shown
by Dunn and Gluecksohn-Schoenheimer (1943) that homozygotes for
complementing genes have distinguishably different lethal phenotypes.
Thus, a combination of the tailless phenotype and complementation
provided not only a way of finding otherwise hidden recessive lethal
mutations, but also a way of classifying them. It should be mentioned
that these facts also provided one of the yet unsolved puzzles with
respect to the T locus, since complementation between alleles at the
same locus is a most unexpected finding. This led in fact to recessive t
mutations being called pseudoalleles, which is still a respectable term
used among geneticists to imply ignorance of genetic structure.

We know also that recessive lethal t mutations are actually physically
(as well as intellectually) complex. As a group, they have two unique
characteristics. First of all, they suppress genetic recombination by
interfering with crossing-over along a considerable length of chromosome 17, stretching from the region of the mutation T to at least the H-2
complex, a distance of about 14 centimorgans (Fig. 2). So, with certain
rare exceptions, all genes in that region are effectively "locked in," and
are inherited en bloc as what has been called by George Snell a "super
gene" complex (Snell, 1968). Rarely, however, recombinational events
do occur in that region in t heterozygotes and about one in a thousand
gametes (instead of the expected 14%) carries a recombinant chromosome. In all such cases that have been analyzed so far it is clear that the
recessive lethal gene has separated into at least two portions: one carrying a factor that interacts with T to produce a tailless animal but is no

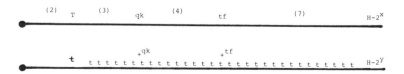

FIG. 2. Diagrammatic summary of T/t heterozygote, with relative positions of marker
genes *quaking* (*qk*), *tufted* (*tf*), and *H-2* indicated. *tttttt* represents region of crossover
suppression associated with lethal recessive t haplotypes.

longer lethal, and one that is lethal in embryos in a way identical to its parent pseudoallele, but no longer interacts with *T* to produce taillessness (Lyon and Meredith, 1964a,b; Bennett, 1975). So, clearly the so-called lethal mutations we detect are composed of at least two separable elements. These two elements are surprisingly widely separated, because, when the positions of exceptional crossovers are mapped in chromosomes with appropriate markers (Fig. 3), all that have so far been studied occur between 3 and 7 units away from the locus of *T* (D. Bennett and K. Artzt, in preparation).

We know very little more about the structure or origin of the abnormal chromosomes that contain recessive *t* mutations, but apparently they play some important role in the natural history of the mouse as a species. It is a surprising fact, but a fact nevertheless, that lethal recessive *t* mutations are polymorphic in wild populations of mice and have been found in virtually every population whose collective genome has been adequately sampled. The frequency of heterozygotes is high, averaging probably about 20% (Bennett, 1978). The role of these genes is unclear, but Klein and Hammerberg (1977) have made the reasonable suggestion that it may be related to the establishment of a super-gene complex that locks together especially compatible elements related to the *H-2* complex.

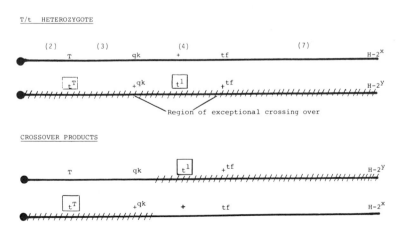

Fig. 3. Diagrammatic representation of exceptional crossovers that occur in *T/t* heterozygotes to separate T interaction and lethal factors of recessive *t*-lethal haplotypes.

At the present time, a panel of about a dozen different embryonic lethal factors has been assembled and studied. Recessive factors have been identified in six different complementation groups, each of which has sharply different effects on early embryonic development. Five different dominant factors that are distinguishably different have also been collected.

Figure 4 shows a precis of normal early development in the mouse embryo, and outlines the major effects of some of the well studied mutations at the T locus. As is seen in the figure, development in the earliest stages seems to involve quite simple transitional steps (horizontal arrows); T-locus mutations seem most often to interfere with these transitions (vertical arrows), and they strike at different points in the pathway of development. A logical but completely unproved assumption is that the genes represented by these mutations are switched on sequentially as development proceeds.

There are some subtle dangers inherent in making interpretations from morphological data like these. The first is the obvious one, that

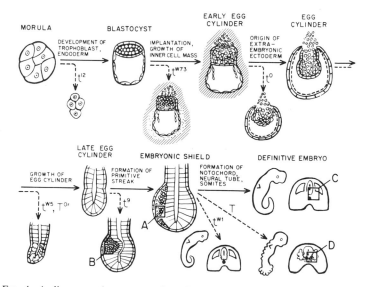

FIG. 4. A diagrammatic representation of early development in the mouse and the defects seen in embryos homozygous for T/t locus mutations. From Bennett (1975). Reprinted with permission of MIT Press.

abnormal morphology reflects only damage that occurred at some earlier, but unknown, stage. The second results from the fact that these very young embryos are extremely simple objects, composed of only a few different cell types, and that they advance from one of the stages pictured here to the next usually by changes that involve only one cell type; one has to wonder then whether the apparent specificity of the effects of these mutations is real, or whether it reflects only the limited repertory of morphological response that such an uncomplicated object is capable of making. In this context it is reassuring that different *T* mutations whose effects are very close in time usually seem to have different primary sites of action in the embryo. We are therefore probably safe in concluding that the various morphological abnormalities that we see are relatively accurate reflections of differential gene activity during these early stages.

We and others have made considerably more intimate studies of normal and abnormal embryos than it is possible to illustrate in such cartoons. I will give just two examples in detail of electron microscopic observations. The first one concerns the defect in embryos homozygous for the mutation t^{w18}. In these embryos the primitive streak becomes abnormally large relative to the rest of the embryo. This is a region of pivotal importance to the development of vertebrates, because it is the area where cells of the "third germ layer," or mesoderm, first differentiate and assemble before migrating to populate the spaces between ectoderm and endoderm. The enlargement of the primitive streak is pronounced, and led my cancer-oriented colleague Karen Artzt to assume wrongly that these embryos might have embryonic tumors of primitive streak cells (Artzt and Bennett, 1972). Electron microscopy showed, however, that far from being tumors these enlarged primitive streaks simply represent regions where the differentiation of presumptive mesoderm cells had been ineffective or incomplete (Spiegelman and Bennett, 1974). The differences between nascent mesoderm cells of normal embryos and mutant embryos are dramatic. In normal embryos mesoderm cells are stellate, with many long pseudopodia connecting them to other similar cells, and, virtually wherever cell contacts are made, intercellular junctions are seen. It is generally thought that the migratory ability of these mesoderm cells depends on junctional specializations that provide footholds for moving cells. In the defective young mesoderm cells of t^{w18} homozygotes, however, none of these features are present; these cells are round, have at best a few lumpy protuberances, and almost never form junctions. The impression from looking at pictures like this is of cells that either do not recognize one another as suitable partners for interaction or are unable to respond to recognition signals, or perhaps both. In any case, the lack of intercellular connections between mesodermal cells of t^{w18} embryos is probably associated with their locomotional paralysis that results in an enlarged primitive streak, but very scanty mesoderm.

Observations on another mutation, the dominant T, have produced yet a different picture. In this case, some of the cells of homozygotes, instead of showing defective or virtually absent associations relative to normal cells, have shown enhanced, in fact promiscuous, relationships between cell types that normally never come into contact (Spiegelman, 1975). A constant feature of normal embryos is the rigid isolation from one another of important axial structures with very different cellular makeup and functional roles; for example, the ectodermal neural tube, the mesodermal somites and notochord, and the endodermal gut. Yet in T/T homozygotes, although all these structures begin to differentiate as entities, they eventually lose their integrity and reassociate (Fig. 5). The impression gained is that of cells that have lost the ability to discriminate self from nonself or to recognize their proper associative partners.

From these and other examples that have been studied in detail, we deduced that T mutations hinder normal organizational processes in ways that may be generally associated with abnormalities of cell–cell interactions, and this in turn led to the hypothesis that these mutations (and their normal counterparts as well) may exert their effects at the level of the cell surface.

I should say immediately that this thinking has not been acceptable to some other students of the T locus. I want to discuss this problem briefly because it has been an embarrassing one to me.

It is the viewpoint of Sherman and Wudl (1977) and Wudl et al., (1977) that at least certain mutations at the T/t locus (and by their implication all of them) (a) act as "generalized cell lethals"; (b) have therefore nothing to do with specific events of differentiation during embryogenesis; and (c) are exceedingly uninteresting as objects for the study of developmental mechanisms. These conclusions were drawn largely because these authors were unable to derive long-term cell cultures from blastocysts homozygous for either of two very early-acting t

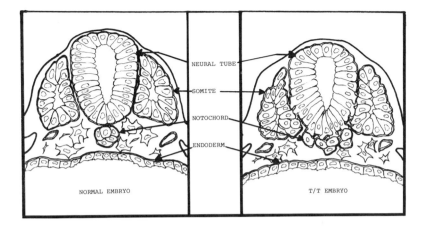

FIG. 5. A diagrammatic representation of axial structures of a normal and a *T/T* embryo: transverse sections at the mid-trunk level at 8¾ days of gestation (8–10 somites).

haplotypes (t^0 and t^{w5}), whereas about 80% of other blastocysts produced continuous cultures of cells that were apparently of extraembryonic origin. Their conclusions have been embarrassing for several reasons. First of all, it is embarrassing to have to admit that I do not know what a "generalized cell lethal" is. (This defect on my part is not aided by Wudl and Sherman, who do not provide a definition.) The original and, so far as I know, still operative definition of "cell lethal" refers to cells, behaving autonomously in *Drosophilia* embryos, that having acquired a lethal genotype by somatic crossing-over die without producing progeny cells (Demerec, 1936). It is readily understandable that a cell lethal results in a dead cell, but then I have to infer that any cell afflicted with cell lethality during embryonic development is *dead* and therefore (in the case of t^0/t^0 and t^{w5}/t^{w5} homozygotes, for example) should be dead as a zygote and incapable of giving rise to embryos that develop quite normally, morphologically speaking, to the stages where they consist of hundreds of cells, of several different types. It has to be remembered in this context that we are dealing not with frog embryos, for example, where stored maternal RNAs and proteins can support development for a surprisingly long time in the absence of essential zygotic gene function, but with mammalian embryos where zygotic gene function begins as early as the 2–4 cell stage, and where aneuploidy can kill at those stages (Gropp, 1975).

I have brought this up here only to air my misgivings that "generalized cell lethal" is a catchy phrase that may have more weight given to it than it rightly deserves. For the record, I should also point out that, whatever "cell lethal" means, about half of the known T-locus mutations cannot by any criterion fall into this category, since their homozygous embryos have been shown to be capable of prolonged growth *in vitro* (Ephrussi, 1935; Hogan *et al.*, in press), to produce teratomas capable of sustained growth (Artzt and Bennett, 1972; Bennett *et al.*, 1977), or to contribute substantial numbers of viable cells in chimeras (Bennett, 1978; Spiegelman, 1978).

Now, to go back to my main theme, I think that a further suggestion of cell surface involvement comes from another effect of T locus recessive mutations. This is a bizarre phenomenon detected in the earliest experiments of Dunn and Glueksohn-Waelsch, but unknown in any other mammalian system, which results in male heterozygotes passing their recessive lethal gene on to most of their progeny. Incidentally, it is this characteristic that is no doubt responsible for maintaining the lethal genes in wild populations of mice, since enhanced transmission of the lethal gene provides a powerful positive selective pressure to counterbalance the negative selection due to embryonic lethality. This infraction of Mendel's rules has been much studied, but no obvious mechanism has so far been found. The situation is further complicated by the fact that males that carry two different but complementing alleles are inevitably completely sterile, instead of showing the superfertility that might have been predicted because of the apparent superiority of gametes that carry the recessive lethal. Almost for want of a better explanation, I think, the notion arose generally that some recognition phenomenon, maybe operating in an immunological way and maybe related to cell surface antigens similar to H-2, was responsible.

Morphological studies with the electron microscope revealed no significant abnormalities in heterozygous males showing distorted transmission, but when Dooher (Dooher and Bennett, 1977) examined spermatogenesis in sterile animals carrying *two* *t*-mutations, he obtained some evidence suggesting that abnormalities of the cell surface were in fact associated with *t* mutations. Part of the morphogenetic maneuvers involved in the differentiation of round spermatids to typically elongate spermatozoa depend on the organization of a cone of microtubules to surround the nucleus. In normal development these microtubules appear to be organized and/or to insert on cytoplasmic densities that aggregate in a very circumscribed ring on the inner face of the plasma membrane. In spermatids of sterile animals this nuclear ring of microtubule organizing sites is very much larger than normal, and the spermatids accumulate such large numbers of microtubules that their morphology becomes grossly distorted, and they apparently are no longer capable of fertilization.

I would like to summarize here the position I was led to by these observations. First, it seemed reasonable to suspect that genes in the *T/t* region regulate early developmental processes through gene products that are switched on in some sequential fashion and appear only on specific cell types; and further that these gene products either directly or indirectly affect the cell surface. On the simplicity principle, I assumed that the same gene products were present in spermatogenic cells and responsible for their differentiation and fertilizing ability, again in ways that operate through the cell surface. I want to be careful to emphasize here that these interpretations, although they seemed the most reasonable ones to me, were chosen with a deliberate bias toward concentrating on the role of the cell surface in developmental interactions. To my mind, all the complexities of embryonic development can be reduced to just three essential processes: the first is the controlled multiplication of cells; the second is the emergence of new cell types from a common parental pool; and the third is the characteristic assembly of similar cells into functional morphological configurations. A wealth of classical embryological data, too extensive to begin to cite here, has demonstrated that the latter two processes are heavily dependent on the ability of cells to recognize and respond to their environment. Both of those abilities in turn must be heavily dependent on the plasma membrane, since in the last analysis it is only through the membrane that the nucleus of a cell can see or interact with the world around it. Molecules of the cell surface must be crucial in modulating the necessary decisions that elicit differential gene function, and presumably serve to provide receptors for positional information coming from the environment, as well as to provide positional signals to other cells. Since the *T* complex obviously constitutes a major locus governing events of early embryogenesis, and since it seemed so likely that these major events were in turn governed by cell surface phenomena, I quite simply decided to concentrate on the cell surface.

So, together with my colleague E. A. Boyse, a search was begun for cell surface antigens specified by *T*-locus mutations. Young embryos not being available in quantities large enough for immunization, we took advantage of effects on sperm and immunized normal mice with sperm from *t*-mutant heterozygotes. Complement-dependent cytotoxicity tests showed that the antisera produced reacted with spermatozoa of all genotypes. This was expected, because the testis is an immunologically privileged organ, effectively unseen by the immune system of the animal, and thus spermatozoa are autoantigenic. Extensive absorption of these "anti-sperm" antisera with normal sperm proved to remove nonspecific autoantibody and to leave detectable but weak cytotoxic activity for sperm of the genotype used for immunization (Bennett *et al.*, 1972). The serological system is in fact a dismayingly weak one to deal with, complicated as it is by the fact that immunizations with sperm evoke such high titers of autoantibodies. The tedious nature of this kind of experimentation has discouraged most laboratories, with the exception of mine and that of François Jacob, from pursuing it. Nevertheless, further work on *T*-locus-defined antigens on sperm has yielded several interesting results. First of all, Yanagisawa *et al.* (1974) showed that members of each of four different complementation groups appeared to define a serologically distinct antigen on sperm. Later Artzt (Artzt and Bennett, 1977) showed that the situation was not that simple, and that t antigens were composed of multiple specificities, like H-2 antigens, although so far at least on a much smaller scale. Of the three t antigens that have been carefully studied so far, all proved to have at least one common cross-reacting specificity, as well as at least one unique specificity. It is especially interesting that when Artzt studied recombinant chromosomes derived from these mutations by the kind of exceptional crossover event I mentioned earlier, she found in each case examined that the unique specificity was associated with the lethal factor, and the common specificity with the tail-interacting piece. This provides a direct correlation between serology and genetics. And finally Dooher (1979) has evidence that members of the same complementation group do not necessarily have identical antigenic specificities, although that is the general rule. This is a particularly interesting observation because it suggests that serology may be a more sensitive tool than complementation tests for discriminating among *t* mutations. For the present purpose two more points need to be made: (*a*) the demonstration by Goldberg (Bennett *et al.*, 1972) that t antigens are found only on spermatozoa, not on any other adult cells; and (*b*) the indirect immunofluorescence topographical evidence of Fellous (Fellous *et al.*, 1974) that showed that t antigens on sperm were localized in the postacrosomal membrane. This is the region that fuses with the egg in fertilization, and thus this observation is in line with our suspicion that t antigens may play a role in that process. In any case, their absence from adult somatic cells, and their classification as "differentiation" antigens, thus left t antigens in the running as candidates for cell surface components important in embryogenesis.

It will be obvious that at that time our highest priority was to use sperm-derived antisera in attempts to detect relevant t antigens on embryonic cells. But we found with some dismay that the serological system we had then was not sufficiently robust to give any answers at all, and, as you will see in a moment, even now it gives disappointingly unclear results.

In any case, another kind of system was available for attempting to test in a more general way the hypothesis that had been derived from the study of *t* mutations, namely that stage-specific and cell-specific surface markers appear and disappear during early stages of embryonic differentiation. A number of teratocarcinoma cell lines had been assembled by François Jacob, to whom they appeared to be valid models for embryonic cells on the grounds that the stem cells (called embryonal carcinoma cells) of these tumors not only resembled uncommitted embryonic cells morphologically and biochemically, but were similar also in their capacity to differentiate into a variety of apparently normal cell types. It is a remarkable feature of these tumors that under many circumstances they maintain a malignant stem cell pool while simultaneously permitting some of those stem cells to enter nonmalignant pathways of apparently normal differentiation. In fact a complete parallel between such embryonal carcinoma cells and normal embryonic cells has recently been demonstrated by Illmensee and Mintz (1976), who showed that a single stem cell, injected into the normal environment of a young embryo at the blastocyst stage, was capable of converting to a normal developmental pathway and contributing normally differentiating cells to every tissue, including functional gametes, of the resulting chimera.

When Jacob was joined by Karen Artzt to make a serological approach to teratocarcinomas, they realized in designing their first experiments that the very fact that conventional teratocarcinoma lines were capable of differentiation might create problems, because then they would be dealing with a heterogeneous mixture of cells of unknown developmental state. So they made a rational decision and decided to study a line of teratocarcinoma cells called F9, which had lost virtually all ability to differentiate, although by any other criterion the embryonal carcinoma cells were unchanged. They initially asked a very simple question of these cells, namely whether they possessed cell surface components that were peculiar to the embryo and therefore recognizable as antigens by a mouse of identical genotype. To make a long story short, they got a very simple answer: F9 cells were highly immunogenic in syngeneic hosts (Artzt et al., 1973). When the resulting antibody was analyzed in detail it defined an antigen (or antigens) with a very limited but exciting tissue distribution: simply the cells of preimplantation embryos, spermatozoa, and embryonal carcinoma cells of any teratocarcinoma cell line including those of species other than the mouse. Neither teratocarcinoma cells in later stages of differentiation, adult cells, nor a variety of other tumor cells reacted with the antiserum. Thus, it seemed that the F9 antibody clearly defined not only an embryonic antigen, but also one that had the characteristics predicted of T-locus antigens.

These observations led to the speculation that the gene coding for the F9 antigen might be a wild-type member of the T locus. Since spermatozoa were known to express both F9 and t antigens, they could provide material for investigating this idea, because if there were a genetic relationship between F9 and t mutations, then populations of sperm from heterozygous mutant animals would be expected to express only half the amount of F9 seen in entirely normal sperm. This question was approached by the sensitive method of quantitative absorption, from which can be obtained reliable estimates of the number of cells necessary to absorb a given amount of antibody activity. When these experiments were exhaustively done, it appeared that sperm from all types of T-locus heterozygotes but one were equivalent to wild-type in removing anti-F9 antibody (Artzt *et al.*, 1974; Marticorena *et al.*, 1978). The one exception occurred with males that carried the mutation t^{12}; it required twice as much of their sperm to absorb the same amount of antibody activity removed by sperm of any other genotype. The conclusion was reached, then, that the F9 antigen was very likely the product of the wild-type form of the t^{12} mutation. It now seemed very significant that embryos homozygous for t^{12} died at the morula stage, without taking any significant step in differentiation, because this was just the stage in normal embryos when F9 antigen was most prominently expressed.

At this point efforts in my laboratory and that of Jacob to try to define t antigens on preimplantation embryos and define their relationship to F9 were understandably intensified. Jacob and co-workers chose to use immunofluorescence techniques, and we continued with cytotoxicity methods. Both groups succeeded quite unequivocally in showing that F9 antigen exists in small quantity on the egg, increases in prominence to the late morula stage, and then declines—but does not completely disappear—at the blastocyst stage. But, as we began to use anti-t antisera and mutant embryos, our results began to diverge in a most disappointing way. Our own cytotoxicity data showed a straightforward picture, comfortably compatible with the other data and ideas I have so far presented. A smaller proportion of embryos of 8–16 cells in litters from parents both of which carried the t^{12} mutation were susceptible to anti-F9 cytotoxicity than in normal controls; the proportion of embryos susceptible to anti-t^{12} antiserum was correspondingly increased. But litters containing another t mutation, t^{w5}, responded like wild-type—that is, they all seemed to be equally sensitive to anti-F9 antiserum. This suggested that embryos that expressed t^{12} had less F9 antigen than normal, and vice versa. The point that t^{12} homozygotes were depleted of F9 was tested by allowing embryos to develop further in tissue culture after treatment with anti-F9. In litters containing t^{12} homozygotes after treatment with anti-F9, many of the embryos that had remained alive failed to make the transition to blastocyst, suggesting that indeed the anti-F9 serum had preferentially killed the normal embryos and left behind a preponderance of defective t^{12}/t^{12} homozygotes (Marticorena *et al.*, 1978). On the other hand, Jacob and his associate Kemler (Kemler *et al.*, 1976) made quite different observations— specifically first that several t antigens (not just t^{12}, but also t^0 and t^{w5})

were present on morulae obtained from matings where at least one parent carried the relevant mutation. This obviously presented a serious obstacle to the notion of sequential gene activation that had been postulated, because t^0 and t^{w5} are mutations that affect development some days later than the morula stage. Furthermore, although the results from sperm had indicated that only the products of the mutation t^{12} stood in a mutually exclusive relationship to F9, Kemler and co-workers found that not only t^{12} homozygotes, but also t^{w5} homozygotes, seemed to be devoid of F9 antigen. Clearly in this case what was thought to have been learned from sperm was not compatible with data obtained from the embryos that were of so much more interest.

These discrepancies have simply not been resolved, and so our two laboratories have had to agree to disagree for the moment. In any case, we have shared conversation, reagents, and animals; thus the differences in data appear to depend on the methods used. Since there is no reasonable way of deciding which method is more appropriate in this circumstance, some important theoretical points—for example, sequential activation of T-locus genes and the relationship of F9 to t^{12}—will simply have to await clarification by other means.

Further work showed that F9 cells resembled early embryonic cells in yet another way—their failure to express antigens of the major histocompatibility complex, the H-2 locus (Artzt and Jacob, 1974). This is a unique feature of embryonic cells, and, interestingly, one that is shared normally only by spermatozoa (Table I). But as both teratocarcinoma cells and embryonic cells begin to differentiate, F9 disappears from their surface and they begin to express H-2. The apparent reciproc-

TABLE I
"TISSUE" DISTRIBUTION OF F9 AND H-2 ANTIGENS

Tissue	F-9	H-2
Embryonal carcinoma cells	+	−
Spermatozoa	+	−
"Young" embryos	±	±
Differentiated teratoma cells	−	+
"Old" embryos	−	+
Tumors (spontaneous, viral, chemical)	−	+
Adult cells	−	+

ity of F9 and H-2 expression was especially interesting because not only are the *T* locus and the *H-2* locus on the same chromosome, but recessive lethal *t* mutations are inextricably linked to *H-2* as part of a "super-gene" complex. The availability of teratocarcinoma cell lines provided not only unlimited quantities of cells, but also anti-F9 antisera far more potent than those made on sperm, and this encouraged attempts to try to analyze the biochemistry of this *T*-locus related antigen. We were eager to do this for obvious reasons, among them the possibility that the apparent reciprocal expression of F9 and H-2 antigens on differentiating cells might indicate some degree of relatedness between them. This notion was supported by the observations of Vitetta (Vitetta *et al.*, 1975), who showed in immunoprecipitation experiments that the cell surface components recognized on F9 cells by anti-F9 antiserum had the same molcular weight and subunit structure as those recognized on spleen cells by anti-H-2 antiserum. Both sets of antigens recognized in this way were comprised of a molecule of about 44,000 daltons plus a smaller, noncovalently bound molecule, of about 12,000 daltons. This finding led already in 1975 to further flights of speculation, namely that the *T* locus might be a candidate for an evolutionary precursor of the *H-2* locus, and that genes responsible for cell surface molecules involved in the relatively simple cell–cell interactions required for early embryonic development had at some time in evolution become duplicated and given rise to the more sophisticated recognition devices used in the functions of the immune system (Artzt and Bennett, 1975). Unexpected problems in sequencing the F9 molecules have so far prevented a straightforward biochemical solution to this interesting question, but a report from Qvist *et al.* (1978), demonstrating that a xenogenic antiserum (made in a rabbit against H-2) was capable of immunoprecipitating F9, suggests that there is still life in the old idea.

I have tried so far to provide a logical and consistent summary of how a genetic complex in a mammal appears to operate, via the specification of changing cell surface components, to govern specific steps in determination and differentiation during early embryonic development. The data on which this picture rests are probably in general sound (with the exceptions already noted), and the conceptual framework is reasonable. Nevertheless, it should be noted that both the data that have been sought and the theoretical arguments used to interpret them have been subject to a self-inflicted bias, namely that the cell surface plays an essential role in mediating cell differentiation. Obviously, what is badly needed now are both functional and molecular insights into how this system works. Conventional serology, although it has been a powerful tool, probably cannot—if used unassisted—take us much further in analyzing important cell surface components from embryos and sperm, since they necessarily carry so many genetically undefined autoantigenic molecules that are unrelated to those we are interested in; however, the new methods of monoclonal antibody production may surmount this problem.

As an example of what we must do in the future, I will discuss two already fruitful approaches taken by young postdoctoral fellows in our laboratory. First of all I want to mention the question put by Barry Shur, who came from the laboratories of Roseman and Roth, who are primary proponents of the idea that glycosyltransferases and their substrates may provide a way for cells simultaneously to recognize and modify one another. The basic idea is that if, on their surfaces, one cell involved in an interaction has a substrate and the other an enzyme specific for it, the two cells will be transiently bound together during the enzymic reaction, and then leave that kiss with at least one of them carrying an altered molecule on its surface (Roth, 1973). These glycosyltransferase enzymes come in families showing the kind of co-ordinate expression that might be expected of T-locus mutations. Shur came to us with the question whether specific abnormalities of glycosyl-transferase enzymes might correlate with specific t mutations. He found in fact that *all* sperm carrying t mutations have enhanced levels of a specific enzyme, galactosyltransferase; three other transferase activities and a number of other enzymes were identical to wild type (Shur and Bennett, 1979). Galactosyltransferase also appears to be important for the development of preimplantation embryos. In a very clear and well controlled experiment, Shur and Oettgen (Shur *et al.*, 1979) demonstrated that normal mouse morulae grown in the presence of the galac-tosyltransferase substrate, UDP-galactose, failed to differentiate into blastocysts, and therefore were phenocopies of t^{12} homozygous em-bryos, which also fail to make that transition. Neither galactose nor UDP-glucose, nor both in combination, had any effect on embryonic development. Interestingly, anti-F9 antiserum protects embryos against the teratogenic effects of UDP-galactose. Although nothing is known about the mechanism at this point, it seems clear that T-locus associated cell surface antigens appear to be integrated in some way with galactosyltransferase activity.

A different kind of attack has been made by Lee Silver, a postdoctoral fellow working with Artzt. He chose to tackle the problem of T-locus gene products somewhat more directly, by comparing the proteins manufactured by normal testicular cells with those produced in males that carry either recessive lethal *t* mutations, or a well defined deletion of part of the T region (a dominant factor called T-hairpin) or both. The hairpin deletion is apparently a fairly extensive one; by genetic tests it evokes pseudodominance of the marker mutation *quaking,* but not the marker *tufted,* so it spans at least the region between T and qk. It is to this region, as you may remember, that tail-interacting factors of all recessive *t* mutations are mapped. In his experiments, Silver radiolabeled testicular cells metabolically with ^{35}S, lysed them, and analyzed their proteins in a variation of the two-dimensional electrophoretic separation system invented by O'Farrell, which separates proteins both by charge and molecular weight. What he has found, in essence, is that a major protein of normal spermatogenic cells (a molecule of about 63,000 daltons) is produced by a gene in the region covered by the hairpin deletion, and further, that the charge of this protein is altered to a more acidic form by recessive *t* mutations. Since the more acidic protein appears to be a constant and indistinguishable feature of the several different recessive genotypes that have been studied so far, we infer that a mutant protein associated with the tail interaction factor of recessive *t* mutations has been identified and will no doubt be important in exploring both the functional and genetic properties of these mutations (Silver *et al.,* 1979).

I will conclude now simply by reemphasizing my belief that the study of nature's experiments, even one so apparently trivial as a short-tailed mouse, can give some insight into what Harvey called secret mysteries, and what we today call so much more mundanely "molecular biology."

REFERENCES

Artzt, K., and Bennett, D. (1972). *J. Natl. Cancer Inst.* **48,** 141–158.
Artzt, K., and Bennett, D. (1975). *Nature (London)* **256,** 545–547.
Artzt, K., and Bennett, D. (1977). *Immunogenetics* **5,** 97–107.
Artzt, K., and Jacob, F. (1974). *Transplantation* **17,** 632–634.

20   D. BENNETT

Artzt, K., Dubois, P., Bennett, D., Condamine, H., and Babinet, C. (1973). *Proc. Natl. Acad. Sci. U.S.A.* **70**, 2988-2992.

Artzt, K., Bennett, D., and Jacob, F. (1974). *Proc. Natl. Acad. Sci. U.S.A.* **71**, 811-814.

Bennett, D. (1975). *Cell* **6**, 441-454.

Bennett, D. (1978). *Nature (London)* **272**, 539-540.

Bennett, D. (1978). NIH Workshop, "Origins of Inbred Mice" (H. C. Morse, ed.), pp. 615-632. Academic Press, New York.

Bennett, D., Goldberg, E., Dunn, L. C., and Boyse, E. A. (1972). *Proc. Natl. Acad. Sci. U.S.A.* **69**, 2076-2080.

Bennett, D., Artzt, K., Magnuson, T., and Spiegelman, M. (1977). "Cell Interactions in Differentiation" (M. Karkinen-Jaaskelainen and L. Saxén, eds.), pp. 389-393. Helsinki, Finland.

Chesley, P., and Dunn, L. C. (1936). *Genetics* **21**, 525-536.

Demerec, M. (1936). *Proc. Natl. Acad. Sci. U.S.A.* **22**, 350-354.

Dobrovolskaia-Zavadskaia, N. (1927). *C. R. Soc. Biol.* **97**, 114-119.

Dobrovolskaia-Zavadskaia, N., and Kobozieff, N. (1932). *C. R. Soc. Biol.* **110**, 782-784.

Dooher, G. B. (1979). "3rd Int. Symp. Spermatozoon" (D. W. Fawcett and J. M. Bedford, Eds.), pp. 231-238. Urban and Schwartzenberg, Baltimore and Munich.

Dooher, G. B., and Bennett, D. (1977). *Biol. Reprod.* **17**, 269-288.

Dunn, L. C. (1941). *Harvey Lect.* **35**, 135-165.

Dunn, L. C., and Gluecksohn-Schoenheimer, S. (1939). *Genetics* **24**, 587-609.

Dunn, L. C., and Gluecksohn-Schoenheimer, S. (1943). *Genetics* **28**, 29-40.

Ephrussi, B. (1935). *J. Exp. Zool.* **70**, 197-204.

Fellous, M., Gachelin, G., Buc-Caron, M.-H., Dubois, P., and Jacob, F. (1974). *Dev. Biol.* **41**, 331-337.

Gropp, A. (1975) *Embryogenesis in Mammals, Ciba Found. Symp.* pp. 155-175.

Hogan, B., Spiegelman, M., and Bennett, D. (1980). *J. E. eM*, in press.

Illmensee, K., and Mintz, B. (1976). *Proc. Natl. Acad. Sci. U.S.A.* **73**, 549-553.

Kemler, R., Babinet, C., Condamine, H., Gachelin, G., Guenet, J. L., and Jacob, F. (1976). *Proc. Natl. Acad. Sci. U.S.A.* **73**, 4080-4084.

Klein, J., and Hammerberg, C. (1977). *Immunol. Rev.* **33**, 70-104.

Lyon, M. L., and Meredith, R. (1964a). *Heredity* **19**, 301-312.

Lyon, M. L., and Meredith, R. (1964b). *Heredity* **19**, 313-325.

Marticorena, P., Artzt, K., and Bennett, D. (1978). *Immunogenetics* **7**, 337-347.

Qvist, S., Ostberg, L., and Peterson, P. (1978). *Scand. J. Immunol.* **7**, 265-276.

Roth, S. (1973). *Quart. Rev. Biol.* **48**, 541-563.

Sherman, M. I., and Wudl, L. R. (1977). *In* "Concepts of Mammalian Embryogenesis" (M. I. Sherman, ed.), pp. 134-234. MIT Press, Cambridge, Massachusetts.

Shur, B. D., and Bennett, D. (1979). *Dev. Biol.* **71**, 243-259.

Shur, B. D., Oettgen, P., and Bennett, D. (1979). *Dev. Biol.* **73**, 178-181.

Silver, L. M., Artzt, K., and Bennett, D. (1979). *Cell* **17**, 275-284.

Snell, G. D. (1968). *Folia Biol. (Prague)* **14**, 335-358.

Spiegelman, M. (1975). *Embryogenesis in Mammals, Ciba Found. Symp.*, pp. 199-220.

Spiegelman, M. (1978). "Genetic Mosaics and Chimeras in Mammals" (L. B. Russell, ed.), pp. 59-80. Plenum, New York.

Spiegelman, M., and Bennett, D. (1974). *J. Embryol. Exp. Morphol.* **32,** 723–738.

Vitetta, E., Artzt, K., Bennett, D., Boyse, E. A., and Jacob, F. (1975). *Proc. Natl. Acad. Sci. U.S.A.* **72,** 3215–3219.

Wudl, L. R., Sherman, M. I., and Hillman, N. (1977). *Nature (London)* **270,** 137–140.

Yanagisawa, K., Bennett, D., Boyse, E. A., Dunn, L. C., and Dimeo, A. (1974). *Immunogenetics* **1,** 57–67.

THE MEDICAL TREATMENT OF GALLSTONES: A CLINICAL APPLICATION OF THE NEW BIOLOGY OF BILE ACIDS*

ALAN F. HOFMANN

*Division of Gastroenterology,
Department of Medicine (H-811D),
University of California at San Diego
Medical Center,
San Diego, California*

I. OVERVIEW: THE NEW BIOLOGY OF BILE ACIDS

IN vertebrates, cholesterol, which is insoluble in water, is eliminated by conversion in the liver to a group of water-soluble anions known as bile salts or bile acids (Haslewood, 1978). Although work on the chemistry and physiology of these compounds began well over a century ago (for review see Sobotka, 1937), a quantitative description of the physiology of these compounds became possible only when Bergström and his colleagues in Lund, Sweden, synthesized radioactive bile acids that could be used to define synthesis rates and metabolic biotransformations (see Bergström *et al.*, 1960).

During the past two decades, our laboratory has worked to define the metabolism of bile acids in man and to determine the importance of altered bile acid metabolism in intestinal and hepatic disease (for reviews see Fromm and Hofmann, 1975; van Berge Henegouwen and Hofmann, 1978). The experiments have involved a number of disciplines because of the multiple functions of bile acids and the multiple organ systems involved. Initially, the approach involved descriptive physical chemistry. We focused on the dispersant properties of bile acids (Hofmann and Borgström, 1962; Hofmann, 1963) because bile acids are detergents with a striking capacity to disperse polar lipids in micellar form (Hofmann and Small, 1967). This ability to solubilize lipids is important biologically, for bile acids mediate the excretion of

---

*Lecture delivered October 19, 1978.

cholesterol in bile—as a mixed micelle composed of bile acids, lecithin, and cholesterol (Small *et al.*, 1966)—and bile acids mediate the absorption of fat-soluble vitamins—as mixed micelles of bile acids, fatty acids and monoglycerides, and ˙fat soluble vitamins (Hofmann, 1976; Borgström, 1977; Simmonds, 1974).

We turned from these *in vitro* experiments, which had defined the dispersant properties of bile acids, to *in vivo* experiments, in which we showed that a micellar solution could be isolated by ultracentrifugation from human intestinal content during digestion (Hofmann and Borgström, 1964) and that fat was rapidly absorbed from a micellar solution when this was infused into the jejunum in man (Borgström *et al.*, 1963). In other studies, we measured hourly biliary lipid secretion in man, permitting quantitation of the diurnal variation in the composition of the mixed micelle in bile (Northfield and Hofmann, 1975; LaRusso *et al.*, 1975).

A second line of endeavor involved a quantitative description of the enterohepatic circulation of bile acids in healthy man (Hofmann, 1977). Bile acids have a unique anatomic description compared to other drugs. They are secreted in bile, efficiently absorbed from the intestine, and resecreted in bile. Hepatic extraction is remarkably efficient (60–90% per single pass), so that the amount of bile acids reaching the systemic circulation is small. The efficient coupled extraction systems of the liver and intestine are responsible for the enterohepatic circulation of bile acids. First, we defined the metabolism of the two major bile acids made in the liver from cholesterol—the primary bile acids. Then, we defined the metabolism of the two major secondary bile acids made in the cecum by dehydroxylation of the primary bile acids. We then could construct a pharmacokinetic model describing every aspect of bile acid metabolism in man (Hoffman and Hofmann, 1974, 1977; Hofmann, 1977; Hofmann *et al.*, 1979b).

There were reasons for believing that this descriptive physiology would have clinical relevance. Since the amount of bile acids reaching the systemic circulation depended on liver extraction, impaired liver function should result in decreased hepatic extraction and increased serum bile acid levels; accordingly, serum bile acid levels should be a sensitive indicator of hepatic function, and this fact is now well documented (Osuga *et al.*, 1977). We (Simmonds *et al.*, 1973) and others (Roda *et al.*, 1977; Murphy *et al.*, 1974; Matern *et al.*, 1976;

Bagir, *et al.*, 1979; Mäentausta and Jänne, 1979) developed sensitive radioimmunoassays for serum bile acids, which are being widely studied to assess their clinical utility.

While quantitating the metabolism of bile acids, we found that certain dihydroxy bile acids induce secretion from the small and large intestine (Mekhjian *et al.*, 1971) in man. Thus bile acids are secretory cathartics, and increased bile acid concentrations in the colon might cause diarrhea. We showed that patients with ileal resection do have increased bile acid concentrations in the colon, and that such patients show a clinical response to bile acid binding resins has been demonstrated in controlled studies (Hofmann and Poley, 1972).

By far the most common disease involving the biliary tract is cholesterol cholelithiasis, a disease caused by an excess of cholesterol in bile. In 1971, our group found that chenodeoxycholic acid, one of the primary bile acids, greatly decreases the relative cholesterol concentration in bile and induces gallstone dissolution in man (Danzinger *et al.*, 1972). Because of the high prevalence of gallstone disease, and because this observation has led to the first practical medical treatment for gallstones, I have decided to focus here on the role of bile acids in the formation and dissolution of gallstones.

II. FORMATION AND DISSOLUTION OF CHOLESTEROL GALLSTONES

A. *Introduction*

Cholesterol cholelithiasis is commonly found today in Caucasian adults of the Western world. Its incidence increases with age and approaches 30% by late middle age in some European population groups (Lindstrom, 1977) (Fig. 1). Cholelithiasis is a very ancient disease (Thudicum, 1863). Prior to the development of oral cholecystography 50 years ago, the asymptomatic state of the disease could not be diagnosed except at laparotomy. Even today, cholecystography is rarely done in the absence of symptoms, so that little information exists on the true prevalence of cholelithiasis (see Bainton *et al.*, 1976).

During the past 15 years, great advances have occurred in 'our understanding of the mechanism of gallstone formation, even though some of the initial steps remain unclear. When it was shown that the oral admin-

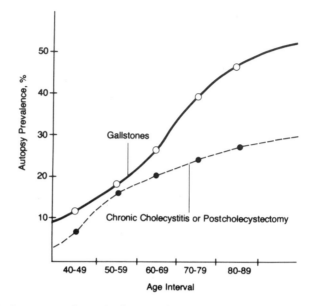

Fɪɢ. 1. Autopsy prevalence of gallstones and gallbladder disease in Sweden. Gallbladder disease was documented as chronic cholecystitis or presumed to be present if a cholecystectomy was done. The greater prevalence of gallstones than gallbladder disease is consistent with the view that gallstone formation precedes the development of gallbladder disease. From Lindstrom (1977).

istration of two naturally occurring bile acids, chenodeoxycholic (chenic) acid or its 7β epimer, ursodeoxycholic acid, caused decreased cholesterol saturation of bile, a topic of exciting pathophysiology was transformed into one of immediate clinical relevance. In Section II, I will summarize three current aspects of bile acid metabolism: first, the physical chemistry of bile; second, the physiology of biliary lipid secretion as it relates to gallstone disease; and third the physiological basis for bile desaturation and gallstone dissolution by exogenous bile acids. Only cholesterol cholelithiasis will be considered, since bile pigment cholelithiasis is a different disease that is poorly understood and for which no medical treatment has been proposed.

One must distinguish cholelithiasis, the cause, from gallbladder disease, the result. This is a crucial distinction, since gallstones may occur

with or without gallbladder disease. Although chenic and ursodeoxycholic acids are effective for treating cholelithiasis, they probably have no effect on gallbladder disease, except in its early and reversible stages. Early treatment of gallstones with these agents may be
considered a prophylactic approach to gallbladder disease.

B. Pathogenesis of Gallstones

1. Physical Chemistry of Bile

a. The Micelle.   Bile is a concentrated micellar solution; that is,
most of its solutes are present not as single hydrated ions or molecules,
but as aggregates of molecules held together by hydrophobic forces. In
1966, Donald Small, on the basis of physicochemical studies carried out
at the Institut Pasteur in Paris, proposed an imaginative model of the
molecular structure of the mixed micelle present in bile (Small *et al.,*
1966) (Fig. 2). According to this model, the micelle has a core of
lecithin and cholesterol that exists as a bilayer in which the rigid cholesterol molecules interdigitate between the flexible hydrocarbon chains of
the lecithin; also, the outside of the micelle is coated by a layer of bile
acid molecules, two molecules across. Small proposed that the bile
acids, as bifacial detergents, are arranged so that their hydrophobic
sides are against the fatty acid chains of the lecithin. Thus, in this model
for the mixed micelle of bile, cholesterol molecules are dissolved by the
lecithin molecules, which in turn are dispersed by bile acid molecules.
The micelle resembles a portion of cell membrane in which the bile
acids replace transmembrane proteins.

Thus, the micelle is a molecular aggregate, the interior of which is a
liquid hydrocarbon. This structure enables it to solubilize cholesterol
and other polar or nonpolar lipids. In addition, the outside of the micelle
provides a second mode of solubilization for bifacial molecules such as
bilirubin diglucuronides or certain drug metabolites. Such molecules
may adsorb to the micelle with their hydrophobic side against the fatty
acid chains of the lecithin molecules. The term "micellar sink" has
been proposed, since the micelle offers a means of transporting any
amphipathic compound in bile. Thus, the micelle offers a simple,
elegant solution to the problem of solubilizing, transporting, and
eliminating cholesterol from the body.

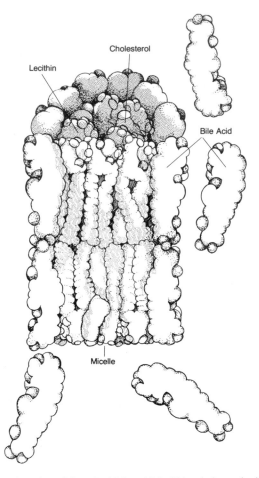

Fig. 2. Coronal section of the mixed bile acid–lecithin–cholesterol micelle present in bile. The hydrocarbon chains of the lecithin are in a liquid state. The interior of the micelle may also contain some dimers of bile acid molecules. The bile acid molecules coating the micelle are believed to be exchanging rapidly and continuously with the low concentration of bile acids in true molecular solution, which surround the micelle.

Solubilization of lecithin by bile acid in mixed micelles is quite similar to lecithin solubilization by the apoprotein of α-lipoprotein. An important difference is that the bile acids are adsorbed loosely to the micelle and are in dynamic equilibrium with a definite concentration of molecularly dispersed bile acids (about 1 mM) (Duane, 1977). In contrast, the concentration of molecularly dispersed apoprotein is considered to be extremely low.

The molar ratio of bile acids to lecithin is fairly constant at a ratio of about 3:1. The ratio of bile acids to cholesterol is 10–20:1, depending on the degree of saturation of bile. Hepatic bile has a concentration of about 50 mM in man, but in the gallbladder, bile is concentrated severalfold; gallbladder bile in man has a concentration of 100–150 mM.

b. Behavior of Biliary Lipids in Model Systems. Conjugated bile acids are colorless crystalline powders that are extremely water soluble. A 2% solution (about 40 mM) of a conjugated bile acid is water-clear and will foam slightly when shaken, since bile acids have some surface activity (for review see Small, 1971). Small aggregates of bile acid molecules are present as oligomers, but these are difficult to detect unless techniques of macromolecular chemistry are used (i.e., light scattering or analytical ultracentrifugation) (Shankland, 1970; Kratohvil, 1975).

If one adds pure phosphatidylcholine (lecithin) to the solution, the added phospholipid will dissolve. The solution will remain clear, although it may have a faint opalescence. The lecithin forms mixed micelles. The size of the mixed micelle depends on the ratio of lecithin to bile acid and increases as the ratio of lecithin to bile acids increases (Mazer *et al.*, 1980). The mixed micelles are believed to have the simple structure of a bilayer with bile acids on the outside. Some bile acids may be incorporated, probably as dimers, into the lecithin bilayer (Zimmerer and Lindenbaum, 1979).

When the proportion of lecithin to bile acid exceeds about 0.3, the turbidity of the solution increases abruptly owing to the formation of much larger aggregates. These aggregates are probably liquid crystalline, since they have sufficient order to give a well defined X-ray diffraction pattern, but are microscopically liquid. In such circumstances, there is insufficient bile acid to fully coat the micelles; as a result, they coalesce. As more lecithin is added to the bile acid solution, the concentration of molecularly dispersed bile acids falls. This is because bile acids adsorb to the lecithin bilayer in direct proportion to their concentration. In this simple system, "saturation" is signaled by the appearance of turbidity. The large aggregates do not aggregate because

they are charged. Further, they remain dispersed because their density
does not differ significantly from that of the solution.

The situation is very different when cholesterol is the solute. If one
adds cholesterol to the clear micellar bile acid solution, only a small
amount dissolves. This is because simple bile acid micelles are poor
solvents for cholesterol. When saturation is reached, the solution remains clear, but the added cholesterol simply precipitates from solution
as crystals of the monohydrate. If cholesterol is added to bile acid–
lecithin solutions containing mixed bile acid–lecithin micelles, its behavior is similar. It does, however, have a higher solubility, since the
mixed bile acid–lecithin micelle is a much better solvent for cholesterol.
When saturation is reached, cholesterol again precipitates as crystals of
the monohydrate (Carey and Small, 1978). The amount of cholesterol
that dissolves in the solution depends on the ratio of the lecithin to the
bile acid, since lecithin provides most of the solvent capacity of the
solution. Thus, cholesterol dissolves in the lecithin, but the bile acids
are necessary to keep the lecithin dispersed in micellar form.

The solubility of cholesterol in a bile acid–lecithin micelle increases
with temperature (Carey and Small, 1978). If a saturated solution at
60°C is cooled to body temperature, it will be supersaturated. Eventually, when nucleation occurs, the cholesterol will crystallize out. The
process is considered analogous to the first stage of cholesterol gallstone
formation.

The behavior of solutes in water is described by phase diagrams in
which the physical state of the constituent is shown in relation to its
proportion by weight. Bile has five major constituents: bile acids,
lecithin, cholesterol, bilirubin diglucuronides, and water. To show these
using conventional phase equilibria, one requires a figure in four dimensions since there are four degrees of freedom; i.e., if one knows the
proportion of four of the substances, the proportion of the fifth is fixed.
Donald Small, however, reasoned that it was permissible to ignore the
bilirubin diglucuronide, as it is the least common constituent of the
biliary lipids. If this were true, one could represent bile in three dimensions, i.e., by a tetrahedron. Furthermore, if one held the percentage of
water constant, one could then show biliary lipid composition in two
dimensions by using triangular coordinates (Admirand and Small,
1968). The idea of holding the proportion of water constant was also
reasonable. Bile, like most body fluids, is largely water—90 to 95%. As

a result, one can fix biliary composition at a constant percentage of solid (e.g., 10%) and then show the saturation line for cholesterol. This would be a system of bile acid–lecithin–cholesterol–water at a constant water composition. With this approach, there were only two degrees of freedom, which thereby permitted the use of triangular coordinates. Thus, bile composition could be shown in two dimensions (Fig. 3).

Triangular coordinates came into use nearly a century ago in mathematics and had been used even earlier in the medical literature to show dietary composition (Ahrens, 1957). It was common practice for colloid chemists, when depicting phase equilibria, to hold one variable constant in the phase diagram while the proportions of others were varied. This was shown by rectangular or triangular coordinates. But no one had ever used triangular coordinates for bile before Small. He buttressed his idea by meticulous experiments with model systems simulating bile. In 1968, the hypothesis was clearly stated: bile could be simulated by mixtures of bile acid, lecithin, cholesterol, and water. In these mixtures, the saturation solubility of cholesterol was clearly defined and, using triangular coordinates, could be shown as a line (Small, 1967).

    c. Application of the Model System to Bile. The next step was to ascertain whether the model system would apply to bile. Small returned to Boston and worked with Admirand. They obtained bile at surgery

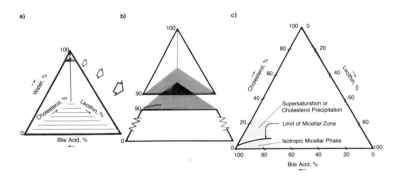

FIG. 3. Phase equilibria of model system of bile acid–lecithin–cholesterol–water used to simulate bile. A plane through the tetrahedron (a) at 90% water (and 10% total solids) is shown enlarged in (b) and then depicted as conventional triangular coordinates (c). The line depicting the limit of the micellar zone is slightly lower in very dilute bile, e.g., bile with less than 5% total solids.

from patients, both with and without gallstones, and determined the
nature and the concentration of biliary lipids. Using triangular coordinates, they plotted the experimentally determined concentrations (Admirand and Small, 1968). In general, patients with gallstones had bile
that fell in the supersaturated zone, whereas patients without gallstones
had unsaturated bile. Suddenly, a clinical disease had been expressed as
a simple deviation of physical chemistry. This was truly molecular or
biophysical pathology.

However, to strengthen the theoretical basis for the model, it had to
be shown that the line of cholesterol saturation for the model system was
the same as the line for bile. This was done subsequently by Holzbach
et al. (1973). Holzbach determined the line of saturation using bile
samples obtained at surgery and also carried out experiments using
model systems. Holzbach and associates, and still earlier Hegardt and
Dam (1971), found that the true equilibrium solubility line for cholesterol was somewhat lower than that proposed by Admirand and Small
(1968). This new line, now widely accepted as the true line for equilibrium solubility, offered good agreement between saturation in model
systems and in bile samples obtained at surgery.

The clear definition of gallstone disease in terms of physical chemistry is often considered to originate with Admirand and Small, but this is
probably not true. The idea that bile contains an excess of cholesterol in
gallstone patients is an old one, perhaps most clearly stated in the
American literature of 1957 by Johnston and Nakayama (1957). They
knew that although human bile was saturated with cholesterol, this was
not the case for most animal species. They also stated the rationale of
medical therapy for cholelithiasis in simple terms: the goal of therapy is
to decrease the cholesterol saturation in bile. Johnston and Nakayama
knew that, if human bile could be made as unsaturated as canine bile,
gallstones would dissolve. In the 1880s researchers found that human
gallstones would rapidly dissolve if transplanted into the gallbladder of
the dog, which was known to have extremely unsaturated bile (Naunyn,
1896).

d. Determination of Bile Saturation.   To determine the saturation
of gallbladder bile, the concentrations of bile acids, lecithin, and cholesterol are determined. Thus, the concentration of bile acids is determined
using a specific bacterial enzyme, 3-hydroxysteroid dehydrogenase,
that oxidizes the 3-hydroxy group to a 3-keto group; the oxidation

is coupled to nicotinamide adenine dinucleotide, which is monitored spectrophotometrically (Palmer, 1969) or spectrofluor - ometrically (Osuga et al., 1977). The concentration of lecithin is determined enzymically (Takayama et al., 1977) or by using a standard technique for phosphorus after the lipid has been ex- tracted into chloroform and ashed (Bartlett, 1959). Cholesterol is best determined enzymically (Roda et al., 1975) or by gas-liquid chroma- tography. Based on these values, a calculation is made of percentage of saturation, i.e., of the solubility of cholesterol in the sample divided by the solubility of cholesterol in a hypothetical sample that contains the same proportion of bile acid and lecithin as the actual sample.

The triangular coordinates proposed by Admirand and Small for de- noting bile lipid composition can be transformed into rectangular coor- dinates by expressing the abscissa as a ratio of phospholipid to bile acids (Thomas and Hofmann, 1973). Using this technique, it is possible to describe the line for cholesterol saturation by a polynomial equation. When the molar proportion of bile acids, lecithin, and cholesterol is known, one can then develop numerical tables from which the percent- age of saturation can be read. The line of cholesterol saturation has been determined for varying concentrations of bile (Carey and Small, 1978), and "critical tables" have been published (Carey, 1978).

2. Enterohepatic Circulation of Bile Acids and Biliary Lipid Secretion

a. *Biliary Secretion in Cholelithiasis.* The presence of supersatu- rated bile in the gallbladder must reflect the secretion of either too much solute (cholesterol) or too little solvent (lecithin or bile acid or both). The lipid composition of gallbladder bile is believed to be determined primarily by biliary lipid secretion from the liver. The subsequent modification of secreted biliary lipids during passage along the biliary tree or storage in the gallbladder is considered of little quantitative importance. It seems likely that if there is any modification in biliary lipids during gallbladder concentration, it is a reduction in cholesterol saturation because of some cholesterol absorption (Duane et al., 1976).

Bile acids are the prime movers in biliary lipid secretion. When bile acids return to the liver, they are efficiently extracted and promptly secreted in bile. As they are secreted, they induce the synthesis and secretion of lecithin (Schersten et al., 1971; Schersten, 1973; Bennion

ALAN F. HOFMANN

and Grundy, 1975; Wheeler and King, 1972). The induced synthesis
and secretion is often termed a "coupling." This is because the induced
lecithin output is almost stoichiometric at low and moderate rates of
secretion of bile acids. In some animals, bile acids also induce, directly
or indirectly, the secretion of cholesterol (Hoffman *et al.*, 1975;
Wheeler and King, 1972); but the stoichiometry of this coupling in man
has not been well characterized.

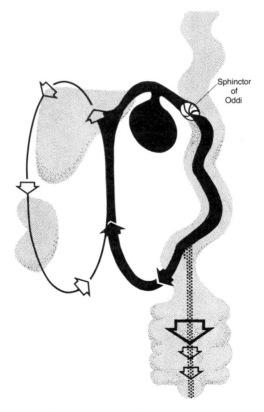

FIG. 4. Schematic depiction of the enterohepatic circulation of bile acids in man.
Gallbladder filling is determined by contraction of the sphincter of Oddi. The movement
of the enterohepatic circulation is largely mediated by intestinal motility. The serum level
of bile acids is determined by the fraction of bile acids returning from the intestine that are
removed by the liver. In healthy man, individual bile acids are eliminated from the body
only in feces.

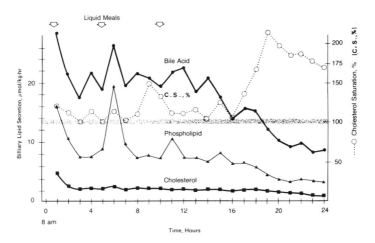

Fig. 5. Hourly secretion of the three major biliary lipids into the intestines of six gallstone patients and calculated percentage saturation (C.S.). Bile is supersaturated during overnight fasting because bile acid and lecithin secretion abate more rapidly than cholesterol secretion. From LaRusso *et al.*, (1975).

The enterohepatic circulation of bile acids is a continuous flow of detergent molecules. This flow accelerates during digestion and slows during overnight fasting when the major portion of the bile acids is stored in the gallbladder (Fig. 4). In man, the secretion of cholesterol appears to continue rather unabated during overnight fasting. As a consequence, nocturnal bile is supersaturated in many adults (LaRusso *et al.*, 1975) (Fig. 5).

The output of bile acids into the biliary tract derives largely from the return of bile acids to the liver. This return depends on gallbladder contraction, intestinal motility, and intestinal absorption (in the jejunum and especially the ileum). The current view is that the presence of supersaturated gallbladder bile in gallstone patients is explained by defective hepatic secretion of biliary lipids (for review, see Bennion and Grundy, 1978)—i.e., cholesterol cholelithiasis is a hepatic disease. In the nonobese patient, it seems that either the secretion of bile acids is low or there is a combination of a moderate decrease in the output of bile acids and a moderate increase in cholesterol output (Shaffer and Small, 1977). In the obese patient, the major defect is excessive secretion of cholesterol in bile (Bennion and Grundy, 1975). The role of the gallbladder, if any, in the pathogenesis of cholesterol cholelithiasis remains unclear. An important role seems unlikely (van Berge Henegouwen and Hofmann, 1977). As noted above, it could be that a healthy gallbladder absorbs cholesterol, thereby decreasing bile saturation (Duane *et al.*, 1976). When gallbladder disease occurs, the protective effect would be lost, accelerating stone growth.

   b. Enterohepatic Circulation of Bile Acids.   The bile acids participating in the enterohepatic circulation consist principally of primary bile acids formed in the liver, and secondary bile acids formed from primary bile acids in the intestine by bacteria (Danielsson, 1963; Hofmann, 1977) (Fig. 6). In man, two primary bile acids are formed in the liver from cholesterol. Cholic acid, a trihydroxy acid, is $3\alpha,7\alpha,12\alpha$-

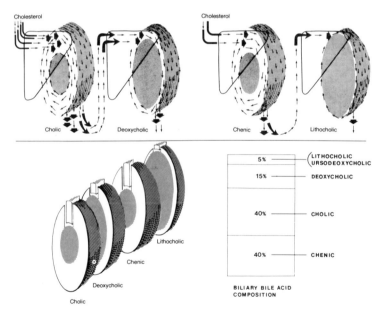

FIG. 6. Enterohepatic circulation of the major primary and secondary bile acids in man. The size of the pool of any bile acid reflects the balance between input (from synthesis or intestinal absorption of newly formed secondary bile acids) and the efficiency of intestinal conservation. The relative sizes of each of the individual bile acid pools determine the pattern of biliary bile acids. The formation and enterohepatic circulation of ursodeoxycholic acid is not shown because of its complexity.

trihydroxycholanoic acid; and chenic acid, a dihydroxy acid, is $3\alpha,7\alpha$-dihydroxycholanoic acid. After formation, bile acids are conjugated in amide linkage with glycine or taurine. The cholyl and chenyl conjugated bile acids are excreted in bile, and most are reabsorbed from the small intestine without further biotransformation (Hepner *et al.*, 1972a). Each day, about one-third to one-fourth of the pool of primary bile acids is lost from the enterohepatic circulation. Bile acids not absorbed in the small intestine pass into the cecum, where they are converted by enteric bacteria to secondary bile acids. The most important change is a 7-dehydroxylation that converts cholic acid to deoxycholic acid and chenic acid to lithocholic acid.

The fates of these two secondary bile acids differ. About one-third to one-half of the deoxycholic acid that is formed is reabsorbed (Hepner *et al.*, 1972b). The absorbed, unconjugated deoxycholic acid passes to the liver, where it is conjugated with glycine or taurine. These deoxycholyl conjugates are secreted in bile and reabsorbed with an efficiency similar to that of the dihydroxy primary bile acid conjugates chenylglycine and chenyltaurine. Lithocholic acid, however, has a unique metabolism when it reaches the liver. It is first conjugated with glycine or taurine, but the majority of the lithocholyl conjugates are then sulfated (Cowen *et al.*, 1975a) at the 3 position to form two new lithocholyl conjugates: sulfolithocholylglycine and sulfolithocholyltaurine. These sulfated conjugates are excreted in bile but are poorly absorbed from the small intestine (Cowen *et al.*, 1975b; Allan *et al.*, 1976b). They pass rapidly into the colon and are eliminated with little enterohepatic cycling. Thus, lithocholic acid is eliminated rapidly from the enterohepatic circulation because it is conjugated to a form that is not recycled enterohepatically (Hofmann, 1977).

In many people, ursodeoxycholic acid (the 7β epimer of chenic acid) has recently been recognized to be the fourth most common billiary bile acid. Ursodeoxycholic acid can be shown by isotopic techniques to originate from chenic acid (Fedorowski *et al.*, 1977; Hofmann and Klein, 1978). It is thought that chenic acid is hydrogenated in the small intestine by bacterial enzymes to form 3-hydroxy-7-ketocholanoic acid. The latter is absorbed and reduced in the liver to both ursodeoxycholic acid and chenic acid (Fromm *et al.*, 1980). When these two compounds reach the small intestinal lumen, they are again oxidized at the 7 position to 3-hydroxy-7-ketocholanoic acid. This is then reabsorbed and once again reconverted in the liver to ursodeoxycholic and chenic acids. Thus, chenic acid and ursodeoxycholic acid are interconvertible. Since most ursodeoxycholic acid is derived from a secondary bile acid, we have suggested that it be termed a tertiary bile acid. However, some recent experiments suggest that ursodeoxycholic acid can also be formed by intestinal bacteria alone (Fedorowski *et al.*, 1979).

C. Medical Therapy

1. Desaturation of Bile with Chenic Acid: Rationale

Therapy is aimed at correcting the disproportion of supersaturated bile that contains too little bile acid or too much cholesterol or both. The simplest approach would be to feed bile acids. This might increase biliary bile acid secretion, and, if cholesterol secretion remained unchanged, bile should become less saturated. This intriguing idea appears several times in the older literature. In 1967, Schoenfield and Thistle planned to feed cholic acid to women with gallstones and then determine the effect that the administration of this bile acid exerted on the saturation of their bile. The decision to feed cholic acid was based on its commercial availability. Chenic acid, the other primary bile acid, was prohibitively expensive ($200 per gram). However, beginning in the mid-1960s the manufacture of chenic acid was commenced on a small scale in London by Weddel Pharmaceuticals and became available to our group. With chenic acid on hand, it was added to the Schoenfield–Thistle protocol because of the possibility that chenic acid might increase the secretion of bile acids more than cholic acid per se.

The effect of cholic acid and chenic acid on bile saturation was then studied in 1968 and 1969. After 4 months of treatment with chenic acid, bile became desaturated in all four women; in contrast, cholic acid had no effect (Thistle and Schoenfield, 1969) (Fig. 7). But no clear-cut changes in gallstones were seen on the radiographs.

2. Efficacy and Toxicity

By 1971, convincing evidence had begun to accumulate for a cholelitholytic effect of chenic acid (Danzinger *et al.*, 1972). Stimulated by these findings, we initiated a control trial comparing chenic acid with cholic acid or placebo and confirmed its unique efficacy. We

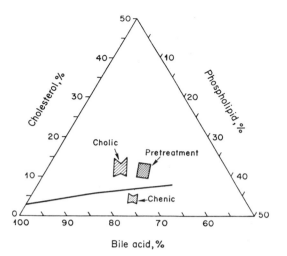

Bile acid,%

FIG. 7. Effect of cholic or chenic acid on biliary lipid composition (mean ± standard error). Pretreatment data are also shown. The saturation line is that of Holzbach *et al.* (1973). From LaRusso *et al.* (1975).

achieved a response rate of greater than 70% (Thistle *et al.*, 1978). Similar efficacy has been subsequently reported by others from different parts of the United States and Europe (Hofmann and Paumgartner, 1974). The response rate is not 100% for both biological and physical reasons, but the major reason is that some radiolucent stones are not composed of cholesterol. Makino's laboratory showed that ursodeoxycholic acid, the 7β epimer of chenic acid, could also induce gallstone dissolution (Makino *et al.*, 1975).

There was widespread concern from the beginning that chenic acid might be hepatotoxic. Chenic acid is eliminated exclusively by the fecal route, and largely in the form of a bacterial biotransformation product—lithocholic acid. This is a known hepatotoxin in many animals (Palmer, 1976). However, the evidence that chenic acid is not toxic in man is now nearly overwhelming (Hofmann and Paumgartner, 1975). Liver biopsies have been carried out in several hundred patients, and no appreciable morphological abnormalities have been observed. The only abnormality in serum enzymes has been a modest, usually transient, increase in serum transaminases. This abnormality occurs in about one-fourth of the patients receiving chenic acid and is dose related (Gerolami *et al.,* 1977; Thistle *et al.,* 1978). The elevation seems to be a "false positive," since it is not associated with morphological change. Nor is it related to the level of lithocholic acid in serum or bile (Allan *et al.,* 1976a). It seems likely that chenic acid may alter the membrane permeability of the hepatocyte, thereby allowing certain cytosolic enzymes to leak into the plasma compartment.

Despite the ever-increasing evidence that chenic acid is safe in man, the drug is quite hepatotoxic in a number of animals, including the rabbit (Fisher *et al.,* 1974) and two nonhuman primates, the rhesus monkey (Dyrska *et al.,* 1975, 1976) and baboon (McSherry *et al.,* 1976). No other drug that is currently in widespread usage is toxic in nonhuman primates, since a drug that was proved to be toxic in primates would never be introduced into man. The striking animal toxicity of chenic acid was not noted until 1973, five years after chenic acid had been first used in man. By this time, considerable evidence for human safety of the drug had already been accumulated. Because of this, the human trials were allowed to continue, with careful patient monitoring. Simultaneously, vigorous efforts were made to explain the anomalous toxicity. The explanation came quickly and was related to the unique pharmacology of chenic acid (Fig. 8). Chenic acid is converted by intestinal bacteria to lithocholic acid in most animals; the lithocholic acid is then absorbed, and passes to the liver. In the rabbit, rhesus monkey, and baboon, the lithocholic acid is amidated with glycine or taurine and circulates in the enterohepatic circulation. It then induces portal tract inflammation and ultimately induces severe liver damage. In man, lithocholic acid is not only amidated with glycine or taurine, but is also sulfated when it reaches the liver. Sulfation alters the subsequent fate of lithocholic acid because sulfated lithocholic acid is poorly reabsorbed in the intestine. Consequently, it does not accumulate in the enterohepatic circulation and liver damage does not occur. It would be remarkable if man had a unique ability to sulfate lithocholic acid. Indeed, we have recently shown that the chimpanzee appears to sulfate lithocholic acid as well as man (Schwenk *et al.,* 1978). At present, it is not known whether chenic acid is toxic in the chimpanzee.

The effect of chenic acid on lipid metabolism in man is not yet entirely clear. There appears to be no change in serum cholesterol levels (Thistle *et al.,* 1978; Dowling, 1977) or the size of the exchangeable cholesterol pools (Hoffman *et al.,* 1974). There is decreased bile acid

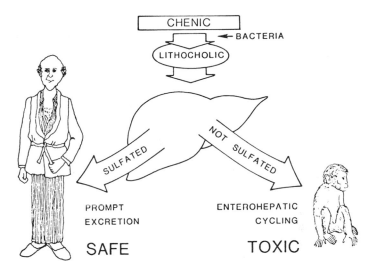

Fig. 8. Metabolism of chenic acid in man (left) and rhesus monkey (right). In man, the hepatotoxic secondary bile acid, lithocholic acid, is sulfated and rapidly eliminated; in the rhesus monkey, lithocholic acid is poorly sulfated. It accumulates, causing portal tract inflammation that leads to cirrhosis.

synthesis (LaRusso *et al.*, 1975) and presumably decreased cholesterol synthesis (Pedersen *et al.*, 1974). Serum triglyceride levels may show a lowering of 15–20% (see, for example, Angelin *et al.*, 1978), but in many studies, the effect is transient. It is still unclear whether chenic acid, as such, will become an important hypolipidemic drug.

3. Mechanism of Action

The initial rationale for the feeding of bile acids was to increase acid secretion and thereby decrease the saturation of bile. Astonishingly, the desaturating effect of chenic and ursodeoxycholic acid seems to be achieved by an entirely different mechanism, i.e., decreased biliary cholesterol secretion (Northfield *et al.*, 1975; Einarsson *et al.*, 1980; von Bergmann *et al.*, 1979). Both cholic and chenic acid increase bile acid secretion, but only chenic and ursodeoxycholic decrease cholesterol secretion into bile (LaRusso *et al.*, 1975). The explanation for this remarkable finding remains unclear. It is correlated with a fall in the activity of hydroxymethylglutaryl–coenzyme A (HMG–CoA) reductase (Ahlberg, 1979; Coyne *et al.*, 1976), a rate-limiting enzyme in cholesterol synthesis. Bile acids are thought to have little direct effect on the activity of this enzyme (Cooper, 1976). Therefore, it has been postulated that chenic acid, rather than cholic acid, inhibits the formation (or increases the turnover) of this crucial enzyme. A second possibility, suggested by recent experiments of Lindblad *et al.* (1977), is that the effect of chenic acid on this enzyme is secondary. Here, the major effect of chenic acid would be to evoke less cholesterol secretion and, pari passu, induce the formation of unsaturated bile, thereby allowing cholesterol to accumulate in the liver. The accumulation of cholesterol locally causes a direct inhibition of the activity of HMG–CoA reductase, presumably by an allosteric mechanism.

These two different hypotheses have not yet been tested, because only man is known to manifest an immediate desaturation response to chenic acid. The lack of a suitable animal model for the desaturating effect of chenic acid has prevented the elucidation of its mechanism of action, as well as the development of a cheaper analog.

4. Stone Dissolution Kinetics

When chenic acid is fed, bile becomes unsaturated and cholesterol slowly passes from the stone to the bile. Stone dissolution is rate-limiting because bile remains unsaturated during chenotherapy. *In vitro,* under well stirred conditions, stone dissolution is much slower than would be predicted from theoretical considerations (Hofmann *et al.*, 1979a). This is due to the presence of lecithin, which greatly slows the dissolution rate (Kwan *et al.*, 1977a). Lecithin's retarding effect on the dissolution of cholesterol can be abolished by the addition of quaternary amines (Kwan *et al.*, 1977b). Whether this finding can be used to accelerate dissolution *in vivo* is still not known. A critical question is whether dissolution is limited by diffusion through the unstirred layer surrounding the stone or by the presence of an interfacial barrier. When chenic acid is given in adequate dosage, dissolution takes 4–12 months on the average. Small stones with greater surface-to-volume ratio dissolve much more rapidly than large stones. Large, single cholesterol stones dissolve at a fairly linear rate (about 1 mm in diameter per month) so that in the future it may be possible to predict the time required for dissolution (C. Wolpers, personal communication).

5. Stone Recurrence

When chenic acid is fed, it is efficiently absorbed from the intestinal tract (van Berge Henegouwen and Hofmann, 1977). Within a week or so, the bile acid pool becomes greatly enriched in chenic acid. The effect is proportional to the dose. The degree of desaturation decreases as the proportion of chenic acid increases. In nonobese individuals, bile becomes unsaturated when biliary acids contain more than 70% chenic acid (Thistle *et al.*, 1977). In obese patients, in whom basal cholesterol secretion is higher, bile must contain a higher proportion of chenic acid to become desaturated. When chenic acid is stopped, biliary bile acids revert to their pretreatment composition and bile becomes resaturated (Thistle *et al.*, 1978).

Gallstones recur in one-fifth to one-third of patients. A stone may be redissolved, and stone recurrence prevented, by maintenance therapy, or the patient may undergo cholecystectomy. Thus, dissolution of gallstones with chenic acid may be considered to be a "medical cholecystotomy." In contrast to cholecystotomy, however, which was abandoned because of the high incidence of stone recurrence, chenic acid offers a medical approach in which recurrence is easily managed by retreatment or can be prevented by maintenance therapy.

D. Prophylaxis with Chenic Acid

If chenic acid were effective at microgram doses and were added to drinking water, table salt, toothpaste, or vitamin tablets, the prevalence of cholesterol cholelithiasis would be strikingly reduced. But this proposal is clearly unthinkable at present because the cost of such an approach would be great. Furthermore, the benefit would be difficult to assess, given our ignorance of the natural history of cholelithiasis. It seems clear that symptomatic cholelithiasis carries a moderately severe prognosis: that is, most patients with symptomatic cholelithiasis will eventually develop gallbladder disease requiring surgery (Wenckert and Robertson, 1966). The corollary of this principle, given the known very high prevalence of gallstone disease at autopsy, is that many patients have no manifestations of this disease (see Fitzpatrick *et al.*, 1977). Our present knowledge is insufficient to indicate whether the patient with a truly silent stone has enough risk of developing gallbladder disease so that his health prognosis would be improved if the stone were dissolved with chenic acid. When a patient develops symptoms, however, there appears to be a brief interval in the history of the disease when it can be effectively treated with chenic acid. A state of unsaturated, isotropic bile is achieved with stone dissolution, and either amelioration or stabilization of existing gallbladder disease.

For other diseases involving organs with vital biological functions, preventive agents are much more important, e.g., vaccines for poliomyelitis or other infectious diseases, and penicillin for rheumatic heart disease. The dispensability of the gallbladder, together with the safety of elective cholecystectomy, has caused a guarded reception of what might otherwise be deemed another pharmacological triumph. Thus, chenic acid does all that a drug can do. For many chronic metabolic diseases, such as diabetes, duodenal ulcer, or Wilson's disease, drugs offer, at best, reversible improvement, but not cure.

E. Perspective

Application of the laws of physical chemistry transformed cholelithiasis into a molecular disease. Understanding of the enterohepatic circulation and serendipity led to the discovery of a medical treatment. Surgeons contributed both the superb diagnostic technique of oral cholecystography and cholecystectomy, one of our safest, curative surgical procedures. Now the challenge is epidemiological: we must learn whether it is better to abolish gallbladder disease by preventing or dissolving gallstones, or to permit gallbladder disease to develop and become symptomatic before curing it with elective cholecystectomy.

Acknowledgments

The author's work is supported by NIH Grant AM 21506, as well as grants-in-aid from the Rorer Company and Canada Packers Limited. Previous work at the Mayo Clinic was supported by Mayo Foundation, NIH Grants AM 16770, AM 6908, and RR 585, as well as grants-in-aid from the Eli Lilly Foundation and Mead Johnson & Company. Clinical work carried out with Dr. Johnson L. Thistle was supported by NIH Grants AM 15887 and RR 585. The concepts presented here have been developed with the aid of many colleagues, including Tim Northfield, Rudy Danzinger, Nicholas LaRusso, Gerard van Berge Henegouwen, Alistair Cowen, Gershon Hepner, Neville Hoffman, Thomas Gadacz, Eberhard Mack, Robert Allan, Michael Schwenk, Paul Thomas, and Gerald Carlson. Collaborative work at the College of Pharmacy of the University of Michigan was carried out with William Higuchi, Henry Kwan, Sompol Prakongpan, and Abdul

Molokhia. Technical assistance was provided by Beverly Ott, Paulina Yu, Janet Carter, and Jacqueline Turcotte. The art work was created by Aviva Rahmani, Leslie Litwiler, and Ione Koch.

REFERENCES

Admirand, W. H., and Small, D. M. (1968). *J. Clin. Invest.* **47,** 1043.
Ahlberg, J. (1979). *Acta Chir. Scand. Suppl.* **492** (thesis).
Ahrens, E. H., Jr. (1957). *Am. J. Med.* **23,** 928.
Allan, R. N., Thistle, J. L., Hofmann, A. F., Carter, J. A., and Yu, P. Y. S. (1976a). *Gut* **17,** 405.
Allan, R. N., Thistle, J. L., and Hofmann, A. F. (1976b). *Gut* **17,** 413.
Angelin, B., Einarsson, K., and Leijd, B. (1978). *Clin. Sci. Mol. Med.* **54,** 451.
Bagir, Y. A., Ross, P. E., and Bouchier, I. A. D. (1979). *Anal. Biochem.* **93,** 361.
Bainton, D., Davies, G. T., Evans, K. T., and Gravelle, I. H. (1976). *N. Engl. J. Med.* **294,** 1147.
Bartlett, G. R. (1959). *J. Biol. Chem.* **234,** 466.
Bennion, L. J., and Grundy, S. M. (1975). *J. Clin. Invest.* **56,** 996.
Bennion, L. J., and Grundy, S. M. (1978). *N. Engl. J. Med.* **299,** 1161.
Bergström, S., Danielsson, H., and Samuelsson, B. (1960). *In* "Lipide Metabolism" (K. Bloch, ed.), p. 291. New York.
Borgström, B. (1977). *In* "Gastrointestinal Physiology II" (R. K. Crane and A. C. Guyton, eds.), pp. 305–323. Univ. Park Press, Baltimore, Maryland.
Borgström, B., Lundh, G., and Hofmann, A. F. (1963). *Gastroenterology* **45,** 229.
Carey, M. C. (1978). *J. Lipid Res.* **19,** 945.
Carey, M. C., and Small, D. M. (1978). *J. Clin. Invest.* **61,** 998.
Cooper, A. D. (1976). *J. Clin. Invest.* **57,** 1461.
Cowen, A. E., Korman, M. G., Hofmann, A. F., and Cass, O. W. (1975a). *Gastroenterology* **69,** 59.
Cowen, A. E., Korman, M. G., Hofmann, A. F., Cass, O. W., and Coffin, S. B. (1975b). *Gastroenterology* **69,** 67.
Coyne, M. J., Bonorris, G. G., Goldstein, L. I., and Schoenfield, L. J. (1976). *J. Lab. Clin. Med.* **87,** 281.
Danielsson, H. (1963). *Adv. Lipid Res.* **1,** 335.
Danzinger, R. G., Hofmann, A. F., Schoenfield, L. J., and Thistle, J. L. (1972). *N. Engl. J. Med.* **286,** 1.
Dowling, R. H. (1977). *Clinics in Gastroenterology* **6,** 141.
Duane, W. C. (1977). *Biochem. Biophys. Res. Commun.* **74,** 223.
Duane, W. C., Ginsberg, R. L., and Bennion, L. J. (1976). *J. Lipid Res.* **17,** 211.
Dyrska, H., Chen, T., Salen, G., and Mosbach, E. H. (1975). *Gastroenterology* **69,** 333.
Dyrska, H., Salen, G., Zaki, F. G., Chen, T., and Mosbach, E. H. (1976). *Gastroenterology* **70,** 93.
Einarsson, K. A., Grundy, S. M., and Hardison, W. G. M. (1980). *Gut* (in press).
Fedorowski, T., Salen, G., Colallilo, A., Tint, G. S., Mosbach, E. H., and Hall, J. C. (1977). *Gastroenterology* **73,** 1131.
Fedorowski, T., Salen, G., Tint, G. S., and Mosbach, E. H. (1979). *Gastroenterology* **77,** 1068.

Fisher, M. M., Prize, V. M., Magnusson, R. J., and Yousef, I. M. (1974). *Lipids* **9,** 786.

Fitzpatrick, G., Neutra, R., and Gilbert, J. P. (1977). *In* "Costs, Risks, and Benefits of Surgery" (J. P. Bunker, B. A. Barnes, and F. Mosteller, eds.), pp. 246–261. Oxford Univ. Press, London and New York.

Fromm, H., and Hofmann, A. F. (1975). *Ergeb. Inn. Med. Kinderheilk,* **37,** 143.

Fromm, H., Farivar, S., Hofmann, A. F., Carlson, G. L., and Amin, P. (1980). *Am. J. Physiol.* (in press).

Gerolami, A., Sarles, H., Brette, R., Paraf, A., Rautureau, J., Debray, C., Bermann, C., Etienne, J. P., Chaput, J. C., and Petitie, J. P. (1977). *Digestion* **16,** 299.

Haslewood, G. A. D. (1978). "The Biological Importance of Bile Salts". North-Holland Publ., Amsterdam.

Hegardt, F. G., and Dam, H. (1971). *Z. Ernaehrungswiss.* **10,** 223.

Hepner, G. W., Hofmann, A. F., and Thomas, P. J. (1972a). *J. Clin. Invest.* **51,** 1889.

Hepner, G. W., Hofmann, A. F., and Thomas, P. J. (1972b). *J. Clin. Invest.* **51,** 1898.

Hoffman, N. E., and Hofmann, A. F. (1974). *Gastroenterology* **67,** 887.

Hoffman, N. E., and Hofmann, A. F. (1977). *Gastroenterology* **72,** 141.

Hoffman, N. E., Hofmann, A. F., and Thistle, J. L. (1974). *Mayo Clin. Proc.* **49,** 236.

Hoffman, N. E., Donald, D. E., and Hofmann, A. F. (1975). *Am. J. Physiol.* **229,** 714.

Hofmann, A. F. (1963). *Biochem. J.* **89,** 57.

Hofmann, A. F. (1976). *In* "Lipid Absorption: Biochemical and Clinical Aspects" (K. Rommel and H. Goebell, eds.), pp. 3–18. MTP Press, Lancaster, England.

Hofmann, A. F. (1977). *Clinics in Gastroenterology* **6,** 3.

Hofmann, A. F., and Borgström, B. (1962). *Fed. Proc.* **21,** 43.

Hofmann, A. F., and Borgström, B. (1964). *J. Clin. Invest.* **43,** 247.

Hofmann, A. F., and Klein, P. D. (1978). *In* "Stable Isotopes" (T. A. Baillie, ed.), p. 309. Univ. Park Press, Baltimore, Maryland.

Hofmann, A. F., and Paumgartner, G. (1974). "Chenodeoxycholic Acid Therapy of Gallstones." Schattauer, Stuttgart.

Hofmann, A. F., and Paumgartner, G. (1975). "Chenodeoxycholic Acid Therapy of Gallstones. Update 1975." Schattauer, Stattgart.

Hofmann, A. F., and Poley, J. R. (1972). *Gastroenterology* **62,** 918.

Hofmann, A. F., and Small, D. M. (1967). *Annu. Rev. Med.* **18,** 333.

Hofmann, A. F., Higuchi, W. I., Kwan, K. H., Prakongpan, S., Thistle, J. L., and Molokhia, A. (1979a). *In* "Biological Effects of Bile Acids" (G. Paumgartner, A. Stiehl, and W. Gerok, eds.), pp. 79–89. MTP Press, Lancaster, England.

Hofmann, A. F., Milanese, M., Belforte, G., and Molino, G. (1979b). *Gastroenterology* **77,** A16.

Holzbach, R. T., Marsh, M., Olszewski, M., and Holan, K. (1973). *J. Clin. Invest.* **52,** 1467.

Johnston, C. G., and Nakayama, F. (1957). *Arch. Surg.* **75,** 436.

Kratohvil, J. P. (1975). *Colloid Polymer Sci.* **253,** 251.

Kwan, K. H., Higuchi, W. I., Molokhia, A. M., and Hofmann, A. F. (1977a). *J. Pharm. Sci.* **66,** 1094.

Kwan, K. H., Higuchi, W. I., Molokhia, A. M., and Hofmann, A. F. (1977b). *J. Pharm. Sci.* **66,** 1105.

LaRusso, N. F., Hoffman, N. E., Hofmann, A. F., Northfield, T. C., and Thistle, J. L. (1975). *Gastroenterology* **69**, 1301.

Lindblad, L., Lundholm, K., and Schersten, T. (1977). *Eur. J. Clin. Invest.* **7**, 383.

Lindstrom, C. G. (1977). *Scand. J. Gastroenterol.* **12**, 341.

McSherry, C. K., Morrissey, K. P., Swarm, R. L., May, P. S., Niemann, W. H., and Glenn, F. (1976). *Ann. Surg.* **184**, 490.

Mäentausta, O., and Jänne, O. (1979). *Clin. Chem.* **25**, 264.

Makino, I., Shinozaki, K., Yoshino, K., and Nakagawa, S. (1975). *Jpn. J. Gastroenterol.* **72**, 690.

Matern, S., Krieger, R., and Gerok, W. (1976). *Clin. Chim. Acta* **72**, 39.

Mazer, N. A., Benedek, G. B., and Carey, M. C. (1980). *Biochemistry* **19**, 601.

Mekhjian, H. S., Phillips, S. F., and Hofmann, A. F. (1971). *J. Clin. Invest.* **50**, 1569.

Murphy, G. M., Edkins, S. M., Williams, J. W., and Catty, D. (1974). *Clin. Chim. Acta* **54**, 81.

Naunyn, B. (1896). "A Treatise of Cholelithiasis," p. 22. New Sydenham Soc., Ed., London.

Northfield, T. C., and Hofmann, A. F. (1975). *Gut* **16**, 1.

Northfield, T. C., LaRusso, N. F., Hofmann, A. F., and Thistle, J. L. (1975). *Gut* **16**, 12.

Osuga, T., Mitamura, K., Mashige, F., and Imai, K. (1977). *Clin. Chim. Acta* **75**, 81.

Palmer, R. H. (1969). *In* "Methods in Enzymology" (S. P. Colowick, and N. O. Kaplan, eds.), Vol. 15, "Steroids and Terpenoids," pp. 280–288. Academic Press, New York.

Palmer, R. H. (1976). *In* "The Hepatobiliary System. Fundamental and Pathological Mechanism" (W. Taylor, ed.), pp. 227–240. Plenum, New York.

Pedersen, L., Arnfred, T., and Hess Thaysen, E. (1974). *Scand. J. Gastroenterol.* **9**, 787.

Roda, A., Festi, D., Sama, C., Mazzella, G., Aldini, R., Roda, E., and Barbara, L. (1975). *Clin. Chim. Acta* **64**, 337.

Roda, A., Roda, E., Aldini, R., Festi, D., Mazzella, G., Sama, C., and Barbara, L. (1977). *Clin. Chem.* **23**, 2107.

Schersten, T. (1973). *Helv. Med. Acta* **37**, 161.

Schersten, T. Nilsson, S., Cahlin, E., Filipson, M., and Brodin-Persson, G. (1971). *Eur. J. Clin. Invest.* **1**, 242.

Schwenk, M., Hofmann, A. F., Carlson, G. L., Carter, J. A., Coulston, F., and Greim, H. (1978). *Arch. Toxikol.* **40**, 109.

Shaffer, E. A., and Small, D. M. (1977). *J. Clin. Invest.* **59**, 828.

Shankland, W. (1970). *Chem. Phys. Lipids* **4**, 109.

Simmonds, W. J. (1974). *In* "Gastrointestinal Physiology" (E. D. Jacobson and L. L. Shanbour, eds.), p. 343. Univ. Park Press, Baltimore, Maryland.

Simmonds, W. J., Korman, M. G., Go, V. L. W., and Hofmann, A. F. (1973). *Gastroenterology* **65**, 705.

Small, D. M. (1967). *Gastroenterology* **52**, 607.

Small, D. M. (1971). *In* "The Bile Acids, Chemistry, Physiology and Metabolism" (P. P. Nair and D. Kritchevsky, eds.), Vol. 1, pp. 249–356. Plenum, New York.

Small, D. M., Bourges, M. C., and Dervichian, D. G. (1966). *Nature* (*London*) **211**, 816.

Sobotka, H. (1937). "Physiological Chemistry of the Bile." Williams & Wilkins, Baltimore, Maryland.

Takayama, M., Itoh, S., Nagasaki, T., and Tanimizu, I. (1977). *Clin. Chim. Acta* **79**, 93.

Thistle, J. L., and Schoenfield, L. J. (1969). *J. Lab. Clin. Med.* **74**, 1020 (abstract).

Thistle, J. L., Hofmann, A. F., Yu, P. Y. S., and Ott, B. (1977). *Am. J. Dig. Dis.* **22**, 1.

Thistle, J. L., Hofmann, A. F., Ott, B. J., and Stephens, D. H. (1978). *J. Am. Med. Assoc.* **239**, 1138.

Thomas, P. J., and Hofmann, A. F. (1973). *Gastroenterology* **65**, 698.

Thudicum, J. L. W. (1863). "A Treatise on Gall-stones: Their Chemistry, Pathology, and Treatment." Churchill, London.

van Berge Henegouwen, G. P., and Hofmann, A. F. (1977). *Gastroenterology* **73**, 300.

van Berge Henegouwen, G. P., and Hofmann, A. F. (1978). *Neth. J. Med.* **21**, 257.

von Bergmann, K., Gutsfeld, M., Schulze-Hagen, K., and von Unruh, G. (1979). *In* "Biological Effects of Bile Acids" (G. Paumgartner, A. Stiehl, and W. Gerok, eds.), pp. 61–66. MTP Press, Lancaster, England.

Wenckert, A., and Robertson, B. (1966). *Gastroenterology* **50**, 376.

Wheeler, H. O., and King, K. K. (1972). *J. Clin. Invest.* **51**, 1337.

Zimmerer, R. O., Jr., and Lindenbaum, S. (1979). *J. Pharm. Sci.* **68**, 581.

THE MAJOR HISTOCOMPATIBILITY COMPLEX: ITS EVOLUTION AND INVOLVEMENT IN CELLULAR IMMUNITY*

GEORGE D. SNELL

*The Jackson Laboratory,
Bar Harbor, Maine*

I. What Is the Major Histocompatibility Complex?

THE *H-2* complex is a paragraph in Nature's book that was read out of context. We are still trying to find out what it means. The complex was discovered by Peter Gorer in 1936 as a blood group and histocompatibility locus in mice. I came across it later as a histocompatibility locus linked to fused tail in chromosome 17. In a joint study (Gorer et al., 1948), Gorer and I proved that our loci were one and the same. We named it *H-2*. Subsequent work showed that *H-2* is actually a nest of closely linked loci, that compared to other histocompatibility loci even its individual components are unique in the strength of their effect on graft rejection, and that homologs exist in all mammals and perhaps all vertebrates. There are even tempting hints of ancestral loci in invertebrates. These findings led to the concept of the major histocompatibility complex, or MHC. They also led me (Snell, 1968) to refer to the complex as a super gene. Bodmer (1978) has now gone me one better—in a recent Harvey Lecture, he called the human version, HLA, a super super gene. The MHC is still important as a histocompatibility locus, especially to surgeons doing organ transplants, but causing the rejection of transplants obviously is not its function, at least at the present time. We are still not sure of its true context in Nature's book.

Before trying to see where *H-2* fits in Nature's scheme, we must briefly examine known facts about its structure. I cannot begin to cover the extensive literature. Reviews will be found in Klein (1975), Snell *et*

---

*Lecture delivered November 16, 1978.

al. (1976), Götze (1977), McDevitt (1978), and Gill *et al.* (1978). My outline will be highly selective.

Basic information in regard to chromosome 17 and the *H-2* complex is summarized in Fig. 1. There are now three known loci in *H-2* with the properties originally demonstrated by Gorer (Démant *et al.*, 1976). These are called *H-2K*, *H-2D*, and *H-2L* (abbreviated *K*, *D*, and *L*; when written K, D, and L, not italicized, they refer to gene products). Crossing-over between *K* and *D* is about 0.5%. There are no known crossovers between *D* and *L*, which are therefore separable only by the distinctness of their end products. The products of *K*, *D*, and *L* are widely distributed, perhaps present on all cells except those of the early embryo. This makes it possible to study them by a variety of methods. Lymphocyte cytolysis by alloantiserum and complement is now often the method of choice. The H-2 molecules are glycoproteins, 45,000 molecular weight, paired with a non-H-2 product of 12,000 molecular weight, β_2-microglobulin (β_2-m), whose amino acid composition shows similarities to the immunoglobulins. Both they and their human homologs, HLA-A, B, and C, are highly polymorphic, with variation occurring throughout much of the molecule (Coligan *et al.*, 1978). Polymorphism appears to be substantially less in the rat (Cramer *et al.*, 1978).

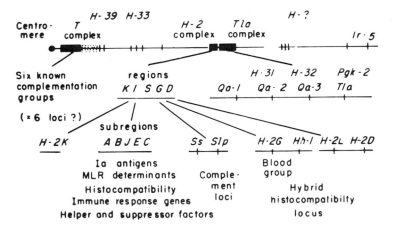

FIG. 1. Mouse chromosome 17 and the *H-2* complex. The unlabeled cross-lines on the chromosome 17 map represent known loci not relevant to this paper.

The *I* region of the *H-2* complex was originally identified by McDevitt and Chinitz (1969) as the seat of an immune response locus (*Ir-1*). Subsequent studies demonstrated multiple, closely linked loci that determine the capacity of mice of particular *H-2* haplotypes to respond or not respond to particular antigenic determinants. While the *Ir-1* loci probably remain the key to *I*-region function, the most useful markers for the area are now the serologically demonstrable cell surface Ia antigens (review in McDevitt, 1978). These are demonstrated by the same methods of lymphocyte cytolysis now regularly used in studying K,D,L. Some of the *Ia* loci probably will turn out to be identical with the *Ir-1* loci, but pending proof of identity they are treated as distinct. The two groups of loci, between them, serve to identify five *I* subregions, *I-A, I-B, I-J, I-E, I-C*. These five subregions have been identified by means of only eight proven recombinants within the *I* region (Klein, 1975; David *et al.*, 1978). Moreover, there is evidence that the *I-A* subregion determines more than one cell surface alloantigen. In all probability, therefore, further subregions remain to be discovered. The Ia antigens, unlike the K,D,L antigens, occur on only a few cell types other than lymphocytes and macrophages. An important clue to their function is their unequal distribution on the different categories of lymphocytes and macrophages, a property that makes them valuable markers for lymphocyte subclasses. The Ia products are glycoproteins that show some diversity among themselves and little similarity in their protein structure to K,D,L. However, like K,D,L, they are associated with a second molecule, probably not of *H-2* origin, and their carbohydrate component is similar, or perhaps identical, to that of K,D,L (Freed and Nathenson, 1977). In one case, the associated molecule is reported to be β_2-m (Katz *et al.*, 1976).

The *S* region of the *H-2* complex, approximately midway between the *K* and *D* ends, is marked by several closely linked genes that control components of serum complement (Shreffler, 1976; Carroll and Capra, 1978; da Silva *et al.*, 1978).

Klein (1977) refers to the products of the *K,D,L*, the *I*, and the *S* regions as Class I, Class II, and Class III region products, respectively. I shall make occasional use of these terms.

The *G* region, although at least as long as the *I* region, is currently less well marked. It was originally defined by a blood group locus, *H-2G*, mapping between *S* and *D* (Klein *et al.*, 1975). Perhaps also in the G region is the gene, or one of the genes, controlling the curious phenomenon of hybrid resistance, that is, the resistance of F_1 hybrids to parental transplants of bone marrow or tumors of lymphoid origin. This was originally mapped as being at the D end of H-2 (Cudkowicz and Stimpfling, 1964), but a recent report indicates that it may map within G (Clark et al., 1977). A locus, Rfv-1, that influences recovery from Friend leukemia virus-induced splenomegaly, has been mapped in either the G or D regions of H-2 (Cheseboro and Wehrly, 1978).

We now come to an area of chromosome 17 about 1.5 centimorgans (cM) in length that maps immediately to the right of H-$2D$ (review in Snell, 1979). It is marked by four loci, Qa-1, Qa-2, Qa-3, and Tla, which determine serologically demonstrable alloantigens (Boyse et al., 1966; Flaherty, 1976; Stanton and Boyse, 1976; Flaherty et al., 1978). Like the Ia antigens, the antigens determined by these loci show limited tissue distribution, in fact even more limited than Ia since they appear to be present only on lymphocytes and almost entirely on specific categories of T lymphocytes. Unlike the Ia antigens, however, their chemistry is remarkably similar to that of K,D,L. Their molecular weight is 43,000–44,000, and, more significantly, they occur in association with β_2-m (Vitetta et al., 1976; Michaelson et al., 1977; Uhr et al., 1977). Moreover, since there are histocompatibility effects in this region (review in Snell et al., 1976), it is possible that the products of some of these loci, like those of H-$2K$, D, and L, are histocompatibility alloantigens. Their effects on transplantation, however, are much weaker than those of K,D,L.

Whether the Qa—Tla region should be regarded as part of the H-2 complex or as a separate region or complex is a semantic problem on which no consensus has been reached.

Turning now to the other end of chromosome 17, we find about 15 cM to the left of H-$2K$ the remarkable T complex. This has been thoroughly reviewed by Gluecksohn-Waelsch and Erickson (1970) and Klein and Hammerberg (1977). Briefly, the T complex consists of a group of probably at least six loci that determine alloantigens demonstrable in early embryos and on spermatozoa. The loci were originally detected because of their effects on development. They also influence crossing-over, segregation ratios, and fertility. The end product of at least one of the loci has a molecular weight similar to that of the H-2 product, and it is associated, like H-2, with a smaller molecule of about

12,000 molecular weight, which, however, is not β_2-m (Vitetta *et al.*, 1975; Dubois *et al.*, 1976).

We know a great deal about MHC structure; we are only beginning to get some insight into its function. I have briefly reviewed the structure; I now turn to the problem of function. Any conclusions that I draw are speculative, although in some areas we are approaching firm ground.

II. FUNCTION OF THE *I* REGION

I shall start with the function of the *I* region. Although this is the infant among MHC regions, it has grown lustily and is relatively well understood. I shall give only a brief summary of its possible functions, without documentation. Major reviews will be found in Katz and Benacerraf (1976), McDevitt *et al.* (1976), and McDevitt (1978). While my interpretation is in accord with current thinking, the details are obviously my own.

The *I* region is the major regulator of the immune response. It controls the interactions of the different classes of lymphocytes one with another and with macrophages, and, to at least some extent, the interaction of all these cells with antigen. We can distinguish four ways in which the products of the *I* region act.

1. They play an important role in the presentation of antigen by macrophages.
2. They are part of antigen-specific helper factors released by helper cells and of antigen-specific suppressor factor released by suppressor cells. They probably comprise the constant rather than the variable region of these factors.
3. They are part of nonspecific helper and suppressor factors.
4. They form the receptors to which these factors bind, thereby permitting the factors to deliver the appropriate message to the appropriate cell.

This list suggests the range of functions of *I*-region products, but may turn out to be very incomplete.

An important gap in our understanding of *I*-region products concerns the mechanisms by which *Ir-1* genes exert their surprisingly specific effect on a great variety of immune responses. This could be explained if Ia antigens comprised the variable regions of antigen-specific helper and suppressor factors, but the variable regions of these factors appear to be more akin to the immunoglobulins than to *I* products. Two interesting suggestions have been offered (Benacerraf, 1978; von Boehmer *et al.*, 1978); I shall discuss these later. Another puzzle is the function of Ia antigens on epidermal cells (Frelinger *et al.*, 1978).

I-region products are certainly not the only regulators of the immune response. Antibodies undoubtedly play an important role through a variety of complex feedback mechanisms (Snell *et al.*, 1960; Jerne, 1976; and many others). In view of the highly specific B-cell and T-cell distribution of the Ly and the Qa—Tla antigens, these probably play a regulatory role, but their manner of operation is still obscure. Perhaps some of them govern the circulatory patterns of the different lymphocyte subpopulations.

III. Apparent Relationship between Class I and *T*-Locus Products

We have reviewed the function of the Ia products. The function of the Class I (K,D,L) antigens is a more difficult, and in some ways a more intriguing, problem. The early appearance and wide cell distribution of these substances suggests that they serve some rather generalized purpose. Of the various clues as to what this purpose may be, the most specific point to a role for K,D,L in cell interactions. These clues we shall now examine.

The *T* complex at the left end of chromosome 17 (Fig. 1) clearly plays an important role in early development. If *H-2* could be tied to *T*, this would suggest a developmental function. The two are linked, but about 15 cM apart. This distance would seem to rule out a super gene relationship. However, despite the relatively high crossover frequency, a strong linkage disequilibrium between *T* and *H-2* has been demonstrated. Mutant alleles at particular *T* ''complementation groups'' show a strong association with particular *H-2* haplotypes (Hammerberg and Klein, 1975; Levinson and McDevitt, 1976). How this linkage disequilibrium is maintained is unknown. Crossover inhibitors that are associated with some of the *T*-locus lethal alleles probably account for part of it. Hammerberg and Klein (1975) have suggested additional mechanisms.

Another suggestion of communality between T and H-2 is, as noted in Section I, the presence of a smaller companion molecule and a similarity of molecular weight. This area, however, requires a great deal more study.

Perhaps the most important evidence for a functional relationship between K,D,L and the T antigens comes from studies indicating that these antigens appear sequentially on the cells of early embryos. This was suggested by early investigations of T-locus lethal alleles and of H-2 ontogeny (review in Snell et $al.$, 1976). More precise information has come from recent serological studies (review in Jacob, 1977). These studies were made possible by the identification of an embryonic antigen, F9, presumed to be a product of one of the normal T alleles. F9 is defined by an antiserum produced by immunizing strain 129 with an undifferentiated embryonal carcinoma of 129 origin. Subsequent absorptions yield an operationally monospecific antibody. F9 is present on morulae of normal embryos and segregates in crosses with lethal T gene t^{w32}, indicating allelism at this T locus (Kemler et $al.$, 1976). A rabbit antiteratoma antiserum has also been produced that seems to identify the same antigen.

Anti-F9 and anti-H-2 can be used by various methods to study the ontogeny of the F9 and H-2 antigens on the cells of early embryos and of undifferentiated and differentiated teratocarcinomas. Studies up to 1977 have been reviewed by Jacob (1977). By the use of combined absorption and fluorescein labels, it can be shown that, while some F9 is present on both undifferentiated and differentiated teratocarcinomas, the number of cells carrying it steadily decreases when multipotential teratomas are allowed to differentiate in culture. In contrast to this, H-2 is absent on all undifferentiated teratomas, but gradually appears on the differentiating cell lines. The fraction of cells with H-2, however, always remains small (very small according to one study: Edidin and Gooding, 1975).

Confirmatory evidence of a mutually exclusive relationship between an antigen found on teratomas and MHC antigens comes from work with human embryonal carcinomas. Several such carcinomas that have been investigated show a cross-reaction with mouse anti-F9, suggesting the presence of a homologous antigen. Using this reaction, in combination with anti-HLA-A and -HLA-B by double immunofluorescence on a human testicular teratoma, Hogan et $al.$ (1977) found that cells with F9

lacked HLA and vice versa. Holden *et al.* (1977), using anti-β_2-m as
the marker for HLA, found a similar mutually exclusive relationship on
two other human embryonal carcinomas. It should be noted, however,
with respect to the study of Holden *et al.*, that Hakansson and Peterson
(1976) have found β_2-m on blastocysts in association with surface structures other than MHC products.

Klein (1977) questions the significance of these studies suggesting
sequential development of T and K,D,L antigens. He cites a variety of
evidence indicating that overlapping occurs. His criticisms cannot be
taken lightly. However, it seems to me that a considerable overlap can
be explained by the assumption that different *T* loci are expressed on
different cell lineages and are turned off at different times. As each one
is turned off it is succeeded by *H-2*, but only on that particular cell
lineage. The use of teratomas in which developmental processes are
presumably simplified overcomes this difficulty.

That the F9 antigen, as expected of a *T*-locus antigen, does, in fact,
play a regulatory role in early differentiation, is suggested by a study of
Kemler *et al.* (1977). Mouse embryos in the early cleavage stages were
treated with mouse anti-F9, rabbit anti-F9, and with Fab fragments of
these antibodies. The Fab fragment of the rabbit anti-F9, but none of the
other antibodies, while not interfering with cleavage, prevented formation of compact morulae and blastocysts. The antiserum had this effect
when added from the 2-cell to the 8-cell stage or even later, but not after
the start of blastocoel formation. The effect was reversible; 30-cell
embryos washed free of the antibody were capable of reorganization and
of normal development when reimplanted. Why only the Fab fragment
of the rabbit anti-F9 produced this effect is unknown, although the
identity of the antigen with which the Fab fragment reacted was established by blocking experiments.

IV. POSSIBLE ROLE OF CLASS I PRODUCTS IN CELL INTERACTIONS

If the *H-2* complex was derived from a primitive *T* complex of early
invertebrates, and if the *T* complex exerts its effect on development
through a regulation of cell interactions, then it is reasonable to assume
that at least parts of the *H-2* complex are concerned with cell interactions. This is a tenuous sort of evidence. There are several reports that
more directly suggest a role for K,D,L in cell interactions.

Bartlett and Edidin (1978) have studied the effect of *H-2* type on the adhesion of isolated fibroblasts to fibroblast monolayers. All fibroblasts were passed through at least two generations in culture before use. Monolayers were prepared from both embryonic and adult (lung or mesentery) fibroblasts. The isolated fibroblasts were prepared by trypsinization, labeled at once with [^{3}H]leucine, and added to wells bearing the monolayers. Supernatant fluids were removed at 5-minute intervals, the layers were washed, and adherent radioactivity was determined.

After a very brief lag, adhesion occurred rapidly, reaching 30% in 30 minutes. *H-2* incompatible cells showed as good adhesion as *H-2* compatible cells. The *H-2* genotype of the monolayers, but not of the free cells, however, did affect adhesion. With young monolayers, *H-2^k* cells bound fewer free cells and *H-2^s* monolayers more free cells than other genotypes. This was confirmed with *H-2^k* and *H-2^s* on several different backgrounds and with cells from an *H-2^k* backcross. In an F_1, high adhesion was dominant. This effect was reversed when adult rather than embryonic cell monolayers were used, but whether this was due to age or to cell source is uncertain. With respect to the surprising influence of *H-2^k*, the authors suggest that it may be related to low levels of cAMP associated with this genotype.

Tests of the effect of various antisera on adhesion implicated H-2K, D, and/or L as the active cell surface components. Of various antisera tested, including anti-Ia, anti-Thy-1, and a xenogeneic "anti-major cell surface protein" (CSP), only classical anti-H-2 sera affected adhesion. These sera reduced binding by 30–40%. With F_1 cells, the effect of anti-H-2 against the separate parental genotypes was additive. The effect of the anti-H-2 cannot have been due to capping, since fibroblasts do not show this phenomenon. The absence of effect of anti-Thy-1 and anti-CSP was not due to lack of the corresponding antigens on the cell surface; tests showed them to be present.

The authors found 10–20% variation in adhesion rates between experiments, but this was limited by comparing results obtained only under conditions as similar as possible, and in any case did not introduce an element that impaired the statistical significance of the results.

These results strongly suggest that the classical H-2 antigens play a role in cell adhesion. Since the free cells were used soon after trypsinization, it may be that the effect of H-2 is undirectional, requiring the presence of H-2 (or substantial amounts of H-2) on only one of the two cells. The results do not tell us whether H-2 or some substance associated with it is the agent immediately responsible for the adhesion, but the authors express a preference for the latter alternative.

Zelený et al. (1978) have reported a study similar to that of Bartlett and Edidin (1978), but with differences in detail and substantially different results. Here too, however, H-2 played the predominant role. The studies were similar in that adhesion of radiolabled free cells to an adherant cell layer was the basis of the tests, but instead of using fibroblasts, Zelený et al. used bone marrow or peritoneal exudate cells (presumably therefore mostly macrophages) for the cell layer and bone marrow or lymph node cells (presumably mostly lymphocytes) as the test cells. Since the test cells had not been trypsinized, they could well have played an active role in any observed adhesion and, insofar as they were lymphocytes, could have done this through recognition structures that would be lacking from fibroblasts. The results, in any case, were quite different, since in this study H-2 isogenicity vs allogenicity was the determining factor, with the matched, isogeneic cells showing the greater adhesion. It must be added that the test system used by Zelený et al. yielded results with a high level of uncontrollable variability. The authors believe that the observed differences were nevertheless significant, but their results certainly need confirmation.

Another pair of studies that implies a role for H-2, and more specifically for the K,D,L products of H-2, in cell interactions, used the homing of ^{51}Cr-labeled lymphocytes to the lymph nodes. It is known that one of the major circulating pathways of certain classes of lymphocytes is directly from the blood to the nodes via the endothelium of small venules. The lymphocytes pass through, not between, the cells of the endothelium (Marchesi and Gowans, 1964). When labeled lymphocytes are injected, it is therefore not surprising that substantial radioactivity can be recovered from the nodes. In separate studies, Viklický et al. (1976) and Degos and Colombani (1979) tested the effect on this homing to the nodes of H gene disparity. In both studies it was found that in H-2 allogeneic combinations there was substantially less homing to the nodes than in H-2 isogeneic combinations. Homing to other organs (liver, lung, spleen) was essentially unaffected. The effect of H-2 disparity was fully apparent at 24 hours. Such a prompt effect, the authors suggest, points to a nonimmunological mechanism. Also X-irradiation of the recipients did not significantly increase homing in the disparate combinations. The study of Degos and Colombani, through the use of appropriate congenic donor–recipient pairs, adds the information that the active *H-2* regions in the homing response were *H-2K* and *H-2D*. A match at *K* and/or *D* was both necessary and sufficient for homing. Non-*H-2* differences had no effect.

In these studies, as in the tests of *H-2* influence on cell adhesion, the question arises whether *H-2* is itself the active agent or whether it acts via some associated molecules. Because the H-2 antigen is widely distributed and not limited to lymphocytes, Degos and Colombani prefer the more complex, interaction mechanism. It will be remembered that Bartlett and Edidin preferred the complex interpretation of their cell adhesion results.

Relevant to the role of the MHC in cell interactions are observations of tissue heterogeneity in allophenic mice (Mintz, 1977). In these mice derived from the fusion of two cleaving eggs of disparate inbred origins, *H-2* incompatible cells coexist in complete harmony. The mixture is extensive but not complete. Nevertheless, the conclusion is inescapable that normal development is possible despite mismatched MHC products or, for that matter, mismatched products of all polymorphic loci. Incompatibility reactions, it would seem, are the exclusive domain of lymphoid cell clones. These observations place severe restrictions on the sort of mechanisms that can be postulated as regulators of cell behavior during development.

Koch and Smith (1978) have reported an observation relevant to the hypothesis that the Class I products play a role in cell interactions. They have found that, in a mastocytoma that exfoliates large amounts of membrane-derived material, *H-2* products and actin are shed together and apparently as a unit. Since actin is an internal microfilament protein, an association with K,D,L would permit transmembrane interactions and possibly the transmission of messages. K,D,L,—actin associations probably do not occur in unstimulated lymphocytes. However, an observation that surface immunoglobulin on lymphocytes becomes attached to actin when cross-linked by rabbit anti-mouse immunoglobulin suggests that association might occur under certain conditions of stimulation (Flanagan and Koch, 1978).

V. A Summary of What We Kknow about T Cell Recognizers

In the cell interaction studies reviewed in Section IV, attention centered on Class I products as the active agent. When we examine cell interactions in which T lymphocytes are one of the interacting parties, a wholly different class of structures, the T cell recognizers,[1] is a potential candidate for involvement. Since, as we shall find, the products of the MHC and, indeed, of several other chromosome 17 loci, are in some unique way the targets of T cell recognizers, this particular class of interaction structures has an important place in this paper.

An enormous literature has developed concerning T cell recognizers. I shall present a condensed and highly selective review. More details will be found in Golub (1977), Snell (1978), and McDevitt (1978).

The chemical nature of the T lymphocyte recognizer(s) has been the subject of intensive debate and still is not fully resolved. A view that now has considerable support, however, is that the T recognizer, or at least a major category of T recognizers, resembles in some but not all respects classical B cell immunoglobulin. In particular, it appears that immunoglobulin and T recognizers share the same or very similar variable regions. Anti-immunoglobulin variable region (anti-idiotype) antibodies show clear cross-reactions with T cell recognizers (Julius *et al.*, 1977; Krammer, 1978; Krawinkel *et al.*, 1978; Mozes, 1978). The constant regions are probably different. More specifically, the T cell-derived antigen-specific T cell helper and suppressor factors have an Ia (Class II) component perhaps analogous to the immunoglobulin constant region. Whether this is the constant region of cell-bound T recognizers is uncertain; it may be added only on release.

Our subsequent review of other aspects of T cell recognizers will, I believe, be easier to follow if I describe here a theory now gaining currency that T lymphocytes, or at least some T lymphocytes, have two recognizers per cell. This theory has been proposed or favored by a number of authors, e.g., Janeway *et al.* (1976), Zinkernagel *et al.* (1978a,b), Snell (1978), and von Boehmer *et al.* (1978). I shall follow in general the scheme developed in detailed and persuasive form by von Boehmer *et al.* The proposed structures and their properties are diagrammed in Fig. 2.

[1]The recognition structures of T cells have been called by a variety of names. The terms *receptors, antigen receptors,* and *recognition structures* have been commonly used. The use of receptor is confusing because the same term is applied to the wide range of cell surface structures that bind such physiologically normal products as hormones and complement. The term *recognizers* has also been used (Bodmer, 1972; Edelman, 1975; Snell, 1978) and is more descriptive than the terms more generally employed. I shall use it here.

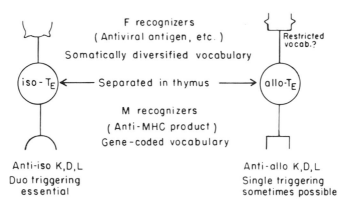

FIG. 2. Hypothesized dual recognizers of T effector lymphocytes. von Boehmer *et al.* (1978) have proposed a very similar theory of dual recognizers.

We may call the two recognizers of the T cell the MHC, or M, recognizer and the foreign, or F, recognizer.

The first is genetically programmed to recognize MHC and MHC-related products. On T helper cells it is slanted toward Class II (*I* region) products and on T effector cells toward Class I (*K,D,L*) products. Its vocabulary includes forms reactive with all (?) allelic forms of these products, although not in any precise one-to-one relationship. The clones can be divided into two groups, those that bear iso-recognizers and those that bear allo-recognizers. The former, in any given individual, are self-reactive (but may have allo cross-reactions); the latter react only with foreign *H-2* products. An important postulate of the theory is that the iso-M clones are not deleted, but rather are altered so as not to be activated through stimulation of the iso-M recognizer alone, a stimulation that must inevitably occur in the individual bearing them. Alternatively, clones with strong iso-reactions may be deleted and only clones with reactions too weak, acting alone, to trigger the cells retained (Janeway *et al.*, 1976). Whatever the precise nature of the events that give the iso-reacting clones their special properties, there is strong evidence that these events occur in the thymus. This has been shown by experiments with chimeras and thymic transplants (Zinkernagel *et al.*, 1978a,b). The M recognizers postulated here are similar to the T_0 recognizers of von Boehmer *et al.* (1978).

The second or F recognizer, like antibody, has a broad spectrum of recognition ability. There is no firm evidence as to how this diversified group of recognizers is generated, and for our purposes it is not important, but somatic processes are probably involved. Zinkernagel *et al.* suggest that the diversity may arise in the thymus by a Jerne (1971, 1976) mechanism. von Boehmer *et al.* also suggest this, and add the postulate that the M and F (their T_0 and T_1) recognizers on any given cell lineage are initially identical. It is essential to our hypothesis, as we shall see from later discussion, that clones with iso-M recognizers bear also F recognizers. The evidence with respect to clones bearing allo-M recognizers is not so clear. However, Heber-Katz and Wilson (1976) found that T-cell clones selected for reactivity to a single foreign MHC genotype could still respond to sheep erythrocytes, suggesting dual responsiveness. [See also the study of Marbrook *et al.* (1978) described below.] One possibility is that allo-M clones have a second recognizer, but one with a more restricted vocabulary than that present on iso-M clones. Such an assumption is in keeping with the Jerne hypothesis since Jerne (1971) postulates that the mutational drive which generates the somatic variability in immunoglobulins occurs in self-recognizing clones. The evidence for the presence of dual receptors is clearest for T effector cells but probably applies also to T helper and T suppressor cells. One interesting point concerns the relationship of the genes that give rise to the two receptors on a single clone. One possibility is that, on any given stem cell, the activated immunoglobulin genes are selected at random. Alternatively, as postulated by von Boehmer *et al.*, the same genes that give rise to the M recognizer might be both retained in unaltered form and, through some process of duplication and somatic variation, used as the source of the F recognizer. This could mean that a special F vocabulary would tend to be associated with a special MHC genotype. This, as argued persuasively by von Boehmer *et al.* (1978), has interesting implications for *Ir-1* gene function.

The reader will see, as we now very briefly summarize some of the evidence concerning T cell recognizers, that there is substantial support for, though certainly not yet firm proof of, this theory of dual recognizers. [See Snell (1978) for more details.]

First, we note two lines of evidence that helper cell recognizers are *I*-region oriented and effector cell recognizers are K,D,L oriented. The mixed lymphocyte reaction, a helper cell phenomenon, is stimulated primarily by Ia (Class II) antigens. There are important exceptions (e.g., *H-2K* mutants), but the general orientation is clear. The target of the effector cell in cell-mediated cell lysis, on the other hand, is typically K,D,L (Class I) products. This points to *I*-region directed helper cell recognizers and *K,D,L*-directed effector cell recognizers. Even more specific evidence of this comes from a study of Nagy *et al.* (1976). These authors found that, when T cells were cocultured with inactivated target cells, the cells with the markers typical of helpers, after several days of culture, had *I*-region antigens bound to their surface, and the cells with the markers typical of effectors had K,D antigens bound to their surface.

Another well established point that clearly applies to T effector cells and probably to T helper cells is that a surprisingly high proportion of all clones respond to MHC antigens. This is a major basis for the postulate that T cells carry a recognizer directed, not to the enormous diversity of antigens in general, but specifically to MHC products. Marbrook *et al.* (1978) have added an important extension of this thesis. They compared the effector activation produced by *H-2* disparities alone as compared with *H-2* plus multiple non-*H-2* disparities. They used a strictly *in vitro* system in which non-H-2 antigens are not effective as targets of cell-mediated lysis (Bevan, 1975). The joint disparities led to a much higher level of clone activation than *H-2* alone. Their proposed explanation is that the allo-recognizing clones do, in fact, have a second, generalized recognizer. Only high-affinity anti-K,D,L clones are activated when the only disparity is at *H-2*. With multiple disparities, permitting stimulation also via the second, F recognizer, many more clones are triggered.

The phenomenon that originally led to the hypothesis of dual receptors is known as *H-2* restriction. *H-2* restriction was foreshadowed by Lawrence (1959) but has only recently become an important part of our thinking. It is documented by an extensive literature and some very complex experiments, but the essential points can be stated briefly. The essence of *H-2* restriction is that T effector lymphocytes are triggered to cytotoxic activity by non-MHC cell-surface antigens, whether native non-H-2 or introduced, only if (*a*) the targets share K or D (or L?) with the immunizing cells; and (*b*) the responders were generated in a thymus sharing K or D (or L?) with the targets and therefore, if they see these particular allelic forms of K,D,L at all, see them as self (Zinkernagel *et al.,* 1978b). There may be partial exceptions (Matzinger and

Mirkwood, 1978). The *H-2* restriction phenomenon, as thus outlined, has been shown to apply to virally infected cells (Zinkernagel and Doherty, 1974), to chemically modified cells (Shearer, 1974), to the H-Y (male) antigen (Simpson and Gordon, 1977), and to a variety of other minor histocompatibility antigens (Bevan, 1975). Similar rules probably hold for T helper cells, except that here the critical H-2 antigens are *I*-region products.

A striking manifestation of *H-2* restriction is seen when the target of the cell-mediated attack is a cultured cell line entirely lacking the K,D,L antigens. Several such lines have been established. With these lines, no lysis occurs whatever the non-MHC target (Bevan and Hyman, 1977; Dennert and Hyman, 1977; Doherty *et al.*, 1977; Zinkernagel and Oldstone, 1976). Apparently the T effector cell cannot be triggered unless the target carries a Class I MHC product, as well as some foreign non-MHC antigen. The Class I product, as we have noted, may be seen as self, and still be an essential component in the triggering.

Besides the hypothesis that *H-2* restriction is due to the presence of two recognizers on T cells (the dual recognition hypothesis), an altered-self hypothesis has been noted as a possibility (Zinkernagel and Doherty, 1974). According to this hypothesis, a single T cell recognizer reacts with a combination product formed by the union of an MHC product and some other antigen. This may very well be a valid hypothesis in some cases (see, e.g., Finberg *et al.*, 1978).

It should be noted that, besides *H-2* restriction of the ability of T effector cells to respond to a variety of antigens on target cells, there also may be cases of *H-2* restriction of cooperation between cell pairs such as macrophages and helper cells (reviewed in Snell, 1978, 1979). The mechanism in these cases is probably quite different.

While the K,D,L restriction of T effector cell activity appears to be a widely applicable rule, there is one highly significant exception. Chromosome 17 products, even those outside the *K–D* boundaries, are not *K,D* restricted. This has been shown to apply to *I*-region products (Billings *et al.*, 1977; Klein *et al.*, 1977), to two distinct antigens determined by loci in the *Qa–Tla* region (Forman and Flaherty, 1978; Klein and Chiang, 1978), and to the F9 antigen presumed to be the product of a locus in the *T* complex (Wagner *et al.*, 1978). It should be emphasized that cell surface alloantigens determined by genes not on chromosome 17 *are H-2* restricted. It would appear that T cell recognizers see a wide range of chromosome 17 products as belonging to a family with properties quite distinct from those of all other cell surface antigens, be they native (minor H antigens) or foreign. There is no specific evidence as to the recognizer involved, but it is logical to suppose that it is the M recognizer. This further emphasizes the uniqueness both of the recognizer and of the class of antigens that it recognizes.

I cannot leave the subject of *H-2* recognition without noting a report that mice can smell H-2 (Yamazaki *et al.*, 1976). The evidence comes from studies of mating preference. What *H-2* product carries the olfactory stimulus is uncertain, and also the nature of the recognizer, but more than one MHC gene may be involved (Andrews and Boyse, 1978, Yamaguchi *et al.*, 1978).

VI. WHY WERE MHC ANTIGENS SINGLED OUT AS T CELL TARGETS?

We saw in Section V that Class I and Class II antigens of the MHC seem, to a unique degree, to be the targets of the T-cell recognizers. Why did this association come into being? Two answers have been proposed. We shall now examine these.

The first possibility is that anti-MHC reactions evolved to prevent fusion with and parasitism by individuals of the same or a closely related species. The commonly cited basis for this hypothesis is the observation that fusion sometimes does occur in nature between adjacent, sessile marine invertebrates. It is seen, for example, in corals (Hildemann *et al.*, 1975) and probably, at a higher level, in ascidians (Oka, 1970; see also Burnet, 1971). Burnet (several papers; summaries in Burnet 1971, 1976) has suggested as possible alternative or supplemental factors the parasitism, at the vertebrate level, of one species of cyclostome by another and the danger of venereal tumors. The latter was previously suggested as a source of *H-2* polymorphism by Gorer (1960). The attraction of these alternatives is that they do not require the postulate that typical cellular immunity appeared at the invertebrate level. A whole lamprey eel, however, would be a formidable object for successful attack by T cells armed with a nascent rejection system. And with respect to venereal tumors, their apparent complete absence in inbred strains of mice, which should be peculiarly susceptible to them, hardly makes them look like a major threat. It seems to me, then, that if we accept natural grafts as the stimulus for T cell evolution, we will probably have to assume a prevertebrate origin.

An inversion of the line of reasoning presented here is to assume that the threat of colony fusion in invertebrates led originally, not to an MHC-directed T cell immunity, but to the evolution of the MHC itself. Hildemann (1977) apparently favors this concept.

In all forms of the fusion-parasitism theory, it is assumed that most invertebrates possess a primitive recognition capacity capable of responding to products of the primitive MHC or some comparable structure. Certainly it is now established that a wide variety of invertebrates possess the ability to reject allografts (reviews in Hildemann and Cooper, 1970; Hildemann, 1977). The possession of this ability implies a capacity to discriminate between self and nonself. Theodor (1970) and Burnet (1976) suggest that this capacity is based on a recognition of *self* rather than of foreignness, although complementary structures rather than the pairing of like with like may be involved.

There is a woeful lack of detailed information on invertebrate recognition structures, but the work of Oka (1970) on the genetics of rejection in ascidians does give some credence to the Theodor–Burnet postulate. Oka found that rejection was determined by a single, polymorphic locus. Unlike the *H-2* situation, however, where a single foreign allele in a graft causes rejection, the presence, in the ascidian graft, of a single native allele causes acceptance. Thus, in the ascidian, a/b can reject c/d but not a/c, a/d, b/c, or b/d. Burnet (1976) suggests that this primitive recognition system may still be present in vertebrates.

With respect of Oka's work, I should note that other studies of the genetics of graft rejection in invertebrates have suggested more complex and less easily interpreted systems (review in Klein, 1977).

When and how the primitive recognition was replaced or had superimposed on it the present T cell system we shall examine in Section VIII.

A second route through which an ancestral MHC might have become tied to T cell immunity is by way of a need, in the evolving vertebrate, for increasingly effective defenses against viral disease.

The first clue that *H-2* is involved with viral disease came from the discovery, independently made by Lilly *et al.* (1964) and Tennant (1963; Tennant and Snell, 1966), that susceptibility to viral leukemogenesis is *H-2* linked. This was confirmed in numerous subsequent studies.

Evidence of a tie between the MHC and viral diseases has come subsequently from many sources. Thus a tie of the MHC not only to viruses but also to T cell immunity is indicated by the *H-2* restriction of cell-mediated immunity against virally infected cells (Section V) (review in Snell, 1978).

The development of adequate protection against intracellular parasitism by viruses must have presented a formidable and important evolutionary problem. In vertebrates, the (or at least a) major function of the whole T cell mechanism is widely regarded as the containment of such diseases (see, e.g., Langman, 1978; Snell, 1978). As one small sample of the evidence, immunity to influenza virus in mice can be adoptively transferred with immune T cells (Yap *et al.*, 1978).

If T cell immunity developed wholly or in substantial part as an agent for the control of viral infections, why should this lead to an involvement of MHC products? A possible answer relates to the functions of the MHC suggested in Sections IV and VI. Class I products, we suggested, may be, like the F9 *T* locus antigen, a necessary agent in organized growth. By subverting this function, viruses could produce uncontrolled or less controlled growth. They might, in so doing, be acting in the way a Fab antibody fragment directed against F9 acts on very early embryonic growth (Kemler *et al.*, 1976, 1977) (Section III), or in a way at least somewhat similar to that in which anti-*H-2* acts to block cell adhesion (Bartlett and Edidin, 1978) (Section IV). Since cell division is often (always?) favorable to viral replication (Bloom *et al.*, 1977) and in at least one case is known to be virus-induced (Butchko *et al.*, 1978), we may assume that viruses have developed the potential to subvert the processes that control growth. One way they might do this is by interaction with Class I products. And indeed, such interactions do occur (review in Snell, 1978). In one case, for example, human and murine Class I products have been found to be cell surface "receptors" for a virus (Helenius *et al.*, 1978). Perhaps also, in the case of leukemias, the Tla antigen may be involved. This T cell antigen is antigenically altered on many leukemic cells (Boyse *et al.*, 1969). Such virus–MHC product interactions suggest at least to some extent why T cells concerned primarily with eliminating a virus should interact also with K,D,L and their homologs. When we discuss the evolution of T cell recognizers in Section VII, we shall spell out in more detail the reasons for this association.

A corollary of this hypothesis of growth subversion via Class I products is that there might be an advantage of the host in having more than one of these products. If the cell regulatory capacity of one of the products was blocked by attachment of a viral antigen, the capacity could still be maintained by the other products. This could be the explanation for the existence of three Class I loci. The same argument can be used to account for the evolution of MHC polymorphism.

Before proceeding we should note that some authors (e.g., Doherty and Zinkernagel, 1975) favor the hypothesis that the active party in the K,D,L–virus interaction is the host, not the virus. The presumption is that the interaction product provides a superior target for the T effector cell. We may call this the virus trap theory. Polymorphism and multiple Class I loci are explained as providing more traps or more kinds of bait, and hence greater protection. Unless some other function is also assigned to K,D,L, this theory implies simultaneous evolution of T cells and the MHC. In any case, it does use, like the other hypothesis we have been discussing, the threat of viral diseases to explain the MHC-T cell association.

We now turn to the evolution of T cell immunity as it relates to the MHC. I shall suggest that both the fusion-parasitism hypothesis and the virus threat hypothesis have a place in explaining the present interdependence of cellular immunity and the major histocompatibility complex.

VII. THE EVOLUTION OF T CELL RECOGNIZERS

Before discussing the evolution of the structures that we have been considering, I want to offer a philosophical comment on evolutionary speculations. It is my impression that the history of all evolutionary studies is marked by early underestimates of the age of the traits under consideration. With further knowledge, origins are pushed back in time. Man's ancestors assumed the upright position earlier than we once supposed. Ability to use language, expressed in symbols, is further developed in the great apes than we imagined. There is now evidence that warm-blooded dinosaurs antedated the birds and animals. Only an historian of science could evaluate the frequency of this sort of situation, but I suspect that it is common enough so that I can espouse early origins without embarrassment.

My discussion of the evolution of the structures I am considering will be at least as much an attempt, in the light of recent evidence, at synthesis of existing ideas as a proposal of new ones. Obviously, the authors I cite are not responsible for my errors.

The major subject to be considered in this section is the evolution of the immunoglobulin-like T cell recognizers. I must point out first, however, that MHC products on T cells and/or macrophages may be involved in less specialized types of interaction with anitgens or a variety of products on other cells.

Burnet (1976) suggests that the capacity to distinguish self from not self (as distinct from foreign), which he dates back to the invertebrate level, still persists in vertebrates. I find this an appealing suggestion. Any firm evidence is lacking, but the results of Degos and Colombani (1979) on the homing of lymphocytes can be explained on this basis. In fact, there is an intriguing parallel between the genetics of homing found in this study and the genetics of graft acceptance in tunicates described by Oka (1970) (Section VI). In both cases, a single match was necessary for ''acceptance'' (homing in the mouse study). In one case, however, the accompanying disparities were inter-locus and in the other case inter-allelic. In the case of vertebrate homografts, of course, a single *non*-match causes rejection. There is an implication in this line of reasoning that the recognition of self, in both invertebrates and vertebrates, is directly due to MHC products, but Burnet does not suggest this and more complex interpretations are possible.

Klein (1977), in discussing *H-2* restriction, proposes a Class I product self-recognition based on a reaction of like with like. According to this view, the Class I products are themselves acting as one of the two recognizers of the cytotoxic T cell.

Whatever the details of these theories asserting that MHC products are involved in self-recognition, they are potentially complementary to theories that the MHC products regulate cell interactions in development. However, it is not easy to see how they can be reconciled with the peaceful coexistence of MHC-disparate cells seen in allophenic mice.

Another possible tie of MHC products to recognition phenomena has been suggested by Benacerraf (1978) in a search for an explanation for MHC-linked immune response gene (*Ir-1* gene) action. There is considerable evidence that an important part of *Ir-1* gene manifestation occurs through a role of *I*-region (Class II) products in the display of antigen on macrophages (see Katz and Benacerraf, 1976; McDevitt, 1978; Snell, 1978). The antigen is actually probably antigen fragments produced by digestion within the macrophage. Benacerraf suggests that the binding involves perhaps only three or four amino acids on the antigen fragment and that it is specific, a given Ia allelic form being able to bind some antigen fragments but not others. The specificity of Ia-binding and Ig-binding are different, but at least some similarity is implied.

I now turn to the major subject of this section, the evolution of T cell recognizers. My basic thesis will be that T cells and their recognizers evolved in response to both of the potential needs listed in Section VII. Of the two presumed immunoglobulin-like recognizers of T cells (Section V), one, the M recognizer, arose, I suggest, to cope with the problem of fusion-parasitism; the other, the F recognizer, arose at a later date to deal with the problem of viral infection. The two needs thus account for the two recognizers of T cells and thereby for a variety of the T cell–MHC product interactions.

The T-cell system as it exists today in vertebrates is an extraordinarily complex system; its evolution must have involved many separate steps. According to current thinking the immunologic system of cyclostomes is much more like that of mammals than like that of invertebrates. The gap between vertebrates and invertebrates is certainly great, but is it quite so big as we suppose?

Specifically, I suggest that M recognizers appeared in late invertebrates on cells that already had T-cell-like properties. They arose in response to the need for protection from fusion-parasitism because they were more effective in preventing fusion than were the self-recognition mechanisms already in existence. The greater efficiency may have taken several forms, but an obvious one is greater genetic discrimination. If equipped with an M recognizer, a/b could recognize a/c or b/c as foreign whereas individuals carrying only self-recognizers would accept these. Such individuals, if a/b, could reject only c/d or comparable genotypes.

Many invertebrates do have lymphocyte-like cells, perhaps with more properties of vertebrate lymphocytes than was at one time supposed. Thus the lymphocytes of earthworms can be stimulated both with the T-cell mitogen concanavalin A and with the B-cell mitogen *Escherichia coli* lipopolysaccharide (Roch *et al.*, 1975). Presumably, therefore, it was in a cell that already had some T cell properties that the M recognizers originated.

As to the genetic source of the M recognizer, an origin from β_2-microglobulin seems probable. Such an origin has been suggested by Burnet (1976) and is supported by evidence of a considerable homology in amino acid sequence with the individual domains of immunoglobulin (Smithies and Poulik, 1972; Peterson *et al.*, 1974). This homology is especially close in the case of the C_H3 domain (Peterson *et al.*, 1974). Because of the closeness of this one resemblance, Smithies and Poulik (1972) suggest that β_2-m arose from immunoglobulin by way of deletion, but the reciprocal hypothesis is also compatible with the data. The first steps, in our view, were a series of duplications of the β_2-m gene. The conversion of these into an MHC-product recognizer might have been aided by the prexisting capacity to pair with these products. If the *Tla* locus, one of the loci whose end product pairs with β_2-m, was already in existence, perhaps the expression of the M recognizer exclusively on primordial T lymphocytes was tied to the expression of *Tla* only on early T cells.

I suggest that the purpose of the M recognizer was to help prevent fusion-parasitism. The MHC became the target of this relatively efficient lymphocyte-borne recognizer because it was already the target of a more primitive recognizer borne on lymphocyte-like cells. In both cases, a wide cell distribution made the MHC a natural target. A necessary property of such a target would be polymorphism, and by the time the M recognizer appeared this polymorphism had already developed. An important strength of this theory is that it accounts for the MHC orientation of the M recognizer and hence of T cells in general.

But at a later (very early vertebrate?) stage of vertebrate evolution, when fusion-parasitism was no longer a threat, why was the T-cell–M-recognizer system maintained? One possible answer is that it was still needed for different but related functions. Burnet (1963) suggested an immune surveillance function for the same mechanisms that are involved in allograft rejection, and both Burnet (1970) and Klein (1977) have suggested that cells with somatic *H-2* mutants may be potentially cancerous and would be both natural and useful targets. Perhaps, also, M recognizers in vertebrates function as recognizers of virus–MHC interaction products so intimately joined that they are seen as altered self. The alloreactivity seen by Finberg *et al.* (1978) in their study of the Sendai virus may be a case in point.

Whether the postulated T cell-equipped invertebrates are still in existence or have become extinct is a question which, because of lack of evidence, we must leave unanswered.

If the need for M recognizers decreased with the appearance of vertebrates (we are not sure that it did), the need for a recognizer that could strengthen the defense against viral diseases may have increased. Viral infections do occur in invertebrates, though there appears to be little evidence as to their importance (Kurstak and Maramorosch, 1971; Farley, 1976). Perhaps because of more active circulation or other characteristics of vertebrates, they became more threatening at this stage of evolution. In any case, we do have reason to believe that the complex T cell immune system is primarily concerned with viral disease. We suggest that the F recognizers appeared early in vertebrate evolution to meet this need.

T cells, we have suggested, were already in existence with an equipment of M recognizers. We have quite good clues, partly outlined in Section V, as to how these could give rise to other recognizers with a much broader vocabulary of specificities capable of reacting with the great diversity of viral antigens. The route selected, apparently, was not a major diversification of immunoglobulin genes, but a resort to a somatic system of diversification, perhaps by the Jerne mechanism. The result was the evolution of a category of lymphocytes with two recognition structures, the M recognizer and the F recognizer. Such lymphocytes are ideally equipped for dealing with viral infection. Their dual equipment led to the phenomenon of MHC restriction of most T cell immune recognition activities. We also found evidence (Section V) for T cells with allo-M recognizers. Because of the homology of a number of chromosome 17 products, cells with these recognizers "see" all these products in much the same way that they "see" Class I antigens. That is why these products are not MHC restricted.

The suggestions that we have offered so far concern primarily T effector cells. T helper cells, perhaps, evolved somewhat later because of a need for precise regulation of an increasingly complex immune system. The appearance, or at least the elaboration, of Class II products occurred simultaneously.

VIII. The Evolution of the MHC

In our review of the major histocompatibility complex and related chromosome 17 loci (Sections I and III), we found evidence of similarities or significant associations between the T locus products, the K,D,L products, the $Qa–Tla$ products, and perhaps the I-region products. We also noted (Section V) that these products, and apparently these products alone of all cell surface components, are not $H-2$ restricted. The T cells seem to be saying to us that these substances are in some unique way the members of a family. They, therefore, are logical candidates for an evolutionary sequence. The evolution would occur by gene duplication as first suggested, in the context of the MHC, by Stimpfling and Richardson (1965). Since the T antigens are the first to appear in development, we may reasonably assume, following the rule that ontogeny recapitulates phylogeny, that they appeared first in evolution. In fact, the embryological evidence would tend to suggest a very primitive origin.

We do not know the function of the T-locus products, but a reasonable assumption, in the light of the Kemler *et al.* (1977) study already cited, is that they are organizers of cell interactions. This may mean that, indirectly, they regulate growth. Whatever their precise role, we may assume that as invertebrate structure became more complex, similar but more complex cell surface products were needed. The K,D,L antigens, with their wide tissue distribution and a development apparently sequential to that of the T antigens, are logical candidates. And indeed, Gluecksohn-Waelsch and Erickson (1970) have hinted at, and Artz and Bennett (1975) have suggested, homology of these structures.

Genetically, the K,D,L system is, if anything, less complex than the T system. Yet we are suggesting that it assumes a developmental role that becomes increasingly complex. To cope with this problem, we adopt the suggestion of Ohno (1977) that the MHC antigens are plasma membrane anchorage sites for organogenesis-directing proteins. There is evidence that some other cell surface components are physically associated with $H-2K$ and $H-2D$ (Boyse *et al.*, 1968). By bringing a variety of different products into the developmental process, they could cope with increasingly complex developmental situations. Perhaps also, as suggested in Section IV, the K,D,L antigens are transmembrane signal transmitters. A third possible function is some form of self-recognition. The report of Degos and Colombani (1979) (see Section IV) could imply such a function, and a role in cell recognition and cell interactions has been suggested by Jerne (1971), Snell (1971), Bodmer (1972), Dausset *et al.* (1972, 1973), Lengerová *et al.* (1977), and McDevitt (1976). A study of Egorov *et al.* (1977) with *H-K* mutants, ingenious but too complex to describe here, also implies self-recognition. However, any postulate of this sort has to be reconciled with the results from allophenic mice already cited.

We are postulating a prevertebrate appearance of Class I products, but certain observations on vertebrates suggest that these products may not be present even in all vertebrates. Thus urodeles do not show the strong graft rejection typical of MHC disparity in mammals. It may well be, however, that this reflects a deficiency in the T cell system in these groups rather than a deficiency in the MHC (Cohen, 1976).

The Qa–Tla antigens are so much like K,D,L that we must assume a common origin. I suggest that, following the gene duplications that brought the *Qa–Tla* loci into being, it was the *K,D,L* gene products that kept their original function. The *Qa–Tla* family arose when the vertebrate lymphocyte system began to expand in complexity and served again in the capacity of some sort of growth organizer. These antigens probably lost the anchorage function, but perhaps they retained a signal transmission function.

The Ia antigens present a difficult problem because of their structural difference from K,D,L. We saw, however, that their carbohydrate component resembles that of K,D,L and that the response to them of T cell recognizers (presumably the T cell M recognizers) indicates an affinity to K,D,L and various other chromosome 17 products. I suggest, therefore, that they are homologous, and that they diversified to assume the roles in macrophage–lymphocyte interaction and behavior described in Section II.

As to the Class III (*S* region) products, the support for homology is so ambiguous that this issue is best left indeterminate.

There remains only the *G* region. Relatively speaking, this is, in our existing maps, underpopulated. I suggest as a possibility that we will find genes here whose end products are localized in rather specific tissues and function in a *T*-complex-like role during the later stages of differentiation. These stages are so complex that the structures regulat-

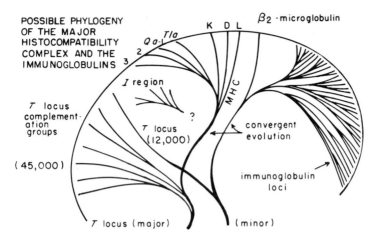

FIG. 3. Proposed evolutionary tree of chromosome 17 products and of the immunoglobulins.

ing them must be complex. A restricted tissue distribution would impede discovery. Perhaps *H-2G* is one of these genes which has been discovered because its product is on red cells.

Figure 3 summarizes the evolutionary progression that I have proposed. I want to emphasize that this is hypothetical; the evidence at present available permits many alternatives. The one thing we can be reasonably sure of is that the ultimate tree will provide an impressive example of gene evolution.

IX. Epilogue

It has been fascinating, as one of the early students of *H-2*, to see this histocompatibility complex, originally the concern only of Gorer and myself and our co-workers, become the center of an enormous research effort. Dausset's discovery of HLA and his realization that this was the homolog of *H-2* was one of the notable steps in this expansion. The outpouring of research has made it abundantly clear that *H-2* and the other MHC systems are extraordinarily complex. Despite the effort expended and the rapidly expanding literature, there still is much to be learned. In this paper I have succumbed to the temptation to theorize on the nature of some of the missing pieces, an occupation, be it said, in which I am not alone. Whether I have read the available portions of Nature's book with sufficient prescience to place the MHC in anywhere near its true context, time alone will tell. The effort has been fun. I hope the result will be at least provocative, and perhaps useful, to some of its readers.

ACKNOWLEDGMENTS

In writing this interpretive review, I have drawn on the work of many authors. The literature is enormous. This makes some sins of omission or commission almost inevitable. I need not say that any such sins were unintentional. I hope and believe that they do not prejudice the line of thought that I have developed.

While I have written from the point of view of someone not now in the thick of major histocompatibility complex research, I would not have undertaken this review had I not devoted many years to histocompatibility studies, first as an active participant, later as a diligent spectator. Throughout my involvement with the subject, I have been helped and encouraged by numerous wonderful colleagues. I cannot name them all, but must acknowledge the contributions of Peter Gorer, William Hildemann, Ralph Graff, Henry Winn, Jack Stimpfling, Judith Tennant, Ivan Hilgert, Marianna Cherry, Peter Démant, Donald Bailey, and Larry Mobraaten. I am indebted to many authors for sending me reprints and preprints, to Drs. Cherry, Heiniger, and Waymouth and Larry Johnson for reading the manuscript, and to Ms. Barbara Dillon for typing.

REFERENCES

Andrews, P. W., and Boyse, E. A. (1978). *Immunogenetics* **6**, 265-268.

Artz, K., and Bennett, D. (1975). *Nature (London)* **256**, 545-547.

Bartlett, P. F., and Edidin, M. (1978). *J. Cell Biol.* **77**, 377-388.

Benacerraf, B. (1978). *J. Immunol.* **120**, 1809-1812.

Bevan, M. J. (1975). *Nature (London)* **256**, 419-421.

Bevan, M. J., and Hyman, R. (1977). *Immunogenetics* **4**, 7-16.

Billings, P., Burakoff, S., Dorf, M. E., and Benacerraf, B. (1977). *J. Exp. Med.* **145**, 1387-1392.

Bloom, R. R., Senik, A., Stoner, G., Ju, G., Nowakowski, M., Kano, S., and Jiminez, L. (1977). *Cold Spring Harbor Symp. Quant. Biol.* **41**, 73-83.

Bodmer, W. F. (1972). *Nature (London)* **237**, 139-145.

Bodmer, W. F. (1978). *Harvey Lect.* **72**, 91-138.

Boyse, E. A., Old, L. J., and Stockert, E. (1966). *Immunopathology, IVth Int. Symp. 4th 1965*, pp. 23-40.

Boyse, E. A., Old, L. J., and Stockert, E. (1968). *Proc. Natl. Acad. Sci. U.S.A.* **60**, 886-893.

Boyse, E. A., Stockert, E., and Old, L. J. (1969). *In* "International Convococation on Immunology" (N. R. Rose and F. Milgrom, eds.), pp. 353-357. Karger, Basel.

Burnet, F. M. (1963). *Med. J. Aust.* **2**, 817-820.

Burnet, F. M. (1970). *Nature (London)* **226**, 123-126.

Burnet, F. M. (1971). *Nature (London)* **232**, 230-235.

Burnet, F. M. (1976). *In* "Receptors and Recognition" (P. Cuatrecasas and M. F. Greaves, eds.), pp. 33–58. Chapman & Hall, London.

Butchko, G. M., Armstrong, R. B., Martin, W. J., and Ennis, F. A. (1978). *Nature (London)* **271**, 66–67.

Carroll, M. C., and Capra, J. D. (1978). *Proc. Natl. Acad. Sci. U.S.A.* **75**, 2424–2428.

Chesboro, B., and Wehrly, K. (1978). *J. Immunol.* **120**, 1081–1085.

Clark, E. A., Harmon, R. C., and Wicker, L. S. (1977). *J. Immunol.* **119**, 648–656.

Cohen, N. (1976). *In* "Phylogeny of Thymus and Bone Marrow-Bursa Cells" (R. K. Wright and E. L. Cooper, eds.), pp. 169–182. North-Holland Publ., Amsterdam.

Coligan, J. E., Kindt, T. J., Ewenstein, B. M., Uehara, H., Nisizawa, T., and Nathenson, S. G. (1978). *Proc. Natl. Acad. Sci. U.S.A.* **75**, 3390–3394.

Cramer, D. V., Davis, B. K., Shonnard, J. W., Stark, O., and Gill, T. J., III. (1978). *J. Immunol.* **120**, 179–187.

Cudkowicz, G., and Stimpfling, J. H. (1964). *Science* **147**, 1056.

da Silva, F. P., Hoecker, G. F., Day, N. K., Vienne, K., and Rubinstein, P. (1978). *Proc. Natl. Acad. Sci. U.S.A.* **75**, 963–965.

Dausset, J., Lebrun, A., and Sasportes, M. (1972). *C. R. Acad. Sci., Ser D* **275**, 2279–2282.

Dausset, J., Sasportes, M., and Lebrun, A. (1973). *Transplant. Proc.* **5**, 1511–1515.

David, C., McCormick, J. F., and Stimpfling, J. H. (1978). *In* "*Ir* Genes and Ia Antigens" (H. O. McDevitt, ed.), pp. 9–19. Academic Press, New York.

Degos, L., Pla, M., and Colombani, J. M. (1979). *Eur. J. Immunol.* **9**, 808–814.

Démant, P., Snell, G. D., Hess, M., Lemonnier, F., Neauport-Sautes, C., and Kourilsky, F. (1976). *J. Immunogen.* **2**, 263–271.

Dennert, G., and Hyman, R. (1977). *Eur. J. Immunol.* **7**, 251–257.

Doherty, P. C., and Zinkernagel, R. M. (1975). *Lancet* **1**, 1406.

Doherty, P. C., Solter, D., and Knowles, B. B. (1977). *Nature (London)* **266**, 361–362.

Dubois, P., Fellous, M., Gachelin, G., Jacob, F., and Kemler, R. (1976). *Transplantation* **22**, 467–473.

Edelman, G. M. (1975). *In* "The Cell Surface, Immunological and Chemical Approaches" (B. D. Kahan and R. Reisfeld, eds.), pp. 260–266. Plenum, New York.

Edidin, M., and Gooding, L. R. (1975). *In* "Teratomas and Differentiation" (M. I. Sherman and D. Solter, eds.), pp. 109–121. Academic Press, New York.

Egorov, I. K., Mnatsakanyan, Y. A., and Popov, L. E. (1977). *Immunogenetics* **5**, 65–74.

Farley, C. A. (1976). *Prog. Exp. Tumor Res.* **20**, 283–294.

Finberg, R., Burakoff, S. J., Cantor, H., and Benacerraf, B. (1978). *Proc. Natl. Acad. Sci. U.S.A.* **75**, 5145–5149.

Flaherty, L. (1976). *Immunogenetics* **3**, 533–539.

Flaherty, L., Zimmerman, D., and Hansen, T. H. (1978). *Immunogenetics* **6**, 245–251.

Flanagan, J., and Koch, G. L. F. (1978). *Nature (London)* **273**, 278–281.

Forman, J., and Flaherty, L. (1978). *Immunogenetics* **6**, 227–233.

Freed, J. H., and Nathenson, S. G. (1977). *J. Immunol.* **119**, 477–482.

Frelinger, J. G., Wettstein, P. J., Frelinger, J. A., and Hood, L. (1978). *Immunogenetics* **6**, 125–135.

78 GEORGE D. SNELL

Gill, T. J., III, Cramer, M. V., and Kunz, H. W. (1978). *Am. J. Pathol.* **90,** 737–777.

Gluecksohn-Waelsch, S., and Erickson, P. P. (1970). *Curr. Top. Dev. Biol.* **5,** 281–316.

Golub, E. S. (1977). "The Cellular Basis of the Immune Response." Sinauer Assoc., Sunderland, Massachusetts.

Gorer, P. A. (1936). *Br. J. Exp. Pathol.* **17,** 42–50.

Gorer, P. A. (1960). *In* "Cellular Aspects of Immunity" (G. E. W. Wolstenholme and M. O'Connor, eds.), pp. 330–347. Little, Brown, Boston, Massachusetts.

Gorer, P. A., Lyman, S., and Snell, G. D. (1948). *Proc. R. Soc. London, Ser. B* **135,** 499–505.

Götze, D., ed. (1977). "The Major Histocompatibility System in Man and Animals." Springer-Verlag, Berlin and New York.

Hakansson, S., and Peterson, P. A. (1976): *Transplantation* **21,** 358–360.

Hammerberg, C., and Klein, J. (1975). *Nature (London)* **258,** 296–299.

Heber-Katz, E., and Wilson, D. B. (1976). *J. Exp. Med.* **143,** 701–711.

Helenius, A., Morein, B., Fries, E., Simons, K., Robinson, P., Schirrmacher, V., Terhorst, C., and Strominger, J. L. (1978). *Proc. Natl. Acad. Sci. U.S.A.* **75,** 3846–3850.

Hildemann, W. H. (1977). *Immunogenetics* **5,** 193–202.

Hildemann, W. H., and Cooper, E. L., eds. (1970). "Phylogeny of Transplantation Reactions." *Transplant. Proc.* **2,** 179–247.

Hildemann, W. H., Linthicum, D. S., and Vann, D. C. (1975). *In* "Immunologic Phylogeny" (W. H. Hildemann and A. A. Benedict, eds.). Plenum, New York.

Hogan, B., Fellous, M., Avner, P., and Jacob, F. (1977). *Nature (London)* **270,** 515–518.

Holden, S., Bernard, O., Artz, K., Whitmore, W. F., Jr., and Bennet, D. (1977). *Nature (London)* **270,** 518–520.

Jacob, F. (1977). *Immunol. Rev.* **33,** 3–32.

Janeway, C. A., Jr., Wigzell, H., and Binz, H. (1976). *Scand. J. Immunol.* **5,** 993–1001.

Jerne, N. K. (1971). *Eur. J. Immunol.* **1,** 1–9.

Jerne, N. K. (1976). *Harvey Lect.* **70,** 73–110.

Julius, M. H., Cosenza, H., and Augustin, A. A. (1977). *Nature (London)* **267,** 437–440.

Katz, D. H., and Benacerraf, B., eds. (1976). "The Role of Products of the Histocompatibility Gene Complex in Immune Responses." Academic Press, New York.

Katz, D. H., Armerding, D., and Eshlar, Z. (1976). *In* "The Role of Products of the Histocompatibility Gene Complex in Immune Responses" (D. H. Katz and B. Benacerraf, eds.), pp. 541–552. Academic Press, New York.

Kemler, R., Babinet, C., Condamine, H., Gachelin, G., Guenet, J. L., and Jacob, F. (1976). *Proc. Natl. Acad. Sci. U.S.A.* **73,** 4080–4084.

Kemler, R., Babinet, C., Eisen, H., and Jacob, F. (1977). *Proc. Natl. Acad. Sci. U.S.A.* **74,** 4449–4452.

Klein, J. (1975). "Biology of the Mouse Histocompatibility-2 Complex." Springer-Verlag, Berlin and New York.

Klein, J. (1977). *In* "The Major Histocompatibility Complex in Man and Animals." (D. Götze, ed.), pp. 339–378. Springer-Verlag, Berlin and New York.

Klein, J., and Chiang, C. L. (1978). *Immunogenetics* **6**, 235–243.

Klein, J., and Hammerberg, C. (1977). *Immunol. Rev.* **33**, 70–104.

Klein, J., Hauptfield, V., and Hauptfield, M. (1975). *Immunogenetics* **2**, 141–150.

Klein, J., Chiang, C. L., and Hauptfield, V. (1977). *J. Exp. Med.* **145**, 450–454.

Koch, G. L. E., and Smith, M. J. (1978). *Nature (London)* **273**, 274–278.

Krammer, P. H. (1978). *J. Exp. Med.* **147**, 25–38.

Krawinkel, V., Cramer, M., Melchers, I., Iwanishi-Kari, T., and Rajewski, K. (1978). *J. Exp. Med.* **147**, 1341–1347.

Kurstak, E., and Maramorosch, K. (1971). "Comparative Virology." Academic Press, New York.

Langman, R. E. (1978). *Rev. Physiol. Biochem. Pharmacol.* **81**, 1–37.

Lawrence, H. S. (1959). *Physiol. Rev.* **39**, 811–859.

Lengerová, A. L., Zelený, V., Haskovec, C., and Hilgert, I. (1977). *Eur. J. Immunol.* **7**, 62–69.

Levinson, J. R., and McDevitt, H. O. (1976). *J. Exp. Med.* **144**, 834–839.

Lilly, F., Boyse, E. A., and Old, L. J. (1964). *Lancet* **2**, 1207–1217.

McDevitt, H. O. (1976). *Fed. Proc.* **35**, 2168–2173.

McDevitt, H. O., ed. (1978). "*Ir* Genes and Ia Antigens." Academic Press, New York.

McDevitt, H. O., and Chinitz, A. (1969). *Science* **163**, 1207–1208.

McDevitt, H. O., Delovitch, T. L., Press, J. L., and Murphy, D. B. (1976). *Transplant. Rev.* **30**, 197–235.

Marbrook, J., Nana, Y., and Miller, J. F. A. P. (1978). *J. Exp. Med.* **148**, 324–328.

Marchesi, V. T., and Gowans, J. L. (1964). *Proc. R. Soc. London, Ser. B* **159**, 283–290.

Matzinger, P., and Mirkwood, G. (1978). *J. Exp. Med.* **148**, 84–92.

Michaelson, J., Flaherty, L., Vitetta, E., and Poulick, M. D. (1977). *J. Exp. Med.* **145**, 1066–1070.

Mintz, B. (1977). *Harvey Lect.* **71**, 193–246.

Mozes, E. (1978). *In* "*Ir* Genes and Ia Antigens " (H. O. McDevitt, ed.), pp. 475–485. Academic Press, New York.

Nagy, Z., Elliott, B. E., and Nabholz, M. (1976). *J. Exp. Med.* **144**, 1545–1553.

Ohno, S. (1977). *Immunol. Rev.* **33**, 59–69.

Oka, H. (1970). *In* "Profiles of Japanese Science and Scientists" (H. Yukawa, ed.), pp. 196–206. Kodansha, Tokyo.

Peterson, P. A., Cunningham, B. A., Beggård, I., and Edelman, G. M. (1974). *Proc. Natl. Acad. Sci. U.S.A.* **69**, 1697–1701.

Roch, P., Valembois, P., and Du Pasquier, L. (1975). *In* "Immunologic Phylogeny" (W. H. Hildemann and A. A. Benedict, eds.), pp. 45–54. Plenum, New York.

Shearer, G. M. (1974). *Eur. J. Immunol.* **4**, 527–533.

Shreffler, D. C. (1976). *Transplant. Rev.* **32**, 140–167.

Simpson, E., and Gordon, R. D. (1977). *Immunol. Rev.* **35**, 59–75.

Smithies, O., and Poulik, M. D. (1972). *Science* **175**, 187–189.

Snell, G. D. (1968). *Folia Biol. (Prague)* **14**, 335–358.

Snell, G. D. (1971). *In* "Immunogenetics of the *H-2* System." (A. Lengerová and M. Vijtisková, eds.), p. 352. Karger, Basel.

Snell, G. D. (1978). *Immunol. Rev.* **38**, 3–69.

Snell, G. D. (1979). *Adv. Genet.* **20,** 291–355.

Snell, G. D., Winn, H. J., Stimpfling, J. H., and Parker, S. J. (1960). *J. Exp. Med.* **112,** 293–314.

Snell, G. D., Dausset, J., and Nathenson, S. (1976). "Histocompatibility." Academic Press, New York.

Stanton, T. H., and Boyse, E. O. (1976). *Immunogenetics* **3,** 525–531.

Stimpfling, J. H., and Richardson, A. (1965). *Genetics* **51,** 831–846.

Tennant, J. R. (1963). The Roscoe B. Jackson Memorial Laboratory 34th Annual Report, pp. 30–31.

Tennant, J. R., and Snell, G. D. (1966). *Natl. Cancer Inst. Monogr.* **22,** 61–72.

Theodor, J. L. (1970). *Nature (London)* **227,** 690–692.

Uhr, J. W., Vitetta, E. S., Klein, J., Poulik, M. D., Klapper, D. G., and Capra, J. D. (1977). *Cold Spring Harbor Symp. Quant. Biol.* **41,** 363–368.

Viklický, V., Peknicová, J., and Polacková, M. (1976). *Folia Biol. (Prague)* **22,** 159–168.

Vitetta, E. S., Artz, K., Bennett, D., Boyse, E. A., and Jacob, F. (1975). *Proc. Natl. Acad. Sci. U.S.A.* **72,** 3215–3219.

Vitetta, E. S., Poulik, M. D., Klein, J., and Uhr, J. W. (1976). *J. Exp. Med.* **144,** 179–192.

von Boehmer, H., Hass, W., and Jerne, N. K. (1978). *Proc. Natl. Acad. Sci. U.S.A.* **75,** 2439–2442.

Wagner, H., Starzinski-Powitz, A., Röllinghoff, M., Goldstein, P., and Jakob, H. (1978). *J. Exp. Med.* **147,** 251–264.

Yamaguchi, M. Yamazaki, K., and Boyse, E. A. (1978). *Immunogenetics* **6,** 261–264.

Yamazaki, K., Boyse, E. A. Miké, V., Thaler, H. T., Mathieson, B. J., Abbott, J., Boyse, J., Zayas, Z. A., and Thomas, L. (1976). *J. Exp. Med.* **144,** 1324–1335.

Yap, K. L., Ada, G. L., and McKenzie, I. F. C. (1978). *Nature (London)* **273,** 238–239.

Zelený, V., Matousek, V., and Lengerová, A. (1978). *J. Immunogenet.* **5,** 41–47.

Zinkernagel, R. M., and Doherty, P. C. (1974). *Nature (London)* **251,** 547–548.

Zinkernagel, R. M., and Oldstone, M. B. A. (1976). *Proc. Natl. Acad. Sci. U.S.A.* **73,** 3666–3670.

Zinkernagel, R. M., Callahan, G. N., Klein, J., and Dennert, G. (1978a). *Nature (London)* **271,** 251–253.

Zinkernagel, R. M., Callahan, G. N., Althage, A., Cooper, S., Klein, P. A., and Klein, J. (1978b). *J. Exp. Med.* **147,** 882–896.

THE ORGANIZATION AND EXPRESSION OF CLONED GLOBIN GENES*

PHILIP LEDER

Laboratory of Molecular Genetics,
National Institute of Child Health and Human Development,
National Institutes of Health,
Bethesda, Maryland

I. INTRODUCTION

G ENETICS has always been an inferential science—that is, the nature and structure of genes have always been inferred from their phenotype. But that approach and system of logic, as elegant and powerful as it is, has undergone a very profound change over the last 4 years, a change brought about by our new ability to clone and quickly determine the structure of genes derived from even the most complex of organisms (1). My colleagues and I at the National Institutes of Health have been extremely fortunate to have been able to bring this new technology to bear on a long-standing, but extremely interesting, set of genetic problems. We are very much honored to have been invited to describe the results of these studies in the form of a Harvey Lecture.

The globin system of the mouse has provided an ideal model for the exercise of both the classical and the new genetics. I shall begin by summarizing, all too briefly, what we have learned of these genes from the classical approach, then describe experiments directed toward cloning and determining the structure of the mouse globin genes and show how we have attempted to identify those elements concerned with their regulated expression. Finally, I should like to describe how we have returned these genes to a cell system in which their function could be tested. Along the way, of course, we were very much surprised by what we discovered regarding the structure of these genes and equally surprised by what we could learn about their evolution and divergence.

This work has proceeded with the inventive participation of a number of valuable colleagues. David Tiemeier and Shirley Tilghman initiated

*Lecture delivered January 18, 1979.

the most recent studies, perfecting the cloning technology that allowed us to visualize the discontinuous structure of the beta globin gene. Aya Leder and David Konkel then joined in the cloning of alpha globin genes and in determining the sequence of the beta genes, respectively. Yutaka Nishioka determined the structure of the prominent members of the alpha gene family, and Dean Hamer and Marian Kaehler then took advantage of the SV40 viral cloning system, developed in large measure by Dean Hamer, to return the characterized globin genes to a cell where their expression could be tested. And finally and most recently, Carol Talkington has used an *in vitro* system to test the validity of the conclusions that we drew from our gene sequence comparisons. Throughout, this work has been carried forward by the enthusiastic contributions of my long-time associates Marion Nau and Barbara Norman.

II. THE MOUSE GLOBINS

The adult BALB/c mouse expresses two alpha and two beta globin genes, each in such a way that alpha and beta peptide chains are produced in fairly equivalent amounts in adult erythrocytes (2). Since the alpha and beta genes are located on separate chromosomes, their coordinated expression suggests that an alpha/beta globin regulatory system must operate *in trans,* possibly mediated by some diffusible control element(s). In addition, the two beta genes, beta major and beta minor, while generally expressed in a fixed 4:1 ratio, seem to vary in expression in response to oxygen supply (3). This variation suggests the operation of yet another regulatory mechanism, in this case functioning to control, *in cis,* the expression of genes that reside upon the same chromosome. While the adult globin genes offer one interesting regulatory paradigm, there is yet another set of globin genes (*X, Y,* and *Z*) that are expressed only in the nucleated red cells of the developing mouse embryo (4) and that offer an additional problem in the reciprocal expression of tightly linked genes. It was really to understand the molecular basis of these problems that we set out in 1975 to develop the tools and strategies that would allow us to clone the globin genes.

III. THE DISCONTINUOUS STRUCTURE OF THE GLOBIN GENES

The astonishing difference between the classic and the new genetics is nowhere more dramatically illustrated than by our current ability directly to visualize genes. When the first globin gene was cloned and purified (5–7), its structure could immediately be determined by making use of a powerful electron microscopic technique, R-loop mapping, that allowed genes to be visualized directly (8). By this technique, an mRNA is annealed to a cloned fragment of DNA that encodes the relevant gene sequence. The mRNA displaces a loop of single-stranded DNA as it anneals to its complementary sequence in the gene, thus forming a bubble-like structure consisting of the RNA–DNA strand and a displaced single DNA strand (Fig. 1). The interesting and surprising feature of the mouse globin gene visualized in this way is that it clearly formed *two* R-loops separated from one another by a double-stranded stretch of DNA that was not represented in the globin mRNA (Fig. 1A).

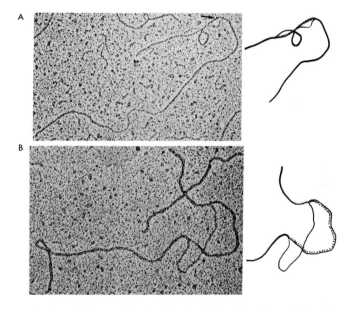

FIG. 1. An electron micrographic visualization of the cloned beta globin minor gene annealed to globin mRNA (A) and to its 15 S precursor (B). The diagrammatic representation illustrates the annealing of globin messenger RNA to the coded globin gene. The heavy line represents double-stranded DNA or RNA–DNA hybrid. The dotted line represents the globin messenger RNA or precursor. An arrow points to the smaller intervening sequence in the globin gene (A). The double-stranded structure visualized in the middle of the gene is the large intervening sequence. These electron micrographs are from Tilghman *et al.* (12).

In fact, there are actually two stretches of DNA that do not occur in the mRNA, a smaller one (see arrow, Fig. 1A) that turns out (as shown by subsequent sequence studies) to divide the gene between codons 30 and 31 and a larger one that divides the gene between codons 104 and 105. The mouse beta globin gene is, in fact, encoded in three discontinuous bits of coding information separated by two intervening sequences of DNA. The rabbit and human genes are divided in an identical fashion (9, 10).

IV. Editing of Coding Sequences Occurs at RNA Level

The fact that the globin gene was shown to be encoded in separate coding blocks immediately raised the problem of how coding information could be assembled so as to remove the noncoding sequences to form a coherent message. The problem of assembly was quickly solved by again making use of R-loop mapping and, this time, by also taking advantage of the fact that Curtis, Mantei, and Weissmann (11) had isolated and purified a 1.5 Kb precursor of the beta globin mRNA. Using their precursor, we were able to show that it annealed to the globin gene in such a way as to form a single, large R loop (Fig. 1B). The precursor obviously was a complete transcript of the globin gene and included both its coding and intervening sequences (12). Formation of a coherent mRNA must, therefore, depend upon a splicing mechanism that removes internal segments of RNA corresponding to the intervening sequence and joins the resulting coding segments (shown diagrammatically in Fig. 2).

V. Potential Consequences of Missplice Mutations: Possible Relevance to Certain Thalassemias

Since this splicing mechanism represented an unexpected series of reactions through which genetic information must pass, it was reasonable to imagine the consequences of mutations that could affect this process. For example, loss of the splicing enzyme system would be lethal. But mutations arising in a sequence that signals splicing within a given gene might either result in loss of function of that gene or reduce the rate of processing of its mRNA. The former situation would prevent the appearance of the product of the mutant gene, but the latter might

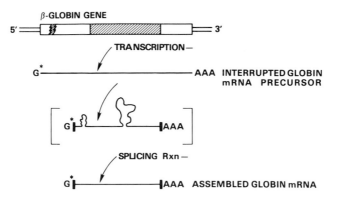

FIG. 2. Diagrammatic representation of a representative globin gene indicating splicing pathway leading from primary transcript to mature mRNA. The uppermost diagram is the gene, with hatched areas representing intervening sequences. The thin lines are RNA with G* and AAA representing the 5'-cap and 3'-poly(A), respectively.

only reduce the amount of the normal gene product. Such a situation is exactly what one sees in certain types of beta thalassemia, an inherited disorder of man characterized by the production of reduced amounts of normal beta globin. While this disease could be accounted for by a variety of mechanisms, the discovery of the interrupted character of the globin genes presents a new possibility in the form of an intervening sequence disease (13).

VI. THE FINE STRUCTURE OF THE ADULT GLOBIN GENES. RECOGNITION OF TRANSCRIPTIONAL INITIATION, POLY(A)-ADDITION, AND SPLICING SIGNALS

We have determined the nucleotide structure of beta globin major and minor and of one of the adult alpha globin genes (14, 15). When these sequences (Figs. 3–5) are aligned and compared, they allow us to identify features of organization and regions of homology that have been selectively preserved throughout vertebrate evolution. Both alpha and beta genes, despite the fact that they evolved from a common ancestral sequence and have been apart for over 500 million years, retain the two intervening sequences that split each gene at homologous positions. From this we conclude that the ancestral sequence was interrupted in

```
                10            20            30            40            50            60            70            80            90
  0    AGTGAGACGTCCTAAGCCAGTGAGTGGCACAGCATGTCCAGGGAAATATCCTTCGTCCTCACCGAGCCTGATTCCGTAGGCCACACCCTGCTGTAA
 100   GGGCCAATCTGCTCACACACCCCAGAAACAGACATCATGGTGCACTGACTGTGCTGAGAAGGCTGCTCTTGCCTGTGTGGGAAAGTGAACTCCGATGAACATATAGT
                                                            ⨁                    ⨁                          cap
       TGTGTTGACTCACACACCCCAGAAACAGACATCATGGTGCACTGACTGTGCTGAGAAGGCTGCTCTTGCCTGTGTGGGAAAGTGAACTCCGATGA
                                                           IleValHisLeuThrAspAlaGluValAlaAlaValSerLeuTrpGlyValLysValAsnSerAspGl
 200
 300   AGTTGGTGGTGAGGGCCCTGGGCAGGTTGGTATCCAGGTTACAAGGCAGCTCACAAGAGAAGAGTTGGGTGTGTTGGACCAGCAGAGGTCTGCTTTTCCAGCACAGAC
       uValGlyGlyGluAlaLeuGlyArg-30
 400   ACTAACTTTCAGTGTCCCCTGCTATGTTTCCCTTTTAGGCTGCTGGTTGTGTACCCTTGGACCAGCAGGTACTTTGATAGCTTTGGAGACCTATCCTC
                                                                                31-LeuLeuValValTyrProTrpThrGlnArgTyrPheGlySerPheGlyAspLeuSerSe
 500   TGCCTCCTCTATCATGGTAATGCAAAGTGAAGGCCCATGGCAAGGTGATAACTCCTTTACCTCCTTTTAACGATGGCCTGAATCACTTGACAGCTCAAGGGC
       rAlaSerAlaIleMetGlyAsnAlaLysValLysAlaHisGlyLysLysValLeuIleThrAlaPheAsnAspGlyLeuAsnHisLeuAspSerLeuLysGly
 600   ACCTTTGCCAGCCTAGTGAGCTCCACTGTGACAAGCTGCATGGAGAACTTCAGGGTGAGTCTGATGGGCACCTCCTGGGTTTCCTTCCCCT
       ThrPheAlaSerLeuSerGluLeuHisCysAspLysLeuHisValAspProGluAsnPheArg-104
 700   GGCTATTCTGCTCAACCTTCCTATCAGAAAAAAGGGAAGGCCATTCTCAGGCACGAGCAGTCTCCATGCACTGTGTGTGGAGTGTTGACAAGAGTTGGGATATT
                                                                                 TER     ⧗    ⧗
                                                                         ⧗8    INSERT
 800   TTATTCTCTACTCAGAATTGCTGCTCCCCCTCCACTGTTCTCTGTTGTCATTTCTCCTCCTCTTCTGTAACGTTTTAATTTCAGTTCCATTTTACTAAA
 900   TTAATTAAGCTCTGGTTATTACTTGGTTATTCAGTTCCCCATCCAGCTTTGTCTTTTGTCTTTTTGCTTTTATGGCTTGTCAGGGACAGAGATATGTTTCTCTAATCCTT
1000   TCCTTTCCCCAGTTGTCTCTGAGATCTCACGTTTGTGATCTACGTTTATCCCAGGTGACAGGGAAGAATATATTTACATATTACTCTGTTT
1100   CTTCTCATAGCTCTGAGAATAGTAGCATAATGGCTTTATGGAATGTCTTTGGCAAATGTCTTTCAGTAGGTTGGTATTTTTGTATGTTCATGGTTC
1200   TTATAATATTTGTCAGTAGGTTAAGGTTGCAGAAATGTCTTGGAATAGCTGCATGATCTCGGTATCTGGTATTTTTTGCTTCTACAGTTATGTGATGGGTC
1300   TTCCATATTCCCAGCTCCTGGGCAATATGTCGGCAATATGCATGTTGCTGGGGCCAATAACCCTTGCTGCTGTTCGCTGCTGGCTGGACAGGCTGCCTTCCAGAAG
       105-LeuLeuGlyAsnValLeuValValLeuValHisHisPheGlyLysGluPheThrProProValGlnAlaAlaTyrGlnLysGlyGlnAlaAlaPheGlnLys
1400   GTGGTGGCTGGAGTGGCCACTGCCCTGGCTCACAAGTACCACTAAGCCCTTGCTGTCCTGTGAACAATGGTTAATTGTCTCCAAGAGAGCAT
       ValValAlaGlyValAlaLeuAlaThrAlaLeuAlaHisLysTyrHisTER-147
1500   CTGTCAGTGTTTGGGAAATGTAGAGACATTTTGGAAATCTGTCTTCTGACAAATAAAAAAGCATTTATTTTCATTGCAATGATGTATTTAAATTATTTCTG
                                                                                           ⊽    pA
1600   TCTCATAGAAGGGTTTATGCAAATTTCAAGAAATAGACAAGAAGTGAGGTCAGGTTCACCTGGGAAAATAAATGAATTACACTTCAAATTGTGTTGT
1700   CAGCTAAGCCAGCAGTAGCCACAGATC
```

exactly as are the contemporary genes and further that these interruptions confer some selective advantage that accounts for their preservation (see later). Several small sequences residing within a few hundred nucleotides of the 5' and 3' borders of the coding regions have also been conserved (indicated in Figs. 3, 4, and 5) and might have functional significance.

At the 5' end of each gene the hexanucleotide, TATAAT A/G, appears 24 base pairs before the putative site of transcriptional initiation, the capped nucleotide of the mRNA (16). This sequence is found similarly placed in several other eukaryotic genes (17, 18) and may serve as a signal for transcriptional initiation in eukaryotes in the same way as does the analogous Pribnow box in prokaryotes (19). The pentanucleotide TTATT corresponds to the UUAUU sequence found in several mammalian mRNAs (20) and may serve as a signal for the addition of poly(A) to the 3' end of the transcript. While the alpha and beta gene intervening sequences differ considerably in sequence and length [the globin intervening sequences appear to be unique, rather than reiterated (21)], the borders of each intervening sequence provide considerable homology (Table I). In particular, Breathnach et al. (22) have pointed out that the intervening sequence can always be removed to restore the coding frame if it is removed between the dinucleotides (GT . . . IVS . . . AG). All six globin genes obey this rule (Table I) and also obey more extensive rules that recently have been drawn to define splicing signals (23). In addition to identifying these potential signals, a comparison of the gene sequences gives us a comprehensive picture of both

FIG. 3. The nucleotide sequence of a mouse beta globin major gene. The amino acid sequence is displayed beneath gene sequences (strand corresponding to mRNA). Symbols are as follows: INI, an initiation codon; TER, a termination codon. The numbers within the sequence refer to the amino acid coding position. The lower-case superscripts indicate a putative promoter site homology sequence, TATAAG, the capping site, cAp; the poly(A) addition site pentanucleotide, AATAAA, and the putative poly(A) addition site, pA. The 5'-putative promoter region sequence TATAAG is boxed; the first in-phase termination codon in IVS-2 is underlined and has a superscript "TER"; stippled bases and amino acids differ from the corresponding position in the β^{maj} sequence (Fig. 4); a ∇ indicates the position of bases deleted in β^{min} relative to β^{maj}, if there are n bases deleted, this is represented by "∇n"; insertions relative to β^{maj} are enclosed by parentheses and have a superscript $+$; the overall region of detectable homology is bracketed. The data are from Konkel et al. (39) as modified (14).

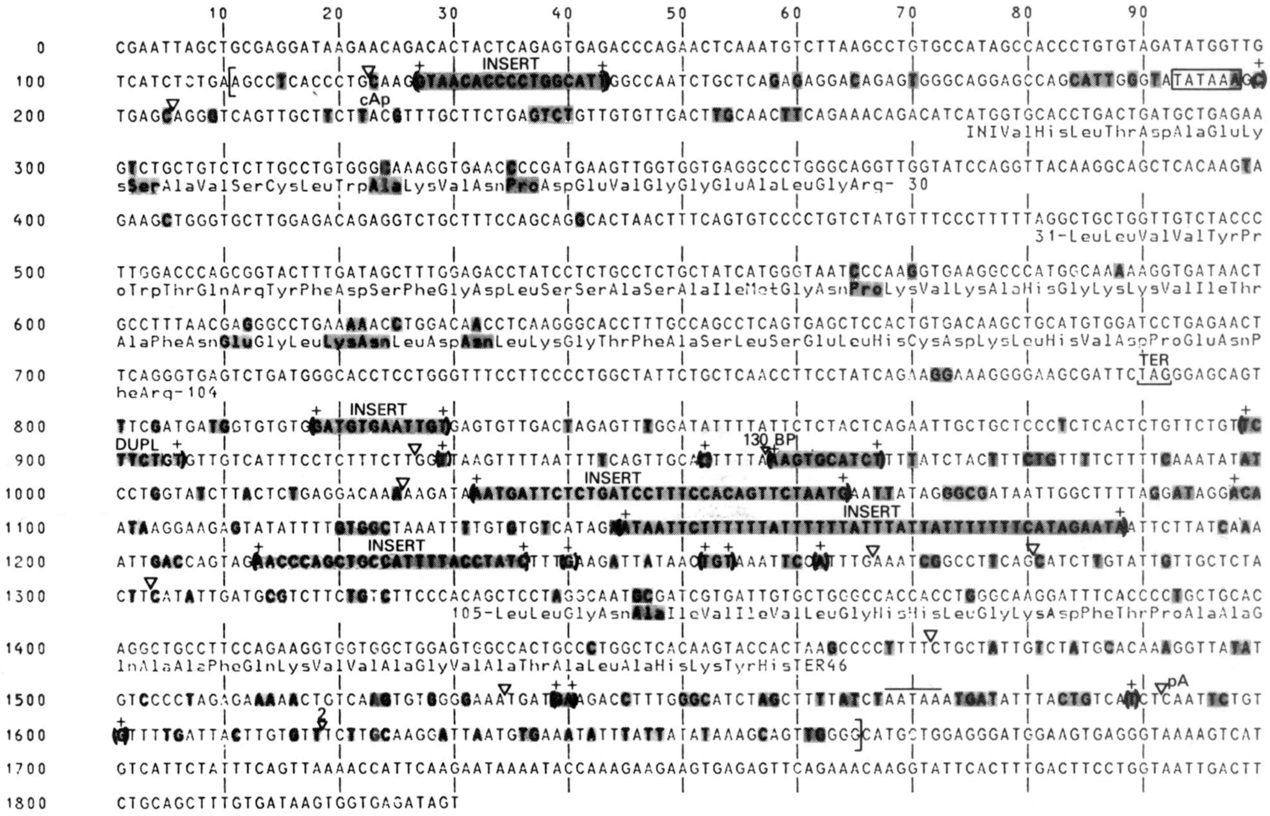

FIG. 4. The nucleotide sequence of a mouse beta globin minor gene. For symbols, see legend to Fig. 3. The data are from Konkel *et al.* (14).

```
                    10        20        30        40        50        60        70        80
                    |         |         |         |         |         |         |         |
0     GTAAGCAGGTTGTGTTGAGAAAGGAAAGTGTGAAACAGGACCCAGAGGGAGAGGTGGGGGATGCGCTGCTTCCTCAGTTTGGTTTGAGGGACTTGCTTCT
100   CTGACCAAGGTAGGAGGATACTAACTTCTTCCCAAACTGCCATCCGTGGGCCCTAACAGTTTACTGGGTAGAGCAAGCACAAACCAGCCAATGAGTAACTGCTCCA
200   TGCACCTAGGGAAGCACAACCCAGCCCCAGAATCTCAGGGGCCCTAACAGTTTACTGGGTAGAGCAAGCACAAACCAGCCAATGAGTAACTGCTCCA
                                                                              tataag
300   AGGGGTGTCCACCCTGCCTGGAGGAGCCCTTGGAGGGCATTATAAGTGCTACTTGCTGCAGGTCCAAGCACTTCTGATTCTGCAGACTCAGGAAGA
                                     cAp
400   AACCATGGTGCTCTCTGGGGAAGCAACAAAAGCAACATCAAGGCTGCCTGGGGAAGATTGTGGCCATGGTGCTGATATGGCTGAAGCCCTGGAAAGG
      INIValLeuSerGlyGluAsnGlyLysSerAsnIleLysSerAlaAlaTrpGlyLysIleGlyHisGlyAlaGluLeuAlaLeuGluGluArg
       -31
500   TGAGAACAGGACCTTGATCGTGTAAGGATCACAGGATCCAATATGGACCTGGCACTCGCCTCAGTGGGCAGCTTCTAACTATGCTTTTCTGTGACCTCAACT
        -31
600   TCTCTTCTCTCCTTCCTCCTTCTCCCAGGATGTTTGCTACCTTCCCCACCACCAAGACCTACTTTCCACTTTGATGTAAGCCACGGCTCTGCCCAGGTCAAGGGT
                                          32-MetPheAlaSerPhePheProThrThrLysThrTyrPhePheAspHisPheProHisPheAspValSerHisGlySerAlaGlnValLysGly
                                           32
700   CACGGCCAAGAAGGTCCCCGATGCGTCGCAGTGCTGCAGGCCACCTGCAGTGCTCGTGCTGTGCTCGAGCCAGCCTGCAGCACCTGCATGCCCACAAGC
      HisGlyLysLysValAlaAspAlaLeuAlaSerAlaGlyHisLeuAspAspLeuProGlyAlaLeuSerAlaLeuSerAspLeuHisAlaHisLysLysL
800   TGCGTGTGGATCCCGTCAACTTCAAGGTATGCGCTGGGACCTGGGACCTGGCAGGGCGGCATCTGGGACCCCTAGGGAAGGGCTTGGGGTCTCGTGCCCAAGGCAGG
      euArgValAspProValAsnPheLys-99
900   GAACATAGTGGTCCCAGGAAGGGGAGCAGAGGGCATCAGGGTGTCCACTTTGTCTCCGCAGCTCCGCAGCTCCGCAGCCTGCCTGGTGACCTTGGCTAGCCACC
                                                                          100-LeuLeuSerHisCysLeuLeuValThrLeuAlaSerHisH
1000  ACCCTGCCGATTTCACCCCCGGTACATGCCTCTCTGGACAAATTCCTTGCCTCTGTGAGCACCGTGCTGACCTCCAAGTACCGTTAAGCTGCCTTCTG
      isProAlaAspPheThrProAlaValHisAlaSerLeuAspLysPheLeuAlaSerValSerThrValLeuThrSerLysTyrArgTER-142
                                                                              aataa           [pA...
1100  CGGGGCTTGCCTTCTGGCCATGCCCTTCTCTCTCCCTTGCACCTGTACCTCTTGGTCTTTGAATAAAGCCTGAGTAGGAAGAAGCCTCATGCCTGGTT
1200  CTCTGCGCTCTGCAAAGGTGTCATGTTTAGTGTGGGGATGCGCGACTCATTTGCCATGGGCGAGTAAGACAAGGTTCAGACAAAAGCATAATTGGAT
1300  GCCTACACACACACACATATGTCTTCTGACTGTTCTGGCAGTGGCAGGCAGCCCTCCCAAGCCCTCCACTGACACCCCATGTGTCTTCTTCCTCTGAGCCCAAGAAGCCAA
1400  AGATCGTCTTTGGAGGGTCCTTATCACAGGACCTCTGAGGG
```

```
       cAp   i    31        32          99           100          t    pA...
      ------------*****--------*************---------**********---******-------------------|
     |------------*******| IVS-1 |*******|       |*********| IVS-2 |*********|            |
     |------------*******--------*************---------**********---******-------------------|
0    |-------------------*-------------------------------------------------------------|  1441
```

Fig. 5. The nucleotide sequence of a mouse alpha globin gene. Coding sequences are indicated by the amino acid abbreviations beneath the sequence. The data are from Nishioka and Leder (15).

TABLE I

The GT/AG Rule of Intervening Sequence Excision[a]

Beta major	
IVS-1	GGCAG(GT . . . . .AG)GCTGCT
IVS-2	TCAGG(GT . . . . .AG)CTCCTG
Beta minor	
IVS-1	GGCAG(GT . . . . .AG)GCTGCT
IVS-2	TCAGG(GT . . . . .AG)CTCCTA
Alpha	
IVS-1	GAAAG(GT . . . . .AG)GATGT
IVS-2	TCAAG(GT . . . . .AG)CTCCTG

[a] The sequence surrounding the two intervening sequences of the indicated globin genes is shown. The segment within parentheses is to be spliced out as the globin mRNA precursors are processed.

selected and apparently random genetic drift in and around these genes over the past 500 million years. We consider these processes below.

VII. A Test for the Function and Universality of Genetic Signals

We have seen how correlation analysis allows us to identify certain regions that might play a role in the expression of these genes. Obviously, we wished to test these predictions by reintroducing these genes into a system in which they could function. This could be done by taking advantage of the monkey virus SV40, which could be modified so as to introduce the globin gene into its chromosome (24). SV40 has two strong promoters, one that governs the transcription of a group of early genes and another that governs the transcription of a group of late genes (25). The late genes can be replaced by a globin gene segment (24, 26) and complemented by a helper virus defective in the early region. When we formed a hybrid virus between the beta globin major gene and SV40 and used it to infect African green monkey kidney cells, authentic mouse beta globin was synthesized in large amounts in infected cells (24). Evidently proper splicing readily occurs across species and organ boundaries (mouse–monkey; red cell–kidney), and the virus system should allow us to assess the function of the cloned globin genes as well as mutants derived from them.

In the experiment just referred to, the beta globin gene was inserted so that it would be transcribed by the late SV40 promoter. In order to determine whether an endogenous promoter was associated with the 5′ end of the globin gene, the alpha globin gene was inserted in two orientations into SV40 (Fig. 6) (27). In one orientation, the SV40 and putative globin gene promoter were oriented in tandem so that both would direct the synthesis of a sense transcript. In the other, the fragment was inserted so that the SV40 promoter transcribed the antisense strand of the globin gene, whereas the putative globin promoter would direct transcription of the sense strand. In the latter orientation, promoters opposed, the appearance of alpha globin would be consistent with a functional promoter on the 5′ side of the alpha gene, as the SV40 promoter would produce only an antisense transcript. Alpha globin was synthesized in response to infection with both hybrid viruses (Fig. 7), indicating that a promoter had been brought in with the cloned gene segment. In more recent experiments, using a cell-free transcription

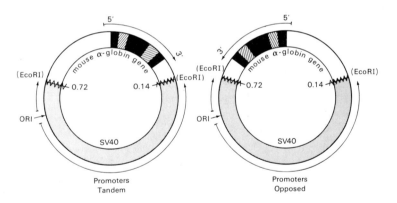

FIG. 6. A diagrammatic representation of the cloned alpha genes in SV40. The gene has been cloned in opposite orientation in each hybrid virus so that the sense strand of the alpha gene will be under control of the late SV40 promoter in the "tandem" orientation and the antisense strand in the "opposed" orientation. Tandem and opposed refer to the presumed orientation of the late SV40 and putative globin gene promoters. Numbers inside the circle represent positions on the SV40 map. Stippled areas are SV40 sequences; clear, filled, and hatched areas represent alpha globin flanking, coding, and intervening sequences, respectively. The "sense" orientation of the globin gene insert is given by the 5′→3′ arrow. ORI indicates the SV40 origin of replication. The globin gene has been inserted using synthetic EcoRI linker sequences. Data are from Hamer et al. (27).

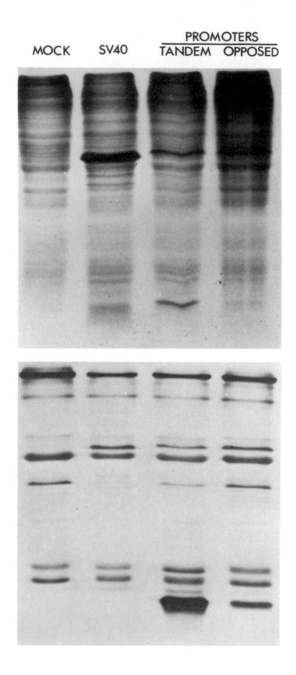

                              PROMOTERS
MOCK   SV40   TANDEM   OPPOSED

system similar to that described by Weil *et al.* (28), similar fragments of the alpha globin gene have been used to direct specific α-amanatin-sensitive transcription of the globin sequence (29), supporting the view that the alpha globin promoter is encoded on the 5' portion of the cloned alpha gene.

VIII. SPLICE SIGNALS AND REQUIREMENT FOR INTERVENING SEQUENCES

Cloning experiments similar to those just described and using sub-fractions of the globin gene allowed us to probe the borders of the splice signal and ask whether such sites were required for gene function (30). A segment of DNA containing 18 bases to the 5' side of large beta major intervening sequence (see Fig. 3) and the remaining 3' portion of the gene was cloned under the control of the late SV40 promoter. The cells infected with this hybrid virus produced a properly spliced and polyadenylated transcript (30), indicating that the splicing signal for this gene resides within 18 bases of the 5' end of the intervening sequence. When this same segment of DNA was inserted in the opposite orientation in such a way that its antisense strand would be transcribed, a transcript was formed, but the large intervening sequence was not deleted. Apparently, the complement of an intervening sequence does not constitute a structure that can be spliced.

Because the globin splicing signal could be eliminated by inverting the gene so as to transcribe its antisense strand, it was also possible to construct a vector that produced transcripts containing splice signals derived from SV40 and/or mouse globin (31). Although each of these hybrid regions was transcribed from the late SV40 promoter, the hybrid that completely lacked splice sites failed to produce a stable transcript (31). The addition of either an SV40 or a globin splice signal restored

FIG. 7. Analysis of mouse alpha globin formed by African green monkey kidney cells infected by SV40 hybrid viruses carrying the mouse alpha globin genes. The top and bottom figures represent autoradiograms of sodium dodecyl sulfate-polyacrylamide gel electrophoretic analyses of total and immunoprecipitated protein products; mock and SV40 lanes are self-explanatory. Tandem and opposed are the hybrids represented in Fig. 6. The data are from Hamer *et al.* (27).

production of a stable cytoplasmic transcript. Evidently intervening sequences play a role during or after the formation of this transcript that is necessary for the appearance of stable mRNA in the cytoplasm.

IX. The Evolution of the Globin Gene Family: Surprising Complexity and Unexpected Mutation

While studies of mouse globin proteins allowed the identification of several active globin genes (see above), the actual globin gene family is far more complex than was originally expected. We have created several libraries of cloned fragments of DNA derived from various mouse organs and cloned these in phage lambda (32). Each library should contain the entire repertoire of the mouse genome, represented as overlapping fragments of cloned DNA (33, 34). In these libraries we have identified at least six beta and seven alpha globin genes, each separately encoded and probably closely linked in chromosomal DNA. In the case of the beta genes we have been able to arrange these genes into a physical map (35). Similar studies have been carried out by M. H. Edgell and C. Hutchinson and their colleagues (personal communication). As shown in Fig. 8, the genes are, in fact, tightly linked and tandemly arranged, head to tail, with the beta major and minor genes at the 3' end of the array. It seems that this family has been expanded from an original duplication event into this larger array, possibly by unequal crossing over.

The evolutionary relationship between the beta major and minor genes can also be recognized (Figs. 3 and 4), as well as two principal, but different, modes of genetic divergence. By comparing their sequences using a computer program written by J. V. Maizel, we have been able to show that coding sequences behave very differently from flanking and intervening sequences (14) (Fig. 9). Coding sequences, as might be expected, exhibit occasional point mutations. On the other hand, large intervening sequences of both genes have clearly diverged principally on the basis of insertions–deletions that occur frequently within their divergent portions (Fig. 9). It is likely that both point mutations and insertions–deletions affect all regions of the chromosome, but that selection operates against their survival in the coding sequences. Elsewhere, we have argued that this rapid divergence of flanking and intervening sequences might serve to stabilize duplicate

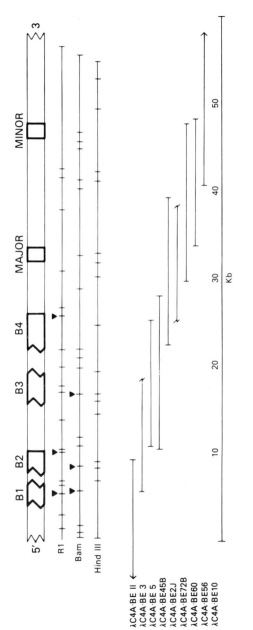

FIG. 8. Physical map of the beta globin genes of the mouse. Each boxed figure represents a beta globin or beta-globin-like gene. The restriction endonuclease sites are shown directly beneath the map and were derived from the randomly cloned fragments shown beneath the restriction map (35).

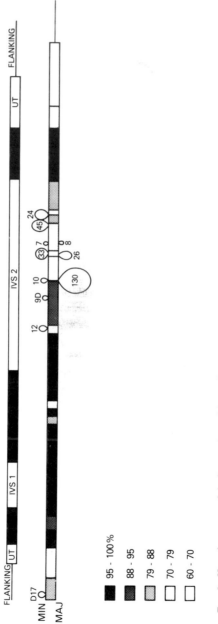

FIG. 9. Homology map of the beta major and beta minor genes. Increased homology is indicated as an increase density of stippling. Large insertions are shown as loops, the associated number indicating the number of bases not represented in the other sequence. Data are from Konkel et al. (14).

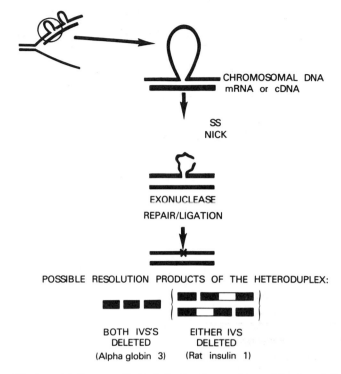

Fig. 10. A model diagrammatically indicating the possible models of resolution of a hypothetical recombinant heteroduplex formed between a single-stranded region of genomic DNA to which globin mRNA or cRNA is annealed. As diagrammed, an mRNA (or cDNA) forms a heteroduplex structure, for example, at a replication fork. One or both intervening sequences loop out as single-stranded structures, is nicked, degraded, repaired, and covalently joined in a sequence corresponding to the mature mRNA, thereby deleting the intervening sequences in accordance with the GT/AG rule. The bottom of the figure diagrammatically represents the alpha-3 gene and rat insulin *I* gene (40, 41).

genes in which extensive homology would permit frequent unequal crossovers resulting in imbalanced loss or gain in gene sequences (36).

In the case of seven alpha genes (though not yet arrayed into a physical map), we have a better idea of the structure of several of the "extra" genes. Two of these, alpha-3 and alpha-4, have been completely sequenced (37, 38). Alpha-4 contains a number of mutations that are similar to those found in two human hemoglobinopathies. In addition to the substitution of a tyrosine for a histidine codon in position 58 (cf. methemoglobinemia associated with hemoglobin M), a frameshift near the normal termination codon has thrown this codon out-of-phase. The next in-phase terminator codon occurs 42 codons away, creating a situation reminiscent of hemoglobin Constant Spring—a human gene with a mutation in its normal terminator and longer-than-normal globin chain.

The sequence of alpha-3 revealed an even more surprising structure (37). This gene completely lacks *both* of its intervening sequences. Moreover, these sequences appear to be lacking in accordance with the GT/AG rule of RNA splicing. An analogous gene has also been cloned and sequenced from a different strain of mouse by O. Smithies and his associates (personal communication). By virtue of an extensive sequence homology between the alpha-3 and the adult alpha gene, it seems that the sequences were lost from a gene that once was similar to all alpha and beta genes inasmuch as the alpha-3 divergence must have occurred long after the alpha/beta divergence. While several mechanisms could account for this loss (37), we favor one akin to gene conversion (Fig. 10) in which the mRNA anneals to a replicating globin gene and forces the looping out of the intervening sequences, which are then cleaved out by DNA repair enzymes.

X. Epilogue

In 1977 it was a great surprise to learn that genes were discontinuous. This observation alone virtually assured us that at least some of the familiar rules established in prokaryotes would provide little guidance in the new analysis of genes in higher organisms. Indeed, we have learned so much about the structure, function, and evolution of genes in the last 4 years that we approach the next 4 years with a sense of expecting the unexpected. In this respect, it is especially ironic to contemplate the structure of the mouse alpha-3 gene just discussed. It is an uninterrupted sequence, and if it had been cloned and sequenced in 1977 it would have left us with the comfortable feeling that evolution created no surprises when dealing with a fundamental structure like a gene. Its discovery today creates quite the opposite impression and provides a prologue for what the future will surely bring.

REFERENCES

1. *Science* **196** (issue No. 4286, entire issue) (1977).
2. Russel, E. S., and McFarland, E. L., *Ann. N. Y. Acad. Sci.* **241**, 25–38 (1974).
3. Whitney, J. B., *Cell* **12**, 863–871 (1977).
4. Fantoni, A., Bank, A., and Marks, P. A., *Science* **157**, 1327–1329 (1967).
5. Leder, P., Tilghman, S. M., Tiemeier, D. C., Polsky, F. I., Seidman, J. G., Edgell, M. H., Enquist, L. W., Leder, A., and Norman, B., *Cold Spring Harbor Symp. Quant. Biol.* **42**, 915–920 (1977).
6. Tilghman, S. M., Tiemeier, D. C., Polsky, F., Edgell, M. H., Seidman, J. G., Leder, A., Enquist, L. W., Norman, B., and Leder, P., *Proc. Natl. Acad. Sci. U.S.A.* **74**, 4406–4410 (1977).
7. Tilghman, S. M., Tiemeier, D. C., Seidman, J. G., Peterlin, B. M., Sullivan, M., Maizel, J. V., and Leder, P., *Proc. Natl. Acad. Sci. U.S.A.* **75**, 725–729 (1978).
8. White, R. L., and Hogness, D. S., *Cell* **10**, 177–192 (1977).
9. Jeffreys, A. J., and Flavell, R. A., *Cell* **12**, 1097–1108 (1977).
10. Lawn, R. M., Fritsch, E. F., Parker, R. C., Blake, G., and Maniatis, T., *Cell* **15**, 1157–1174 (1978).
11. Curtis, P. J., Mantei, N., and Weissmann, C., *Cold Spring Harbor Symp. Quant. Biol.* **42**, 971–984 (1977).
12. Tilghman, S. M., Curtis, P. J., Tiemeier, D. C., Leder, P., and Weissmann, C., *Proc. Natl. Acad. Sci. U.S.A.* **75**, 1309–1313 (1978).
13. Leder, P., *N. Engl. J. Med.* **298**, 1079–1080 (1978).
14. Konkel, D., Maizel, J. V., and Leder, P., *Cell* **18**, 865–873 (1979).
15. Nishioka, Y., and Leder, P., *Cell* **18**, 875–882 (1979).
16. Baralle, F. E., and Brownlee, G. G., *Nature (London)* **274**, 84–87 (1978).
17. Goldberg, M. L., and Hogness, D. S., personal communication.
18. Ziff, E. B., and Evans. R. M., *Cell* **15**, 1463–1475 (1978).
19. Pribnow, D., *J. Mol. Biol.* **99**, 419–443 (1975).
20. Proudfoot, N. J., and Brownlee, G. G., *Nature (London)*, **263**, 211–214 (1976).
21. Miller, H. I., Konkel, D., and Leder, P., *Nature (London)* **275**, 772–774 (1978).
22. Breathnach, R., Benoist, C., O'Hare, K., Gannor, F., and Chambon, P., *Proc. Natl. Acad. Sci. U.S.A.* **75**, 4853–4857 (1978).
23. Seif, I., Khoury, G., and Dhar, R., *Nucl. Acids Res.* **6**, 3387–3398 (1979).
24. Hamer, D. H., and Leder, P., *Nature (London)* **281**, 35–40 (1979).
25. Kelly, T. J., and Nathans, D., *Annu. Rev. Biochem.* **21**, 86–173 (1977).
26. Mulligan, R., Howard, B., and Berg, P., *Nature (London)* **277**, 108–114 (1979).
27. Hamer, D., Kaehler, M., and Leder, P., Cell (in press).
28. Weil, P. A., Luse, D. S., Segall, J., and Roeder, R. G., *Cell* **18**, 469–484 (1979).
29. Talkington, C., personal communication.
30. Hamer, D. H., and Leder, P., *Nature (London)* **17**, 737–747 (1979).
31. Hamer, D. H., and Leder, P., *Cell* **18**, 1299–1302 (1979).
32. Seidman, J. G. Kwan, S.-P., Scharff, M., and Leder, P., unpublished result.
33. Clarke, L., and Carbon, J., *Cell* **9**, 91–99 (1976).
34. Maniatis, T., Hardison, R. C., Lacy, E., Lauer, J., O'Connell, C., Quon, D., Sim, G. K., and Efstratiadis, A., *Cell* **15**, 687–701 (1978).

35. Leder, P., Hansen, N., Konkel, D., Leder, A., Nishioka, Y., and Talkington, C., *Science,* in press.
36. Tiemeier, D. C., Tilghman, S. M., Polsky, F. I., Seidman, J. G., Leder, A., Edgell, M. H., and Leder, P., *Cell* **14,** 237–245 (1978).
37. Nishioka, Y., Leder, A., and Leder, P., *Proc. Natl. Acad. Sci. U.S.A.* **77,** 2806–2809 (1980).
38. Nishioka, Y., Leder, A., and Leder, P., manuscript in preparation.
39. Konkel, D., Tilghman, S. M., and Leder, P., *Cell* **15,** 1125–1132 (1978).
40. Lomedico, P., Rosenthal, N., Efstratiadis, A., Gilbert, W., Kolodner, R., and Tizard, R., *Cell* **18,** 545–558 (1979).
41. Cordell, B., Bell, G., Tischer, E., DeNoto, F. M., Ullrich, A., Pictet, R., Rutter, W. J., and Goodman, H. M., *Cell* **18,** 533–543 (1979).

THE KERATINOCYTE AS DIFFERENTIATED CELL TYPE*

HOWARD GREEN

*Department of Biology,
Massachusetts Institute of Technology,
Cambridge, Massachusetts*

I. INTRODUCTION

T ISSUE culture has been used for a long time to study the epidermis and other stratified epithelia whose dominant cell type is the keratinocyte; for references to early work see Matoltsy (1960). Explantation of tissue fragments was the usual method (Friedman-Kien *et al.*, 1966; Karasek, 1966; Flaxman *et al.*, 1967; Prose *et al.*, 1967; Rowe *et al.*, 1968; Freeman *et al.*, 1976). Many features of epidermal structure could be observed not only within the explants, but also in the epithelium formed by cells that migrated out of the explants. When cultivation of dissociated cells from other tissues became common, it seemed possible that epidermal cells might be grown in this way. Multiplication was found to take place in densely inoculated primary cultures of dissociated epidermal cells (Cruickshank *et al.*, 1960; Prunieras *et al.*, 1965; Briggaman *et al.*, 1967; Yuspa *et al.*, 1970; Vaughan and Bernstein, 1971; Karasek and Charlton, 1971; Fusenig and Worst, 1974, 1975; Kitano and Endo, 1977; Liu and Karasek, 1978; Marcelo *et al.*, 1978; Prunieras, 1979), but serial subculture was difficult or impossible. On the other hand, whatever the method of cultivation, established lines were sometimes obtained from rodent epidermis (Elias *et al.*, 1974; Fusenig *et al.*, 1978; Colburn *et al.*, 1978) and oral epithelium (Jepsen, 1974; Fejerskov *et al.*, 1974).

Our own method of cultivation differed from the methods employed earlier in the use of lethally irradiated fibroblasts (usually 3T3 cells) to support multiplication of the epidermal cells (Rheinwald and Green,

---

*Lecture delivered February 15, 1979.

1975a,b). This method has been applied to keratinocytes of different species (Rheinwald and Green, 1975a; Sun and Green, 1977; Banks-Schlegel and Green, 1980a), but mainly to those of the human (see also Kondo *et al.*, 1979; Taichman *et al.*, 1979; Gilchrest, 1979). Under proper conditions, epidermal keratinocytes of newborn humans may be serially cultivated through many transfers and more than 100 cell generations (Rheinwald and Green, 1977; Green, 1978), but their culture lifetime is finite and, unlike rodent keratinocytes, they do not spontaneously become established as cell lines (see, however, Steinberg and Defendi, 1979).

After inoculation of disaggregated epidermis, colonies are formed by single cells; the size of the inoculum can be as small as desired without reducing colony-forming efficiency appreciably. A colony may begin on top of the 3T3 layer, but as it grows, some epidermal cells soon penetrate between adjacent 3T3 cells and make contact with the surface of the dish; since the epidermal cells adhere more strongly to the surface, they displace the 3T3 cells, a process that continues at the expanding periphery of the colony (Rheinwald and Green, 1975b). Another effect of the cocultivated 3T3 cells is to inhibit the growth of viable dermal fibroblasts present in the inoculum. This inhibition is more effective for human fibroblasts than for those of the mouse. Some viable fibroblasts may remain under epidermal colonies (Green *et al.*, 1979), but most are displaced at the colony periphery, along with the 3T3 cells (Rheinwald and Green, 1975b), and can be removed selectively with ethylenediamine tetraacetic acid (EDTA) (Sun and Green, 1976). This precaution is sufficient to keep the number of viable fibroblasts small in comparison with the number of keratinocytes. By using the improvements described below, keratinocyte colonies can also be easily and cleanly isolated in primary cultures inoculated with as few as 100–1000 cells; clones free of human fibroblasts can then be studied through numerous subcultivations.

It has been known for some time that fibroblast factors are important for the multiplication of keratinocytes (Karasek and Charlton, 1971; Melbye and Karasek, 1973), but the nature of this support has not yet been successfully analyzed. Some established keratinocyte lines can be supported as well by medium conditioned by fibroblasts as by cocultivation (Rheinwald and Green, 1975a). On the other hand, human diploid epidermal keratinocytes cannot be supported nearly as well by conditioned medium. This fact and the difficulties encountered in the purification of the active component in conditioned medium suggest that the supporting function is complex and involves a number of factors (see also Rheinwald, 1980).

II. STRUCTURE OF THE EPITHELIUM FORMED BY CULTURED CELLS

Explants of skin preserve the stratified structure of the epidermis. Proliferation in the basal layer is accompanied by displacement of some of the progeny, which then mature in the superficial layers. When dissociated epidermal cells are inoculated together with supporting 3T3 cells, each colony may begin as a monolayer, but very early in its growth, the central region of the colony begins to stratify and organize into a tissue resembling the epidermis. The cells in all layers are very flattened in comparison with those of intact epidermis (Rheinwald and Green, 1975b). Cell proliferation is confined to the basal layer; the cells in the more superficial layers grow in size and protein content, and in the uppermost layer(s) they form the cross-linked envelopes characteristic of the cells of stratum corneum. The peripheral cells of an expanding colony are not stratified but seem analogous to the basal cells of the inner stratified region. By time-lapse cinematography the basal cells are seen to be very motile and to move as coherent groups (Sun and Green, 1976). The peripheral cells frequently exchange position with basal cells in the interior, and cell division is commonly observed throughout the entire basal layer. In expanding colonies the average division time may be less than 24 hours (Green, 1978).

The epithelium generated by colony growth is, of course, independent of nerves and blood vessels and is essentially without *underlying* connective tissues; it is a self-assembled structure that can be built by the progeny of any colony-forming cell, including clonally isolated ones, and therefore does not require the participation of any of the other cell types resident in the epidermis. Since little or no anucleate s. corneum forms on its surface, the epidermal colony resembles non-keratinized epithelium more than epidermis. This does not imply any irreversible loss in potential of the cultured cells, for their injection into animals (Doran and Sun, 1980) or their application as grafts (Banks-Schlegel and Green, 1980b) leads to formation of typical s. corneum. As long as subcultivation continues, human keratinocytes do not change their basic differentiated phenotype, and they never come to resemble fibroblasts.

When epidermal colonies grow to confluence, the colonial borders remain visible for a time, mainly because of the surrounding cuff of displaced 3T3 cells. Eventually these borders disappear and the colonies fuse to form a single epithelium that covers the bottom of the dish and extends up the vertical walls (Green, 1977; Green *et al.*, 1979). In the confluent epithelium, division continues in the basal layer, but at a rate much lower than in expanding colonies and similar to the rate in the epidermis. Eventually, squames begin to form in the superficial layer of the epithelium and are discharged into the medium. These squames have undergone some of the cytoplasmic organelle destruction characteristic of terminal differentiation and possess cross-linked envelopes, but nuclear destruction takes place more slowly and is usually completed only some days after the squames are discharged. Whether cultured cells have any tendency to form the ordered stacks characteristic of some kinds of epidermis (Mackenzie, 1970; Christophers, 1971; Allen and Potten, 1974) has not been examined, although certain features of silver-stained colonies are suggestive (Sun and Green, 1976). In old confluent cultures, cell movement eventually produces patterns that resemble dermatoglyphs (Green and Thomas, 1978).

Almost as soon as a continuous epithelium is formed by colonial fusion, it is coherent enough to be detached as a unit and handled as a graft (Green *et al.*, 1979). When transferred, the basal cells of a recently confluent epithelium are able to form new colonies quite well, but with increasing time in the confluent state this ability may decline.

III. THE DIFFERENTIATED PROPERTIES OF CULTURED KERATINOCYTES

A large body of literature deals with the particular structures and functions of keratinocytes. I will confine myself here to only three aspects of their differentiation. The first is the keratins, the specialized proteins from which the cell type takes its name. The second is the cross-linked envelope, a structure apparently independent of the keratins, and whose importance to the epidermis is not yet generally appreciated. The third is the destructive process that is the final stage of differentiation, and is usually included under keratinization, a term familiar through long usage, if not very suitable as a designation for the entire process of s. corneum formation.

A. Epidermal Keratins

Keratins are the constituent proteins of the 8 nm filaments of epidermis and its appendages (hair, nail, etc.). Avian feathers also contain keratins, but these are different in molecular size, in filament diameter, and in X-ray diffraction pattern. The keratins of epidermis are easily resolved into a number of proteins of molecular weight 40,000–68,000 (Baden *et al.*, 1973; Steinert and Idler, 1975; Huang *et al.*, 1975; Inoue *et al.*, 1976; Dale *et al.*, 1976; Culbertson and Freedberg, 1977; Brysk *et al.*, 1977; Sun and Green, 1978a; Fuchs and Green, 1980).

Keratins are insoluble in the absence of denaturing agents. Cells may therefore be extensively extracted with dilute neutral buffers to remove other proteins before dissolving the keratins. In the case of living cells, the keratins may then be dissolved in solutions containing 8 M urea or sodium dodecyl sulfate. If the denaturant is removed, the filaments can be reconstituted (Steinert, 1975; Sun and Green, 1978a). In the final stages of terminal differentiation, the plasma membrane becomes permeable and the cell becomes metabolically inert. As a result of the loss of reducing environment of the cytoplasm, the keratins become stabilized by disulfide bond formation (Green, 1977). Once this has occurred, a reducing agent is required in addition to a denaturing agent in order to dissolve them (Sun and Green, 1978a). Filaments can also be reconstituted from reduced keratins (Steinert and Gullino, 1976; Sun and Green, 1978a).

The keratins do not contain detectable carbohydrate, suggesting that their different electrophoretic mobilities in denaturing gel electrophoresis reflect true differences in the size of the polypeptides; but the different polypeptides are obviously related. Their amino acid compositions are very similar (Steinert and Idler, 1975; Fuchs and Green, 1978), they cross-react immunologically, and they give similar polypeptides after partial digestion with protease; but by these same criteria, there are also differences between them (Fuchs and Green, 1978).

The significance of the different molecular sizes of the keratins may be related to different roles in filament formation. According to Steinert *et al.* (1976, 1979) and Lee and Baden (1976), keratin filaments are obligatory heteropolymers of large and small polypeptides, the stoichiometry being variable only within narrow limits. Mouse keratinocytes appear to have substantially one large and one small polypeptide (Steinert *et al.*, 1979), but bovine and human keratins consist of a number of large and of small polypeptides (Steinert, 1975; Sun and Green, 1978a).

As demonstrated immunologically, all cell layers in the epidermis contain keratins (Gray *et al.*, 1977; Sun and Green, 1978b); similarly, all cultured keratinocytes, including the multiplying cells, contain keratins. This does not mean that all cells contain the same keratins, since an antiserum to a single keratin of homogeneous size may cross-react immunologically (particularly by immunofluorescence) with keratins of different size (Fuchs and Green, 1978). Actually the keratinocyte does vary its keratin composition, since different layers of the epidermis do not contain identical keratins (Dale and Stern, 1975; Baden and Lee, 1978; Skerrow and Hunter, 1978; Fuchs and Green, 1980). The cultured keratinocyte (Fig. 1) does not duplicate exactly the spectrum of keratins found in the epidermis; most notably it fails to make the keratins of large molecular weight (>60,000) (Sun and Green, 1978a; Fuchs and Green, 1978). The large keratins appear in cells of the epidermis only in the course of their terminal differentiation (Fuchs and Green, 1980) and it may be surmised that the properties of the filaments are modified as a result (see also Dale *et al.*, 1978).

Keratin filaments are usually estimated at 8 nm in diameter, but this value may not be significantly different from that of other intermediate filaments, usually estimated at 10 nm. It is therefore pertinent to ask to what extent the keratins may resemble intermediate filament proteins of other cell types. It now seems clear that intermediate filament proteins vary in different cell types and in different species (Lazarides and Hubbard, 1976; Starger and Goldman, 1977; Davison *et al.*, 1977; Bennett *et al.*, 1978; Gordon *et al.*, 1978; Hynes and Destree, 1978; Franke *et al.*, 1978b). They may contain a single filament protein or more than one (Granger and Lazarides, 1979). Antibodies to intermediate filament proteins of one species frequently do not cross-react with those of a related species.

The properties of keratins seem different from those of other intermediate filaments. Antiserum to human keratins cross-reacts with kera-

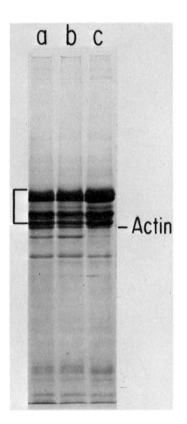

Fig. 1. The keratins of cultured human keratinocytes. Cultures of corneal epithelial cells (a), conjunctival epithelial cells (b), and epidermal cells (c) were harvested and the cells were extracted with neutral buffer. The keratins were then dissolved with the aid of sodium dodecyl sulfate and mercaptoethanol and separated by gel electrophoresis in the presence of the detergent. Each cell type is seen to give rise to keratin bands in the range enclosed by the bracket. There are strong keratin bands at 46,000, 50,000, 56,000, and 58,000 and weaker bands at 48,000, 52,000, and 54,000 (data from Sun and Green, 1977). Keratinocyte cultures derived from nasopharynx and trachea produced the same pattern.

tins of mouse and rabbit, but does not cross-react with any filament proteins in connective tissues or nervous tissue (Franke *et al.*, 1978b; Sun and Green, 1978b; Sun *et al.*, 1979; Franke *et al.*, 1979b). Keratins of different mammalian species give similar polypeptide patterns after partial proteolytic digestion (Fuchs and Green, 1978); but intermediate filaments prepared from NIL fibroblasts by Dr. Richard Hynes did not give a polypeptide pattern resembling that obtained from keratins (E. Fuchs and H. Green, unpublished observations). Fibroblast intermediate filaments may disintegrate at low ionic strength whereas keratins do not (Steinert *et al.*, 1978). One point of similarity between keratins and other intermediate filaments is that both give the α pattern in X-ray diffraction (Steinert *et al.*, 1978); but since fibrous proteins quite unrelated to the keratins, such as myosin, also give the α pattern (Cohen and Holmes, 1963), this property does not indicate a particularly close relation between keratins and other intermediate filament proteins.

It is now quite clear that keratins are not confined to the cells of epidermis, but are found in many other epithelia of different morphology and embryological origin. This has been demonstrated by using antisera to keratins (Sun and Green, 1977, 1978b; Franke *et al.*, 1978a–c; Sun *et al.*, 1979). Among epithelia possessing keratins are the mammary, intestinal, tracheal, urinary, and female genital epithelia, as well as the pancreatic and biliary ductal epithelia, the collecting tubules of the kidney and the ureters (Sun *et al.*, 1979). Cell lines derived from these tissues appear to continue keratin synthesis; this has been shown for HeLa cells, derived from cervical glands, and PtK2 cells, derived from the kidney (Osborn *et al.*, 1977; Franke *et al.*, 1978a,c, 1979c), presumably from the collecting ducts of this organ (Sun *et al.*, 1979). In the case of the HeLa cells, keratins could be purified sufficiently to be visible as bands in denaturing gel electrophoresis (Franke *et al.*, 1979c). It seems likely that tonofilaments are composed of keratins no matter in which cell type they occur and that they play an important structural role in cells exposed at internal as well as external surfaces. Although the endothelial cell is similarly exposed, it does not contain keratins (Franke *et al.*, 1979c; Sun *et al.*, 1979); it probably uses another method of achieving structural strength.

Although keratins are synthesized in many epithelial cell types, they are most abundant in stratified squamous epithelia, in which they have undergone special development as structural proteins. Keratins account for about 30% of the protein of cultured keratinocytes; in s. corneum the value may exceed 80% (Sun and Green, 1978a), but this is not the result of specialized synthesis alone (see below). At least some keratinocytes contain "vimentin"-type filaments in addition to keratins (Franke *et al.*, 1979a).

Since the keratins consist of a family of related polypeptides, a number of questions can be posed with respect to their origin: Do there exist precursor–product relations between keratins of large and small molecular weight, or are they made independently from distinct mRNA molecules? mRNA extracted from cultured keratinocytes translated well in a reticulocyte-based protein-synthesizing system and keratins were prominent among the products (Fuchs and Green, 1979). All the keratins of different molecular size found in the cultured keratinocytes were synthesized within 2 minutes of the addition of labeled methionine to the translation system preincubated with keratinocyte mRNA; no evidence of a keratin precursor was obtained, and no change in the relative abundance of different keratins took place with time after their synthesis. The keratin mRNAs could themselves be separated into two distinct groups by gel electrophoresis under native or denaturing conditions, and there was at least partial separation of different keratin mRNAs within each group (Fuchs and Green, 1979). For these reasons, most of the different keratins must be translation products of different mRNA molecules. Whether there is a corresponding family of different keratin genes, as has been proposed for feather keratins (Kemp, 1975), remains to be explored.

The s. corneum formed on the outer surface of the epidermis contains keratins of larger size than are found in cultured keratinocytes. Consecutive sections through the epidermis parallel to its surface show a gradual transition in synthesis from small keratins (46,000–58,000 MW) in the deepest layers, to large keratins (63,000–67,000) in the more superficial layers (Fuchs and Green, 1980). The basal cells of the epidermis therefore resemble the cultured cells in their keratins, whereas the outer layers account for the differences between epidermis and cultured cells. mRNA extracted from full-thickness epidermis can be translated into both small and large keratins (Fuchs and Green, 1980), whereas the mRNA of cultured cells can be translated only into small keratins (Fig. 2). Maturation of cells as they move through the spinous layer of the epidermis is evidently associated with a change in keratin mRNA formation, the new mRNAs being predominantly those for the large keratins. Whether this process involves a shift in transcription to different keratin genes remains to be established. In addition to the synthesis of new

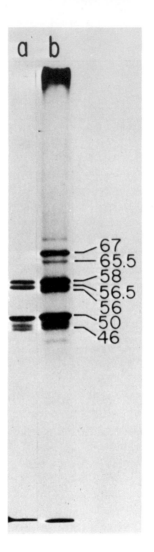

FIG. 2. Translation of keratin mRNA. Poly(A⁺) mRNA extracted and purified from cultured human epidermal keratinocytes and from human epidermis was translated *in vitro* using a reticulocyte lysate and ^{35}S-labeled methionine. The translated keratins were purified by immunoprecipitation and separated by gel electrophoresis. In track a, the fluorogram shows five keratins translated from the mRNA of cultured cells (58K, 56K, 50K, 48K, and 46K; k=thousand). The mRNA of epidermis gave rise to the same keratins (track b), but in addition to two large keratins (67K and 65.5K). Large keratins are made in the outer layers of the living epidermis and dominate in the stratum corneum. Data from Fuchs and Green (1980).

keratins in the maturing cells, there is a small reduction in size of some of the keratins during the last stages of terminal differentiation (Fuchs and Green, 1980).

B. The Cross-Linked Envelope

Since the work of Matoltsy and Balsamo (1955), it has been known that there is something unusual about the plasma membrane of the s. corneum cell. Electron microscopic studies showed that over the entire cytoplasmic surface of the membrane there lies a rather uniform envelope about 12 nm in thickness (Brody, 1959; Farquhar and Palade, 1965; Farbman, 1966; Hashimoto, 1969; Raknerud, 1974). This envelope, sometimes referred to as the marginal band, was found to be insoluble in very alkaline solutions even in the presence of reducing agents (Matoltsy and Balsamo, 1955; Matoltsy and Matoltsy, 1966). Transglutaminase was known to be present in epidermis (Goldsmith *et al.*, 1974; Goldsmith and Martin, 1975; Buxman and Wuepper, 1976; Ogawa and Goldsmith, 1976) and thought to play a role in terminal differentiation of the keratinocyte (Buxman and Wuepper, 1975; Abernathy *et al.*, 1977; Suguwara, 1977). Our investigations showed that the insoluble envelope of s. corneum cells was made of protein (Sun and Green, 1976) assembled from a soluble precursor (Rice and Green, 1979), and cross-linked by tranglutaminase (Rice and Green, 1977, 1978, 1979).

In contrast to the keratins that, as mentioned, are present to some degree in other epithelial cell types, cross-linked envelopes are formed only in keratinocytes. All non-keratinocyte cell types we have tested either dissolve completely in the presence of sodium dodecyl sulfate and β-mercaptoethanol at 100°C or, at most, leave small fragments that do not resemble at all the smooth closed sacs formed by the cross-linked envelopes. It is possible to score 1 cross-linked envelope per 1000 cells with confidence, so the method is sensitive as well as reliable (Sun and Green, 1976; Banks-Schlegel and Green, 1980a). As in s. corneum, cultured cells possessing this marker have a marginal band visible by electron microscopy (Green, 1977).

Stratum corneum cells treated with ionic detergent and reducing agent leave envelopes that reflect the irregular outline of the cells (Sun and Green, 1976; Banks-Schlegel and Green, 1980a), but envelopes that become cross-linked in suspended cell culture are nearly spherical (Fig. 3). The suspended cells that develop cross-linked envelopes may also contain intracellular vesicles that resist the detergent and reducing agent. These may be cross-linked envelopes formed on the cytoplasmic surface of intracellular vesicles. Such vesicles are usually not seen in s. corneum cells (Fig. 3).

In order to examine the nature of the cross-linking, envelopes produced in suspension culture were extracted extensively under denaturing and reducing conditions to remove contaminating non-envelope proteins, and then submitted to exhaustive enzymic degradation. The amount of the isodipeptide ϵ-(γ-glutamyl)lysine recovered indicates the extent of cross-linking (Lorand *et al.*, 1968; Matacic and Lowey, 1968; Pisano *et al.*, 1968). Envelopes generated in culture had the same degree of cross-linking as those formed in s. corneum, about 18% of the lysine residues participating (Rice and Green, 1977).

It soon became clear that transglutaminase was responsible for the ϵ-(γ-glutamyl)lysine bonds (Rice and Green, 1978, 1979). The formation of cross-linked envelopes in suspended keratinocyte cultures was prevented by (*a*) EDTA or EGTA (transglutaminase activity requires

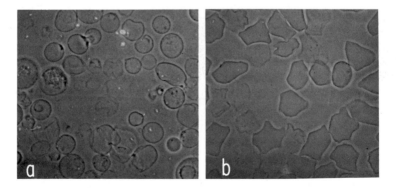

Fɪɢ. 3. Cross-linked envelopes of human epidermal cells. Cells were extracted with 1% sodium dodecyl sulfate and dithiothreitol at 100°C. Only the cross-linked envelopes remain undissolved. (a) Cross-linked envelopes were allowed to form in suspended keratinocyte cultures for several days before extraction. The envelopes are essentially spherical. (b) Sunburned skin was peeled from a subject and extracted. All cells possess cross-linked envelopes, and these retain a flattened and somewhat irregular shape. Photographs by courtesy of Dr. Robert H. Rice.

Ca^{2+}); (*b*) agents that block sulfhydryl groups (there is a cysteine at the active site of the enzyme); (*c*) amines known to be substrates of transglutaminase and therefore able to compete with the lysines that ordinarily act as amine donors in the cross-linking (Lorand *et al.*, 1972).

When keratinocytes grown on surfaces were placed in suspension culture, usually about 50% of the cells formed cross-linked envelopes. If, at the same time, their protein synthesis was arrested with cycloheximide, as many cells formed cross-linked envelopes as in the absence of the drug and there was no detectable diminution either of the amount of cross-linked envelope protein or the degree of cross-linking (Rice and Green, 1978). Before exposure to the drug, these cells must therefore have possessed all the precursor protein they needed to assemble and cross-link the envelope. In the presence of cycloheximide the envelopes formed even more quickly, reaching half-maximal values in about 12 hours instead of 2 days (Rice and Green, 1978).

Although the keratinocyte is unique in making a cross-linked envelope, there are analogous cross-linking processes in other cell types. The entrance of Ca^{2+} into erythrocytes had already been known to result in polymerization of membrane constituents, chiefly spectrin, but also membrane protein band 3 (Carraway *et al.*, 1975). This polymerization was soon shown to be catalyzed by transglutaminase (Lorand *et al.*, 1976), and from erythrocyte membranes a polymer was isolated in which 10% of the lysines were cross-linked (Siefring *et al.*, 1978). The amount of this polymer is small compared with the cross-linked envelope of the keratinocyte, probably too small to form a visible structure, but sufficient to alter the physical properties of the erythrocyte membrane (Kirkpatrick *et al.*, 1975).

As in the erythrocyte, the cross-linking process in the keratinocyte was found to be activated by calcium-transporting ionophores, although very high concentrations were required (Rice and Green, 1979). Disrupting the integrity of the cell membrane with neutral detergents or permeabilizing the membrane with high salt concentrations (Castellot *et al.*, 1978) was also effective in initiating the cross-linking if Ca^{2+} was present in the medium (Rice and Green, 1979). When assisted in this way, the cross-linking proceeded much more rapidly than in the spontaneous process. The number of cross-linked envelopes in suspended epidermal cells increased within 10 minutes after the addition of ionophore X537A and became half-maximal in 30 minutes (Fig. 4).

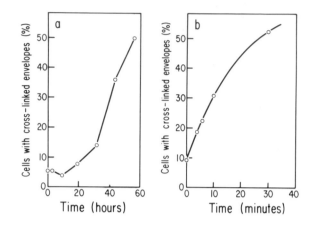

FIG. 4. Spontaneous and ionophore-assisted cross-linking in suspended keratinocyte cultures. Cells were allowed to incubate in suspension culture either in ordinary growth medium (a), or in medium containing the ionophore X537A at 50 μg/ml (b). At intervals, aliquots of cell suspension were removed, the cells were extracted with a solution of sodium dodecyl sulfate and dithiothreitol, and the number of cross-linked envelopes was counted. In the unassisted process cross-linking was not appreciable for over 24 hours and approached completion at about 50% in 60 hours. In the presence of the ionophore, new cross-linked envelopes appeared in 5 minutes, and the number approached a maximum in 30 minutes. The very high ionophore concentration is probably necessary to overcome the calcium sequestering properties of the cell organelles. Data from Rice and Green (1978, 1979).

The existence of a Ca^{2+}-activated, transglutaminase-catalyzed polymerization prompted a search for a molecule that could act as a preferential amine acceptor (Lorand *et al.*, 1972) and in this way be identified as a precursor of the polymeric structure. An amine-accepting molecule had been identified earlier in bovine epidermis (Buxman *et al.*, 1976), but no precise function was assigned. A soluble protein that had the properties expected of a precursor of the cross-linked envelope was identified in extracts of cultured human epidermal cells (Rice and Green, 1979). In a transglutaminase-catalyzed reaction, the protein was found to be a preferential acceptor of the fluorescent amine dansyl-cadaverine and of ^{14}C-labeled ethanolamine. The protein had a molecular weight of 92,000, and was purified to homogeneity by gel filtration and ion exchange chromatography. It was found to be very rich in Glu/Gln residues. Antiserum to the protein was prepared in rabbits and used to examine the relation of the protein to the cross-linked envelope (Rice and Green, 1979). It was concluded that the soluble protein was a precursor of the envelope for the following reasons.

1. Antiserum to the protein reacted with exhaustively washed cross-linked envelopes.
2. The antibodies to the protein were completely removed from the antiserum by absorption with washed cross-linked envelopes.
3. When cross-linking took place, the protein could no longer be extracted from the cytoplasm.

The properties of this molecule are compared with those of keratins in Table I. Except for the fact that they are both products of the keratinocyte, the two molecules are unrelated.

Many cell types possess transglutaminase (Folk and Chung, 1973). The enzyme has been purified from epidermis (Buxman and Wuepper, 1976; Ogawa and Goldsmith, 1976) and from hair follicles (Harding and Rogers, 1972; Chung and Folk, 1972a,b). It is not clear that particu-

TABLE I

COMPARISON OF KERATINS WITH ENVELOPE PRECURSOR[a]

	Keratins		Envelope Precursor	
1. Most abundant amino acids	Gly	20.9	Glu/Gln	45.8
(moles %)	Glu/Gln	13.3	Leu	14.6
	Ser	12.4	Lys	7.4
	Asp	8.5	Gly	6.7
	Leu	8.4	Pro	5.7
	Arg	5.5	His	4.7
2. Solubility in dilute buffers	Insoluble		Soluble	
3. Molecular weight in SDS after reduction	42,000–67,000		92,000	
4. Immunological	No cross-reaction		No cross-reaction	
5. Site in cell	Cytoplasmic (filamentous)		Cytoplasmic, becoming submembranous	
6. Present in all layers of the epidermis	Yes, though keratin size changes		No	

[a] Data from Sun and Green (1978b), Fuchs and Green (1978), and Rice and Green (1979).

lar specificity need be assigned to the epidermal transglutaminase, since fibroblast transglutaminase also acts preferentially on the extracted envelope precursor of keratinocytes (Rice and Green, 1979); it seems that the properties of the envelope precursor determine the molecular specificity of the cross-linking process. This protein, like some erythrocyte proteins, is apparently able to localize to the plasma membrane by a process that is independent of the cross-linking and takes place sometime before it. The protein must be deposited with a certain order, since the final envelope is of fairly uniform thickness.

The cross-linked envelope may be used as a marker for the keratinocyte in studying the development of this cell type during embryonic life. Transglutaminase appears early in the development of the epidermis (Obinata and Endo, 1979). During the first half of the period of gestation of the rabbit, cells of the external epithelium do not possess the ability to make cross-linked envelopes, and when dissociated and placed in surface culture these cells do not give rise to keratinocyte colonies. Early in the second half of gestation some of the epithelial cells acquire cross-linked envelopes, and an increasing number becomes able to make them when dissociated and placed in suspension culture. The ability to make cross-linked envelopes seems to develop at about the time stratification begins in the primitive epithelium (Banks-Schlegel and Green, 1980a).

Stratification plays an important role in envelope formation even in adult epidermis, not only because the cross-linking process is initiated at the time of s. corneum formation, but also because cells begin to accumulate the precursor protein only in the course of their outward movement in the stratified epithelium. Using an antiserum to the purified precursor protein, the location of cells containing the protein could be determined by immunofluorescence. It was found that the deeper layers of human epidermis do not possess this protein; usually it appears about midway through the stratified living cell layers and gradually becomes localized at the cell periphery (Rice and Green, 1979). While the point has not yet been examined, it seems likely, by analogy with the behavior of the keratins, that the mRNA for the envelope protein appears only after the cell reaches a definite position in the stratified epithelium. Differentiation antigens whose location is confined to certain layers have also been revealed by the use of antisera from patients with skin diseases (Bystryn et al., 1978). How the position of the cell might lead to a signal for synthesis of a new protein can only be guessed at. Because of the enlargement of the cells during terminal differentiation, the position of the cell is also correlated with its size (see later).

The use of transglutaminase-catalyzed cross-linking to achieve insolubility of structural proteins is also characteristic of epidermal appendages, such as hair. Highly insoluble proteins present in the medulla and inner root sheath have been found to be cross-linked by ϵ-(γ-glutamyl)lysine bonds (Harding and Rogers, 1971, 1972). These proteins are not keratins; like the envelope precursor, they have an extremely high Glu/Gln content (30–40%), but they differ in that they contain about 10% citrulline (Harding and Rogers, 1976). A urea-soluble precursor was isolated and shown to cross-react immunologically with the cross-linked protein (Rogers *et al.*, 1977). Whether these proteins of the hair follicle are related to the epidermal envelope protein remains to be determined.

C. *The Destructive Process in Terminal Differentiation*

One may say of the epidermal keratinocyte that it is a cell type that carries out its functions better after it is dead than when it is alive. The s. corneum cell not only is unable to proliferate, but has no metabolic activity, a state quite suitable for cells having a purely protective function. This state is achieved in stages, the first being the loss of ability to proliferate. This takes place when a cell leaves the basal layer or, as some evidence indicates, just before (Iverson *et al.*, 1968). Biosynthesis continues through the spinous layer, and there is accumulation of cell mass. Then, when the cell reaches the granular layer, sudden changes take place. Some studies have associated granular cells with specific protein synthesis (Ball *et al.*, 1978), but in the outer granular cells, protein and RNA synthesis are arrested (Fukuyama *et al.*, 1965; Fukuyama and Epstein, 1968) and very soon the destructive process becomes advanced (Lavker and Matoltsy, 1970). The cell then passes into the stratum corneum as a keratin-filled flattened sac without nucleus or cytoplasmic organelles, but with a cross-linked envelope.

The existence of this destructive process raises two questions: What starts it, and how is it carried out? The epidermis itself has no blood supply and it could be imagined that a destructive process might begin in cells at a sufficient distance from the basement membrane for their nutrient supply to become inadequate. But in cell culture, the destructive process takes place in the upper layers of the stratified epithelium or in detached squames even though these cells are closest to the nutrient medium and should be the best nourished of all. Attention should, it seems, be paid to the changes taking place as the cells enlarge and travel from the basal layer outward. Examination of such cells suggests that they are not in a steady state, since their biosynthetic capacity does not increase in proportion to cell mass (T.-T. Sun and H. Green, unpublished observations); it may be that at a certain stage of enlargement the cells are no longer able to carry out effectively their basic metabolic functions.

During the transition from granular layer to s. corneum, the cells appear to become abnormally permeable (Lavker and Matoltsy, 1970). Squame-like cells shed from the surface of epidermal cell cultures are permeable to trypan blue (Green, 1977). The question may be raised whether the permeable state is an early and causative event in the destructive process. The development of membrane permeability might, for example, be essential for the cross-linking process because it makes possible the entrance of Ca^{2+}. This would be consistent with observations that cross-linked envelopes become visible before any destructive process begins in the cytoplasm (Farbman, 1966; Hirone and Eryu, 1977). Artificial induction of a permeable state in cultured keratinocytes by ionophores or neutral detergent rapidly initiates envelope cross-linking by making Ca^{2+} available to the transglutaminase. On the other hand, there are also stores of calcium bound within the organelles of the keratinocyte; Ca^{2+} can be made available from this source and is able to support a slow rate of cross-linking (Rice and Green, 1978). At present it seems impossible to say whether loss of cell membrane function is an early or late step in the destructive process.

Once the cell's destructive capabilities are mobilized there are many cellular enzymes, lysosomal and other, that can participate in organelle destruction. Study of this process is facilitated because the placing of keratinocytes in suspended cell culture leads to a destructive process similar to that in s. corneum formation (Green, 1977). The keratinocytes lose their colony-forming ability (Rheinwald and Green, 1977; Morrissey and Green, 1978; Rheinwald, 1980) and their biosynthetic capacity (Rice and Green, 1978: Morrissey and Green, 1978). When terminal destruction is initiated in suspended keratinocytes, the known ribonucleases (Melbye and Freedberg, 1977) and proteases seem able to complete the destruction of ribosomes very quickly (Morrissey and Green, 1978). Perhaps the same is true for other cellular constituents, but for nuclear destruction the cell requires exogenous plasminogen (Green, 1977). In the absence of a source of plasminogen, nuclear degradation is extremely slow (Morrissey and Green, 1978). Even in the presence of 20% fetal calf serum (Green, 1977) the degradation is probably not as fast as in intact epidermis, where the nucleus disappears cytologically within a period of probably less than a day after biosynthesis is arrested (Fukuyama *et al.*, 1965; Fukuyama and Epstein, 1966, 1968).

If plasminogen originating from plasma plays an important part in this process, how would the granular cell, located so far from the dermal capillaries, obtain the proenzyme? The epidermal–dermal junction is an anatomical unit whose most substantial structure, the basal lamina, appears to constitute a continuous layer (Briggaman and Wheeler, 1975); nevertheless, macromolecules inserted beneath a stratified squamous epithelium penetrate easily into the epithelium and pass between the keratinocytes as far as the granular layer. This is true for horseradish peroxidase, a molecule of 40 kilodaltons (Schreiner and Wolff, 1969; Squier, 1973) and ferritin, whose apoprotein is a molecule of 460K (Nordquist *et al.*, 1966). Even colloidal Thorotrast particles, which are much larger still, penetrate into the epidermis, though not without some hindrance (Wolff and Honigsmann, 1971). When the proteins of epidermal callus are extracted with a dilute neutral salt solution and the extract is subjected to gel electrophoresis, a 68,000 MW protein that migrates with serum albumin is readily apparent (Sun and Green, 1978a). Evidently the normal leak rate for serum proteins through the basement membrane into the epidermis should be sufficient to bring plasminogen (MW 85,000) to the epidermal cells. Since the epidermal cells of the granular layer become permeable, it seems reasonable that plasminogen should gain access to the interior of the cells, either before or after its conversion to plasmin. Such a role for plasminogen is quite consistent with its known relation to tissue remodeling (Ossowski *et al.*, 1979). Neutral proteases of dermal origin are also known (Lazarus and Barrett, 1974) and might play a role in the destructive process.

As already mentioned, keratins account for over 80% of the protein of the s. corneum cell. This concentration of inert but specialized proteins is not achieved by differential synthesis alone; cultured keratinocytes make keratins only to the extent of 30% of cell protein. Presumably it is selective degradation of nonkeratin proteins that is responsible for the higher keratin concentration in s. corneum. When cells leave the granular layer they undergo a remarkable loss of from 45 to 86% of their dry weight (Meyer *et al.*, 1970), and the filamentous proteins appear to become concentrated (Lavker and Matoltsy, 1970). If, as seems likely, the loss is mainly of nonkeratins, the final keratin content would be brought into the range found in s. corneum cells.

IV. Size and Differentiated State in the Keratinocyte

Between the basal layer, in which cells are generated, and the granular layer, in which the destructive process begins, lie cell layers in which there is net biosynthesis but no multiplication. It has been shown in different ways that when cells leave the basal layer of the epidermis or other stratified squamous epithelium, they begin to increase in size (Meyer *et al.*, 1970; Rowden, 1975; Yardley and Goldstein, 1976) and by the time they reach the granular layer their volumes may be as much as 30-fold greater (Meyer *et al.*, 1970). As the cells enlarge they continue to synthesize and accumulate protein; they even make more ribosomes (Fukuyama and Bernstein, 1963). Some proteins and RNA are synthesized even in the deeper cells of the granular layer (Fukuyama *et al.*, 1965; Fukuyama and Epstein, 1966, 1968; Stern and Sekeri-Pataryas, 1972; Bell *et al.*, 1978) shortly before the destructive process begins.

Cultured epidermal cells that have stopped multiplying also accumulate protein (Sun and Green, 1976). The process can be followed simply by measuring cell size. This is most easily done by trypsinizing the culture and measuring the diameter of the now spherical or nearly spherical cells (Fig. 5). Cell diameter varies over a range greater than 3-fold (Sun and Green, 1976), and cell volume over a corresponding range of greater than 20-fold. The largest cells are those at an advanced stage of terminal differentiation. For example, in surface cultures, the modal

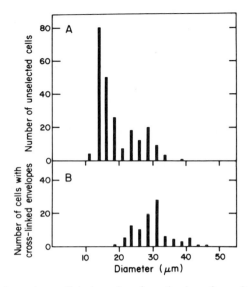

FIG. 5. Cell size and cross-linked envelope formation in surface cultures of keratinocytes. Twelve-day cultures of human keratinocytes were trypsinized, and cell diameters
were measured from a photograph of the cells in a hemacytometer chamber. The modal
diameter was 14 μm (A). After extraction of an aliquot with sodium dodecyl sulfate and
mercaptoethanol, no envelopes were left by small cells (B). The modal diameter of the
cross-linked envelopes was 32 μm. From Sun and Green (1976).

diameter of cells having cross-linked envelopes was 2.3 times the modal
diameter of unselected cells (Sun and Green, 1976), and no cells possessing cross-linked envelopes had a diameter less than 22 μm (Fig. 5).
Evidently in surface culture, as in the epidermis, the program for terminal differentiation ensures that the formation of the cross-linked envelope will be delayed until the cell has grown to a certain size.

Cells capable of multiplication belong to the small-cell category. This
was shown in several ways. Cultures were allowed to incorporate
tritiated thymidine, and then disaggregated. The cells were then cen-
trifuged to equilibrium on Ficoll gradients. Small cells are denser than
large ones, probably because DNA and RNA, which are heavy
molecules, account for a larger proportion of cell mass. The incorporated thymidine was concentrated in the small cells having high buoyant

density. If a chase period of some days was allowed to intervene between labeling and separation of the cells, the thymidine was found concentrated in the large cells (Sun and Green, 1976).

More recently, a method has been developed to relate the size of individual cells to their capacity to synthesize DNA. Cultures were allowed to incorporate [^{14}C]thymidine or [^{125}I]iododeoxyuridine, an analog of thymidine, for 2 hours. The cells were then disaggregated with trypsin and EDTA, and in their now spherical shape they were lightly fixed with glutaraldehyde. They were then mixed with liquid photographic emulsion, and the labeled cells were identified by radioautography. The diameter of the cells was measured from Polaroid photographs made of fields seen through a 16 × objective. The cells were grouped in size classes and the proportion of labeled cells in each size class was determined (Fig. 6). Up to a mean diameter of about 16 μm, cells initiated DNA replication with high frequency, but with increasing diameter the frequency dropped sharply. Above 27 μm, virtually no cells synthesized DNA. If the growth rate of the cells was increased by the inclusion of epidermal growth factor (EGF) and choleragen (cholera toxin) in the medium, the relation between cell size and ability to initiate replication was not affected. It would seem then, that these agents do not influence the probability that cells of any size class will initiate DNA replication. As demonstrated earlier (Green, 1978), choleragen does affect the size distribution of the cells by increasing the proportion of small cells, and this, according to the relation shown in Fig. 6, should increase the overall growth rate.

The effect of choleragen could also be demonstrated more directly. For this purpose, cells were labeled with [^{125}I]iododeoxyuridine rather than [^{14}C]thymidine. When the analog is incorporated into DNA, the emission of Auger electrons damages the DNA very extensively (Feinendegen *et al.*, 1971; Hofer and Hughes, 1971; Bradley *et al.*, 1975), and cell multiplication is prevented. For this reason, all cells that have incorporated the analog increase in size, and there is no dilution of the label. Cultures labeled for 2 hours with [^{125}I]iododeoxyuridine were washed free of the unincorporated label and allowed to incubate in medium for 3 or 6 days more. Most of the labeled cells moved out of the small-size category during the chase period (Fig. 7). The process of cell enlargement was not affected by EGF, but was strikingly reduced by choleragen, for in its presence a large fraction of the cells remained

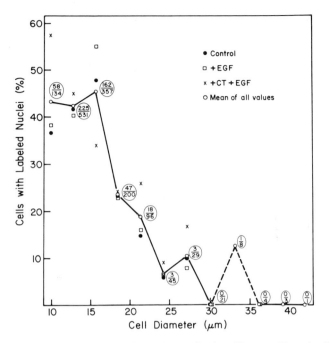

FIG. 6. Cell size and ability to initiate DNA replication. Human epidermal cells were inoculated at 10^5 per 50-mm petri dish already containing 4×10^5 lethally irradiated 3T3 cells. The medium of some cultures was supplemented with epidermal growth factor (EGF) (10 ng/ml) and others with EGF and choleragen (CT) (10^{-10} M). Eight days later the cultures were exposed to 2 μCi or 8 μCi of [^{125}I]iododeoxyuridine (two experiments) or 1 μCi of [^{14}C]thymidine (one experiment) for 2 hours. The cells were then detached and dissociated with trypsin and EDTA. The now spherical cells were fixed with freshly prepared 6% glutaraldehyde in isotonic buffer for 1 hour, suspended in NTB-2 photographic emulsion, and poured into a petri dish for autoradiography. The results of the three experiments are pooled. The symbols indicate for a single culture condition the proportion of DNA-synthesizing cells in each size class. The curve is drawn through the means for all culture conditions, the encircled values giving the number of cells scored as DNA-synthesizing and the number measured. Ability to synthesize DNA dropped sharply for cells over 16 μm in diameter, and the presence of EGF and choleragen did not influence the relation between cell size and the ability to start DNA synthesis. Unpublished experiments of J. Thomas and H. Green.

small 3–6 days later. Since the specific action of choleragen on cells is to increase the activity of adenyl cyclase, it is highly probable that it is the cAMP produced which retards terminal enlargement.

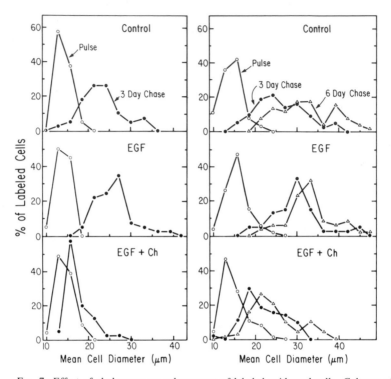

Fig. 7. Effect of choleragen on enlargement of labeled epidermal cells. Cultures of epidermal cells were labeled with [^{125}I]iododeoxyuridine as described in the legend to Fig. 6. After 2 hours, the medium containing the iododeoxyuridine was removed, the cell layer was washed with medium, and fresh medium was added. Immediately after labeling, and 3 days and 6 days later, the cells of a culture were subjected to autoradiography and the size of all labeled cells was measured. The three panels on the left and the three panels on the right show the results of two independent experiments. The enlargement of the labeled cells was greatly retarded by the choleragen (Ch). EGF, epidermal growth factor.

V. The Program of Differentiation

A very incomplete program for the terminal differentiation of the keratinocyte is shown in Fig. 8. The information comes from studies of both epidermis and cultured keratinocytes. The differentiation must be related to a time scale or, as cell size is correlated with time, to a size scale. The three compartments probably correspond to basal layer, spinous layer, and granular layer. When all essential components are ready, it is the death of the cell that eliminates the nonessential components and puts the keratins and envelope protein in their final form. This is associated with a reduction in cell volume (Meyer *et al.,* 1970; Lavker and Matoltsy, 1970).

VI. Factors Affecting Keratinocyte Multiplication

The overall rate of cell multiplication in a culture containing multiplying and terminally differentiating cells should depend on two variables: (*a*) the fraction of the population capable of multiplication; (*b*) the rate of multiplication in that fraction. These variables are difficult to measure and may not be completely independent. The multiplication of cultured keratinocytes is promoted by certain chemical agents, and it seems likely that these effects will shed some light on the means by which multiplication is regulated.

A. Adrenocortical Steroid

In the absence of hydrocortisone, keratinocyte colonies do not expand smoothly as the cells proliferate. Instead, the central region of the colonies tends to form a spherical aggregate, an effect which hinders multiplication. Hydrocortisone at 0.4 μg/ml prevents this and for this reason promotes proliferation (Rheinwald and Green, 1975).

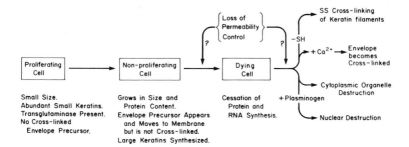

Fig. 8. Terminal differentiation of the epidermal keratinocyte.

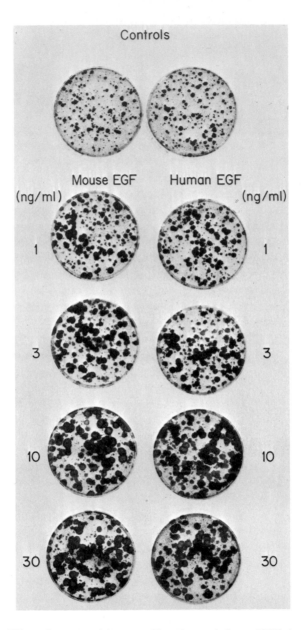

FIG. 9. Effect of mouse and human epidermal growth factor (EGF) in promoting growth of human epidermal colonies. Fifty-millimeter dishes were inoculated with 5×10^3 newborn human epidermal cells and 4×10^5 supporting lethally irradiated 3T3 cells.

B. Epidermal Growth Factor (EGF)

This polypeptide of 53 amino acids, discovered by Dr. Stanley Cohen of Vanderbilt University, has important actions promoting proliferation of many cell types (Cohen and Taylor, 1974; Cohen and Savage, 1974). Although usually obtained in concentrated form from the salivary gland of the male mouse, EGF is also found in blood and urine. The human polypeptide, also known as urogastrone (Gregory *et al.*, 1977), is nearly identical in structure to the EGF isolated from the mouse. It has many of the same effects on different cell types as the mouse polypeptide (Carpenter and Cohen, 1978). The human and the mouse polypeptides have the same effect on human epidermal cells, a concentration of 1 ng/ml increasing the size of the colonies detectably and 10 ng/ml (1.6×10^{-9} M) exerting a maximal effect (Fig. 9).

More detailed analysis has revealed a number of effects of EGF on cultured epidermal cells (Rheinwald and Green, 1977; Sun and Green, 1976).

1. The appearance of the colonies is altered. The cells acquire a tendency to move outward from the center of the colony, thus reducing stratification and the cell density per unit area. This effect often makes it possible to tell from a glance at the appearance of colonies that EGF is present in the culture medium.

2. The average growth rate in the colonies is better maintained. This effect is observed when the colonies contain more than 50–200 cells. At this stage, the growth rate begins to decline in the absence of EGF, but this decline is postponed in the presence of EGF (Rheinwald and Green, 1977). The effect of EGF might be related to the centrifugal tendency of the cells and the consequent reduction of stratification. The supporting 3T3 cells tend to compress the expanding colony, and if they are removed an effect of EGF on growth rate becomes more difficult to demonstrate, the unimpeded epidermal cells now showing a centrifugal tendency

The medium was supplemented with choleragen 10^{-10} M. Additions of EGF were begun 3 days after inoculation. Cultures were fixed and stained with rhodanile blue 14 days after inoculation. Human EGF was kindly provided by Dr. H. Gregory of Imperial Chemical Industries, Cheshire, England.

even in the absence of the polypeptide. The cells of small colonies do not grow faster in the presence of EGF, but when transferred, they give rise to new colonies with higher frequency. The more the cells are subcultured, the greater becomes the effect of EGF on subsequent colony formation. The presence of EGF greatly increases the lifetime of serially cultivated cells (Rheinwald and Green, 1977).

3. In expanding cultures, in which basal cells are able either to multiply or to differentiate terminally, the presence of EGF reduces the proportion of cells possessing cross-linked envelopes (Sun and Green, 1976); but when the culture becomes confluent, there is no room for expansion of the basal population, so that an increased rate of proliferation induced by EGF results in increased production of terminally differentiated squames at the surface of the epithelium (Green, 1977). This may be the explanation for the earlier observation that EGF promotes s. corneum formation in the epidermis (Cohen and Elliott, 1963), an effect often ascribed to increased differentiation.

4. The EGF is known to be mitogenic for numerous cell types (Armelin, 1973; Hollenberg and Cuatrecases, 1973; Cohen and Taylor, 1974), and many or most cell types possess surface receptors for this polypeptide (Carpenter *et al.*, 1975; Fabricant *et al.*, 1977). The A431 line (Fabricant *et al.*, 1977) is an example of a cell type with unusually abundant EGF receptors. This line, which is demonstrably of keratinocyte origin, possesses 25–50 times more EGF receptors than human diploid fibroblasts (Haigler *et al.*, 1978). If this is a general property of keratinocytes, it might make this cell type especially susceptible to the action of EGF *in vivo*.

C. Agents Increasing Cellular Cyclic AMP (cAMP) Content

A survey of the literature on the relation of cAMP to the growth of different cell types gives a rather confusing picture (Abell and Monahan, 1973). On the one hand, the work of most laboratories linked cAMP to the arrest of growth of fibroblasts and other cell types. On the other hand, the multiplication of some cell types seemed to be increased by cAMP or agents that increase cAMP production (Whitfield *et al.*,

1970; Pawalek *et al.*, 1975; Raff *et al.*, 1978; Pruss and Hershman, 1979). Such agents greatly favor multiplication of the keratinocyte (Green, 1978; Marcelo, 1979), and their effects are important both for their practical value in cultivation and for their implications with respect to growth control in this cell type.

Agents known to increase the level of cAMP by different means promote the multiplication of keratinocytes. Choleragen specifically activates adenyl cyclase by covalent modification (Gill, 1977), and it is the most powerful agent for increasing keratinocyte multiplication (Fig. 10). Choleragenoid (Finkelstein, 1976), kindly provided in purified form by Dr. Finkelstein, is without effect. The catecholamine iso-proterenol, which stimulates the activity of adenyl cyclase by acting through adrenergic receptors, also favors multiplication of keratino-cytes. A difference between the two types of activation is shown by the fact that the effect of isoproterenol is abolished by the specific β-adrenergic blocker propranolol, whereas the effect of choleragen is not (Fig. 10).

Methylisobutylxanthine, a phosphodiesterase inhibitor, also increases the multiplication of keratinocytes (Green, 1978). Analogs of cAMP,

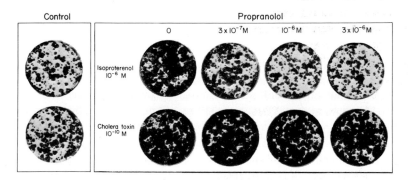

FIG. 10. Effect of agents known to affect cAMP formation on the multiplication of human epidermal cells. Epidermal keratinocytes (10^4; fourth serial transfer) were inoculated together with 4×10^5 lethally irradiated 3T3 cells. The agents indicated were added at each medium change, beginning at the time of inoculation. Mouse epidermal growth factor (10 ng/ml) was added to all cultures beginning 4 days after inoculation. Cultures were fixed and stained 13 days after inoculation. The DL-propranolol prevented the growth-promoting effect of L-isoproterenol but not that of choleragen.

such as dibutryl cAMP and 8-bromo cAMP, promote multiplication (Marcelo *et al.*, 1979), but at least in the 3T3-supported growth of human keratinocytes, the effect of dibutryl cAMP is much weaker than that of choleragen or isoproterenol (Green, 1978).

As the most powerful of the agents affecting cAMP, choleragen has been studied in most detail. Its effects are quite different from those of EGF. As described above, it opposes the terminal enlargement of the keratinocyte. It also inhibits the process of squame detachment that is characteristic of mature confluent cultures. Choleragen has an obvious effect on overall cell multiplication even when the colonies are very small (3–4 days after inoculation in the 3T3-supported system). The cells do not acquire a centrifugal tendency as in the presence of EGF, but pack tightly together and maintain extensive stratification. The addition of EGF produces its usual centrifugal effect and sustains the multiplication rate, so the effect of the combination of choleragen and EGF is superior to that of either agent alone.

The effect of choleragen is specially marked on epidermal cells derived from older donors; these cells can be subcultivated only with great difficulty in the absence of an agent able to increase cAMP, whereas in the presence of choleragen or isoproterenol they can be grown through numerous subcultures.

Disaggregated epidermal cells inoculated into primary culture will form colonies with higher efficiency in the presence of choleragen. For the cells of older donors, the efficiency may increase by two orders of magnitude (Green *et al.*, 1979). In the absence of choleragen, the colonies will often abort at any stage of serial cultivation; all the cells of a colony or of a sector of a colony will, at virtually the same time, become enlarged and stop multiplying, while other colonies or sectors of colonies will contain mostly small cells and maintain multiplication. This suggests that there exist cell cohorts, all of whose members lose proliferative ability at about the same time. In the presence of choleragen the number of colonies that abort is much reduced; most colonies, once initiated, grow until they become confluent.

The action of choleragen and similar agents can be summarized as follows: Only small epidermal cells can multiply (Fig. 6). By raising the cAMP content of the cells these agents retard the process of cell enlargement that is part of the process of terminal differentiation, and more cells remain of a size compatible with proliferation. The proportion of proliferating cells is increased, and thereby the overall growth rate.

VII. The Evolution of Mesenchymal Independence

As mentioned earlier, freshly isolated keratinocytes, even when extensively purified of contaminating dermal fibroblasts (Fusenig and Worst, 1974, 1975), will undergo some multiplication in culture, but the multiplication rate and the retention of proliferative capacity are not comparable to what is obtained in the presence of 3T3 support. At each successive transfer of human keratinocyte cultures, it is necessary again to provide supporting 3T3 cells. The following considerations are relevant to this problem of mesenchymal support.

1. The lower the inoculation density the more critical is the requirement. Sparsely inoculated keratinocytes do not give rise to any colonies without mesenchymal support, whereas densely inoculated ones will undergo some proliferation.

2. If the keratinocytes are inoculated in large clumps, or if single cells are allowed to develop into colonies in the presence of 3T3 cells and the latter are then selectively removed, the keratinocytes will usually grow to confluence (J. G. Rheinwald and H. Green, unpublished experiments). The keratinocytes can therefore multiply for a period after withdrawal of mesenchymal support, if the conditions are not too stringent.

3. Rodent keratinocytes, like rodent fibroblasts, can develop into established lines (references cited earlier). Once this has happened, the cells can become serially cultivable without mesenchymal support. This independence is acquired as a result of selective pressure applied during serial cultivation. Even neoplasms of the keratinocyte are not initially independent of fibroblast support, although they may become independent, even in the case of the human, through serial cultivation. The A431 line of Fabricant *et al.* (1977) is an example. Transformation with oncogenic viruses seems to lead to the same result (Steinberg and Defendi, 1979). Some established keratinocyte lines that can be serially cultivated in the absence of mesenchymal support nevertheless grow better when such support is provided.

4. The attainment of mesenchymal independence by an established keratinocyte line may or may not be accompanied by much deterioration in its differentiated properties. Judging by structural studies, such lines can show very impressive terminal differentiation (Fejerskov *et al.*, 1974). In other lines of keratinocyte origin much of the differentiated function seems to disappear (unpublished observations).

5. Conclusions about proliferative behavior may depend on the medium employed. It remains possible that by modification of the medium the requirements for mesenchymal support might be reduced; this might be achieved either by providing the same components as the mesenchymal cells, or by altering the state of the keratinocytes in such a way as to make these components dispensable.

VIII. BEHAVIOR OF NONEPIDERMAL KERATINOCYTES

Stratified squamous epithelia are distinguished by histologists as keratinizing (s. corneum forming) or nonkeratinizing. The two types contain different keratins (Milstone and McGuire, 1978; Fuchs and Green, 1980). It was of interest to see how cultured keratinocytes of the two types behaved in the presence of 3T3 support. The first to be examined were the cells of corneal and conjunctival epithelia. They were found to form colonies very similar to those of epidermal keratinocytes (Sun and Green, 1977). All three keratinocyte subtypes made the same pattern of keratins (Fig. 1), though small differences could be detected between nonkeratin proteins of rabbit epidermal and corneal keratinocytes. Corneal epithelium *in vivo* has no s. corneum and therefore no cross-linked envelopes, but the cultivated keratinocytes of human corneal epithelium made envelopes just like those of epidermal cells and under the same conditions. Yet when cultured corneal epithelial cells are injected into animals, they do not form s. corneum in the same way as epidermal cells (Doran *et al.*, 1980). The culture conditions therefore permit the expression of those differentiated functions that are common to all the keratinocyte subtypes, but do not necessarily permit the expression of those aspects of terminal differentiation in which epidermal cells differ from the other keratinocyte subtypes.

As mentioned earlier, cultivated epidermal keratinocytes synthesize a family of keratins that resembles that of the basal layer of epidermis, whereas the large keratins appear to be synthesized after the cells leave the basal layer (Fuchs and Green, 1980). In cultured keratinocytes the signal for synthesis of large keratins seems to be absent even though these cells form a stratified epithelium; this is probably the explanation for the similarity of the keratins made by keratinocyte cultures derived from different stratified squamous epithelia.

Keratinocytes have also been cultivated from human oral, pharyngeal, and nasopharyngeal epithelium (Green, 1978; Taichman *et al.*, 1979). The cultured cells contained the same keratins as other cultured keratinocytes and were able to make cross-linked envelopes. They were sensitive to EGF and to choleragen. Though tracheal epithelium is not a stratified squamous epithelium, it can give rise in culture to typical keratinocyte colonies. The implication that some keratinocytes can reside in this epithelium has particular interest for the study of metaplasia.

IX. Cell Culture Can Generate Large Amounts of Human Epithelium—Could Such Epithelium Find Practical Application?

It has been shown many times that epidermis cultured for short periods can be transplanted to animals (Medawar, 1948; Karasek, 1968; Yuspa *et al.*, 1970; Igel *et al.*, 1974; Worst *et al.*, 1974). Naturally the possibility that cultured epidermis could be used to graft humans with epidermal defects was considered very early. There were, however, two serious problems. The first was that of expanding the number of epidermal cells sufficiently by cultivation. This problem has been essentially solved. By the methods I have described, it is possible in two stages of cultivation to generate, from a small biopsy, cultured epithelium in amount comparable to human body surface (Green *et al.*, 1979). This epithelium can be prepared in a form suitable for grafting, takes uniformly when applied to graft beds prepared in athymic mice, and gives rise to histologically normal human epidermis (Banks-Schlegel and Green, 1980b). The second problem is how well such grafted epithelium will perform the functions of natural epidermis. In the most careful study performed on the behavior of grafted (rodent) epidermal cells (Billingham and Reynolds, 1952), serious shortcomings were discovered in the quality of the regenerated epidermis. Since the epidermis of humans behaves differently from that of rodents in important respects, the quality of epidermis constituted from cultured epithelium will have to be determined in the human. Even if the quality should be inferior to that of normal skin, it seems quite probable that covering epidermal defects with autologous or even homologous cultured epithelium will be of value where conventional methods are unable to deal with the problem.

ACKNOWLEDGMENTS

This contribution is dedicated to my associates, the mariners who made all progress possible: Jim Rheinwald, who first paddled strongly in the sluggish currents of epidermal cell culture; (Henry) Tung-Tien Sun and Elaine Fuchs, who fished out the keratins; Bob Rice, who grappled with the cross-linked envelope; Susan Schlegel, who had a hand on many oars; and Olaniyi Kehinde and Judith Thomas, who kept the boat afloat.

REFERENCES

Abell, C. W., and Monahan, T. M. (1973). *J. Cell. Biol.* **59**, 549–558.
Abernathy, J. L., Hill, R. L., and Goldsmith, L. A. (1977). *J. Biol. Chem.* **252**, 1837–1839.
Allen, T. D., and Potten, C. S. (1974). *J. Cell Sci.* **15**, 291–319.
Armelin, H. A. (1973). *Proc. Natl. Acad. Sci. U.S.A.* **70**, 2702–2706.
Baden, H. P., and Lee, L. D. (1978). *J. Invest. Dermatol.* **71**, 148–151.
Baden, H. P., Goldsmith, L. A., and Fleming, B. (1973). *Biochim. Biophys. Acta* **317**, 303–311.
Ball, R. D., Walker, G. K., and Bernstein, I. A. (1978). *J. Biol. Chem.* **253**, 5861–5868.
Banks-Schlegel, S., and Green, H. (1980a). *Dev. Biol.* **74**, 274–285.
Banks-Schlegel, S., and Green, H. (1980b). *Transplantation* **29**, 308–313.
Bennett, G. S., Fellini, S. A., Croop, J. M., Otto, J. J., Bryan, J., and Holtzer, H. (1978). *Proc. Natl. Acad. Sci. U.S.A.* **75**, 4364–4368.
Billingham, R. E., and Reynolds, J. (1952). *Br. J. Plas. Surg.* **5**, 25–36.
Bradley, E. W., Chan, P. C., and Adelstein, S. J. (1975). *Radiat. Res.* **64**, 555–563.
Briggaman, R. A., and Wheeler, C. E., Jr. (1975). *J. Invest. Dermatol.* **65**, 71–84.
Briggaman, R. A., Abele, D. C., Harris, S. R., and Wheeler, C. E., Jr. (1967). *J. Invest. Dermatol.* **48**, 159–168.
Brody, I. (1959). *J. Ultrastruct. Res.* **2**, 482–511.
Brysk, M. M., Gray, R. H., and Bernstein, I. A. (1977). *J. Biol. Chem.* **252**, 2127–2133.
Buxman, M. M., and Wuepper, K. D. (1975). *J. Invest. Dermatol.* **65**, 107–112.
Buxman, M. M., and Wuepper, K. D. (1976). *Biochim. Biophys. Acta* **452**, 356–369.
Buxman, M. M., Buehner, G. E., and Wuepper, K. D. (1976). *Biochem. Biophys. Res. Commun.* **73**, 470–478.
Bystryn, J. C., Nash, M., and Robins, P. (1978). *J. Invest. Dermatol.* **71**, 110–113.
Carpenter, G., and Cohen, S. (1976). *Natl. Cancer Inst. Monogr.* **48**, 149–156.

Carpenter, G., Lembach, K. J., Morrison, M. M., and Cohen, S. (1975). *J. Biol. Chem.* **250,** 4297-4304.

Carraway, K. L., Triplett, R. B., and Anderson, D. R. (1975). *Biochim. Biophys. Acta* **379,** 571-581.

Castellot, J. J., Jr., Miller, M. R., and Pardee, A. B. (1978). *Proc. Natl. Acad. Sci. U.S.A.* **75,** 351-355.

Christophers, E. (1971). *J. Invest. Dermatol.* **56,** 165-169.

Chung, S. I., and Folk, J. E. (1972a). *Proc. Natl. Acad. Sci. U.S.A.* **69,** 303-307.

Chung, S. I., and Folk, J. E. (1972b). *J. Biol. Chem.* **247,** 2798-2807.

Cohen, C., and Holmes, K. C. (1963). *J. Mol. Biol.* **6,** 423-432.

Cohen, S., and Elliott, G. A. (1963). *J. Invest. Dermatol.* **40,** 1-5.

Cohen, S., and Savage, C. R. Jr. (1974). *Recent Prog. Horm. Res.* **30,** 551-574.

Cohen, S., and Taylor, J. M. (1974). *Recent Prog. Horm. Res.* **30,** 533-550.

Colburn, N. H., Bruegge, W. F. V., Bates, J. R., Gray, R. H., Rossen, J. D., Kelsey, W. H., and Shimada, T. (1978). *Cancer Res.* **38,** 624-634.

Cruickshank, C. N. D., Cooper, J. R., and Hooper, C. (1960). *J. Invest. Dermatol.* **34,** 339-342.

Culbertson, V. B., and Freedberg, I. M. (1977). *Biochim. Biophys. Acta* **490,** 178-191.

Dale, B. A., and Stern, I. B. (1975). *J. Invest. Dermatol.* **65,** 220-222.

Dale, B. A., Stern, I. B., Rabin, M., and Huang, L.-Y. (1976). *J. Invest. Dermatol.* **66,** 230-235.

Dale, B. A., Holbrook, K. A., and Steinert, P. M. (1978). *Nature (London)* **276,** 729-731.

Davison, P. F., Hong, B.-S., and Cooke, P. (1977). *Exp. Cell Res.* **109,** 471-474.

Doran, T. I., Vidrich, A., and Sun, T.-T. (1980). *Cell* (submitted).

Elias, P. M., Yuspa, S. H., Gullino, M. Morgan, D. L., Bates, R. R., and Lutzner, M. A. (1974). *J. Invest. Dermatol.* **62,** 569-581.

Fabricant, R. N., De Larco, J. E., and Todaro, G. J. (1977). *Proc. Natl. Acad. Sci. U.S.A.* **74,** 565-569.

Farbman, A. I. (1966). *Anat. Rec.* **156,** 269-282.

Farquhar, M. G., and Palade, G. E. (1965). *J. Cell Biol.* **26,** 263-291.

Feinendegen, L. E. and Bond, V. P. (1971). *In* "Biophysical Aspects of Radiation Quality," pp. 419-430. IAEA, Vienna.

Fejerskov, O., Theilade, J., and Jepsen, A. (1974). *Scand. J. Dent. Res.* **82,** 212-228.

Finkelstein, R. A. (1976). *In* "Mechanisms in Bacterial Toxicology" (A. W. Bernheimer, ed.), pp. 53-84. Wiley, New York.

Flaxman, B. A., Lutzner, M. A., and Van Scott, E. J. (1967). *J. Invest. Dermatol.* **49,** 322-332.

Folk, J. E., and Chung, S. I. (1973). *Adv. Enzymol.* **38,** 109-191.

Franke, W. W., Grund, C., Osborn, M., and Weber, K. (1978a). *Cytobiologie* **17,** 365-391.

Franke, W. W., Schmid, E., Osborn, M., and Weber, K. (1978b). *Proc. Natl. Acad. Sci. U.S.A.* **75,** 5034-5038.

Franke, W. W., Weber, K., Osborn, M., Schmid, E., and Freudenstein, C. (1978c). *Exp. Cell Res.* **116,** 429-445.

Franke, W. W., Schmid, E., Breitkreutz, D., Luder, M., Boukamp, P., Fusenig, N. E., Osborn, M., and Weber, K. (1979a). *Differentiation* **14,** 35–50.

Franke, W. W., Schmid, E., Osborn, M. and Weber, K. (1979b). *J. Cell Biol.* **81,** 570–580.

Franke, W. W., Schmid, E., Weber, K. and Osborn, M. (1979c). *Exp. Cell Res.* **118,** 95–109.

Freeman, A. E., Igel, H. J., Herrman, B. J., and Kleinfeld, K. L. (1976). *In Vitro* **12,** 352–362.

Friedman-Kien, A. E., Prose, P. H., Liebhaber, H., and Morrill, S. (1966). *Nature (London)* **212,** 1583–1584.

Fuchs, E., and Green, H. (1978). *Cell* **15,** 887–897.

Fuchs, E., and Green, H. (1979). *Cell* **17,** 573–582.

Fuchs, E., and Green, H. (1980). *Cell* **19,** 1033–1042.

Fukuyama, K., and Bernstein, I. A. (1963). *J. Invest. Dermatol.* **41,** 47–52.

Fukuyama, K., and Epstein, W. L. (1966). *J. Invest. Dermatol.* **47,** 551–559.

Fukuyama, K., and Epstein, W. L. (1968). *Am. J. Anat.* **12,** 269–274.

Fukuyama, K., Nakamura, T., and Bernstein, I. A. (1965). *Anat. Rec.* **152,** 525–536.

Fusenig, N. E., and Worst, P. K. M. (1974). *J. Invest. Dermatol.* **63,** 187–193.

Fusenig, N. E., and Worst, P. K. M. (1975). *Exp. Cell Res.* **93,** 443–457.

Fusenig, N. E., Amer, S. M., Boukamp, P., and Worst, P. K. M. (1978). *Bull. Cancer* **65,** 271–280.

Gilchrest, B. A. (1979). *J. Invest. Dermatol.* **72,** 219–223.

Gill, D. M. (1977). *Adv. Cyclic Nucleotide Res.* **8,** 85–118.

Goldsmith, L. A. and Martin, C. M. (1975). *J. Invest. Dermatol.* **64,** 316–321.

Goldsmith, L. A., Baden, H. P., Roth, S. I., Colman, R., Lee, L., and Fleming, B. (1974). *Biochim. Biophys. Acta* **351,** 113–125.

Gordon, W. E., III, Bushnell, A., and Burridge, K. (1978). *Cell* **13,** 249–261.

Granger, B. L., and Lazarides, E. (1979). *Cell* **18,** 1053–1063.

Gray, R. H., Brabec, R. K., Brysk, M. M., and Bernstein, I. A. (1977). *J. Histochem. Cytochem.* **25,** 1127–1139.

Gregory, H., Bower, J. M., and Willshire, I. R. (1977). "Growth Factors" (K. W. Kastrup and J. H. Nielsen, eds.), pp. 75–84. Pergamon, New York.

Green, H. (1977). *Cell* **11,** 405–416.

Green, H. (1978). *Cell* **15,** 801–811.

Green, H., and Thomas, J. (1978). *Science* **200,** 1385–1388.

Green, H., Kehinde, O., and Thomas, J. (1979). *Proc. Natl. Acad. Sci. U.S.A.* **76,** 5665–5668.

Haigler, H., Ash, J. F., Singer, S. J., and Cohen, S. (1978). *Proc. Natl. Acad. Sci. U.S.A.* **75,** 3317–3321.

Harding, H. W. J., and Rogers, G. E. (1971). *Biochemistry* **10,** 624–630.

Harding, H. W. J., and Rogers, G. E. (1972). *Biochemistry* **11,** 2858–2863.

Harding, H. W. J., and Rogers, G. E. (1976). *Biochim. Biophys. Acta* **427,** 315–324.

Hashimoto, K. (1969). *Arch. Klin. Exp. Dermatol.* **235,** 374–385.

Hofer, K. G., and Hughes, W. L. (1971). *Radiat. Res.* **47,** 94–109.

Hollenberg, M. D., and Cuatrecasas, P. (1973). *Proc. Natl. Acad. Sci. U.S.A.* **70**, 2964–2968.

Hirone, T., and Eryu, Y. (1977). *In* "Biochemistry of Cutaneous Epidermal Differentiation" (M. Seiji and I. A. Bernstein, eds.), pp. 81–92. Univ. Park Press, Baltimore, Maryland.

Huang, L.-Y., Stern, I. B., Clagett, J. A., and Chi, E. Y. (1975). *Biochemistry* **14**, 3573–3580.

Hynes, R. O., and Destree, A. T. (1978). *Cell* **13**, 151–163.

Igel, H. J., Freeman, A. E., Boeckman, C. R., and Kleinfeld, K. L. (1974). *Arch. Surg. (Chicago)* **108**, 724–729.

Inoue, N., Fukuyama, K., and Epstein, W. L. (1976). *Biochim. Biophys. Acta* **439**, 95–106.

Iverson, O. H., Bjerknes, R., and Devik, F. (1968). *Cell Tissue Kinet.* **1**, 351–367.

Jepsen, A. (1974). *Scand. J. Dent. Res.* **82**, 144–146.

Karasek, M. A. (1966). *J. Invest. Dermatol.* **47**, 533–540.

Karasek, M. A. (1968). *J. Invest. Dermatol.* **51**, 247–252.

Karasek, M. A., and Charlton, M. E. (1971). *J. Invest. Dermatol.* **56**, 205–210.

Kemp, D. J. (1975). *Nature (London)* **254**, 573–577.

Kirkpatrick, F. H., Hillman, D. G., and LaCelle, P. L. (1975). *Experientia* **31**, 653–654.

Kitano, Y., and Endo, H. (1977). *in* "Biochemistry of Cutaneous Epidermal Differentiation" (M. Seiji and I. A. Bernstein, eds.), pp. 319–334. Univ. Park Press, Baltimore, Maryland.

Kondo, S., Aso, K., and Namba, M. (1979). *J. Invest. Dermatol.* **72**, 85–87.

Lavker, R. M., and Matoltsy, A. G. (1970). *J. Cell Biol.* **44**, 501–512.

Lazarides, E., and Hubbard, B. D. (1976). *Proc. Natl. Acad. Sci. U.S.A.* **73**, 4344–4348.

Lazarus, G. S., and Barrett, A. J. (1974). *Biochim. Biophys. Acta* **350**, 1–12.

Lee, L. D., and Baden, H. P. (1976). *Nature (London)* **264**, 377–379.

Liu, S.-C., and Karasek, M. (1978). *J. Invest. Dermatol.* **71**, 157–162.

Lorand, L., Downey, J., Gotoh, T., Jacobsen, A., and Tokura, S. (1968). *Biochem. Biophys. Res. Commun.* **31**, 222–230.

Lorand, L., Chenoweth, D., and Gray, A. (1972). *Ann. N. Y. Acad. Sci.* **202**, 155–171.

Lorand, L., Weissman, L. B., Epel, D. L., and Bruner-Lorand, J. (1976). *Proc. Natl. Acad. Sci. U.S.A.* **73**, 4479–4481.

Mackenzie, I. C. (1970). *Nature (London)* **226**, 653–655.

Marcelo, C. L. (1979). *Exp. Cell Res.* **120**, 201–210.

Marcelo, C. L., Kim. Y. G., Kaine, J. L., and Voorhees, J. J. (1978). *J. Cell Biol.* **79**, 356–370.

Matacic, S., and Lowey, A. G. (1968). *Biochem. Biophys. Res. Commun.* **30**, 356–362.

Matoltsy, A. G. (1960). *Int. Rev. Cytol.* **10**, 315–351.

Matoltsy, A. G., and Balsamo, C. A. (1955). *J. Biophys. Biochem. Cytol.* **1**, 339–360.

Matoltsy, A. G., and Matoltsy, M. N. (1966). *J. Invest. Dermatol.* **46**, 127–129.

Medawar, P. B. (1948). *Quart. J. Microsc. Sci.* **89**, 187–196.

Melbye, S. W., and Freedberg, I. M. (1977). *J. Invest. Dermatol.* **68**, 285–292.

Melbye, S. W., and Karasek, M. A. (1973). *Exp. Cell Res.* **79**, 279–286.

Meyer, J., Alvares, O. F., and Barrington, E. P. (1970). *Growth* **34,** 57–73.

Milstone, L. M., and McGuire, J. S. (1978). *J. Cell Biol.* **79,** CD 148.

Morrissey, J. H., and Green, H. (1978). *J. Cell. Physiol.* **97,** 469–475.

Nordquist, R. E., Olson, R. L., and Everett, M. A. (1966). *Arch. Dermatol.* **94,** 482–490.

Obinata, A., and Endo, H. (1979). *J. Biol. Chem.* **254,** 8487–8490.

Ogawa, H. and Goldsmith, L. A. (1976). *J. Biol. Chem.* **251,** 7281–7288.

Osborn, M., Franke, W. W., and Weber, K. (1977). *Proc. Natl. Acad. Sci. U.S.A.* **74,** 2490–2494.

Ossowski, L., Biegel, D., and Reich, E. (1979). *Cell* **16,** 929–940.

Pawelek, J., Halaben, R., and Christie, G. (1975). *Nature (London)* **258,** 539–540.

Pisano, J. J., Finlayson, J. S., and Peyton, M. P. (1968). *Science* **160,** 892–893.

Prose, P. H., Friedman-Kien, A. E.,and Neistein, S. (1967). *Lab. Invest.* **17,** 693–716.

Prunieras, M. (1979). *J. Invest. Dermatol.* **73,** 135–137.

Prunieras, M., Mathivon, M. F., Leung, T. K., and Gazzolo, L. (1965). *Ann. Inst. Pasteur Paris* **108,** 149–165.

Pruss, R. M., and Herschman, H. R. (1979). *J. Cell. Physiol.* **98,** 469–474.

Raff, M. C., Hornby-Smith, A., and Brockes, J. P. (1978). *Nature (London)* **273,** 672–673.

Raknerud, N. (1974). *Virchows Arch. B* **17,** 113–135.

Rheinwald, J. G. (1980). "Methods in Cell Biology" (C. Harris, ed.), pp. 229–254. Academic Press, New York.

Rheinwald, J. G., and Green, H. (1975a). *Cell* **6,** 317–330.

Rheinwald, J. G. and Green, H. (1975b). *Cell* **6,** 331–344.

Rheinwald, J. G., and Green, H. (1977). *Nature (London)* **265,** 421–424.

Rice, R. H., and Green, H. (1977). *Cell* **11,** 417–423.

Rice, R. H., and Green, H. (1978). *J. Cell Biol.* **76,** 705–711.

Rice, R. H., and Green, H. (1979). *Cell* **18,** 681–694.

Rogers, G. E., Harding, H. W. J., and Llewellyn-Smith, I. J. (1977). *Biochim. Biophys. Acta* **495,** 159–175.

Rowden, G. (1975). *J. Invest. Dermatol.* **64,** 1–3.

Rowe, L., Strasser, F., and Kasten, F. H. (1968). *J. Invest. Dermatol.* **50,** 390–400.

Schreiner, E., and Wolff, K. (1969). *Arch. Klin. Exp. Dermatol.* **235,** 78–88.

Siefring, G. E., Jr., Apostol, A. B., Velasco, P. T., and Lorand, L. (1978). *Biochemistry* **17,** 2598–2604.

Skerrow, D., and Hunter, I. (1978). *Biochim. Biophys. Acta* **537,** 474–484.

Squier, C. A. (1973). *J. Ultrastruct. Res.* **43,** 160–177.

Starger, J. M., and Goldman, R. D. (1977). *Proc. Natl. Acad. Sci. U.S.A.* **74,** 2422–2426.

Steinberg, M. L., and Defendi, V. (1979). *Proc. Natl. Acad. Sci. U.S.A.* **76,** 801–805.

Steinert, P. M. (1975). *Biochem. J.* **149,** 39–48.

Steinert, P. M., and Gullino, M. I. (1976). *Biochim. Biophys. Res. Commun.* **70,** 221–227.

Steinert, P. M., and Idler, W. W. (1975). *Biochem. J.* **151,** 603–614.

Steinert, P. M., Idler, W. W., and Zimmerman, S. B. (1976). *J. Mol. Biol.* **108,** 547–567.

Steinert, P. M., Zimmerman, S. B., Starger, J. M., and Goldman, R. D. (1978). *Proc. Natl. Acad. Sci. U.S.A.* **75,** 6098-6101.

Steinert, P. M., Idler, W. W., Poirier, M. C., Katoh, Y., Stoner, G. D., and Yuspa, S. H. (1979). *Biochim. Biophys. Acta* **577,** 11-21.

Stern, I. B., and Sekeri-Pataryas, K. H. (1972). *J. Invest. Dermatol.* **59,** 251-259.

Sugawara, K. (1977), *In* "Biochemistry of Cutaneous Epidermal Differentiation" (M. Seigi and I. A. Bernstein, eds.) pp. 387-397. Univ. Park Press, Baltimore, Maryland.

Sun, T.-T., and Green, H. (1976). Cell **9,** 511-521.

Sun, T.-T., and Green, H. (1977). *Nature (London).* **269,** 489-493.

Sun, T.-T., and Green, H. (1978a). *J. Biol. Chem.* **253,** 2053-2060.

Sun, T.-T., and Green, H. (1978b). *Cell* **14,** 469-476.

Sun, T.-T., Shih, C., and Green, H. (1979). *Proc. Natl. Acad. Sci. U.S.A.* **76,** 2813-2817.

Taichman, I., Reilly, S., and Garant, P. (1979). *Arch. Oral Biol.* **24,** 335-341.

Vaughan, F. L., and Bernstein, I. A. (1971). *J. Invest. Dermatol.* **56,** 454-466.

Whitfield, J. F., MacManus, J. P., and Gillan, D. J. (1970). *J. Cell. Physiol.* **76,** 65-76.

Wolff, K., and Honigsmann, H. (1971). *J. Ultrastruct. Res.* **36,** 176-190.

Worst, P. K. M., Valentine, E. A., and Fusenig, N. E. (1974). *J. Natl. Cancer Inst. Monogr.* **53,** 1061-1064.

Yardley, H. J., and Goldstein, D. J. (1976). *Br. J. Dermatol.* **95,** 621-626.

Yuspa, S. H., Morgan, D. L., Walker, R. J., and Bates, R. R. (1970). *J. Invest. Dermatol.* **55,** 379-389.

THE ASSEMBLY OF TOBACCO MOSAIC VIRUS: STRUCTURE AND SPECIFICITY*

A. KLUG

MRC Laboratory of Molecular Biology,
Cambridge, England

I. EARLIER HISTORY

TOBACCO mosaic virus (TMV) is one of the simplest and most successful viruses known. Whether or not this very simplicity of design is responsible for its success, its ready availability has made it convenient for biochemical and structural studies and its simplicity has helped turn it, in one sense, into a paradigm for studies of biological structure and assembly. It has also provided an invaluable system for the development and application of new techniques in X-ray analysis and electron microscopy and in biochemistry and genetics, but these are not our main concern here.

Tobacco mosaic virus has now been studied intensively for over 40 years (see Table I). Much of the early understanding of the properties of viruses came from the studies of TMV by W. M. Stanley and his colleagues, first at the Rockefeller Institute and then, in particular with H. C. Fraenkel-Conrat and R. C. Williams at Berkeley, California, and by the group at Rothamsted and Cambridge, England (F. C. Bawden, N. W. Pirie, and J. D. Bernal). While the work at Berkeley and Rothamsted concentrated on the more biological properties of the virus, the X-ray crystallographic study started by Bernal at Cambridge, before he moved to Birkbeck College, London, was stopped because of the war. It was taken up again by J. D. Watson, in a brief interlude from DNA, in Cambridge in 1952, by D. L. D. Caspar at Yale in 1954, and by Rosalind Franklin in 1953 at Birkbeck, where I joined her early in 1954. Investigations on the more chemical and physicochemical aspects of TMV were also started by G. Schramm during the war, and continued by himself, A. Gierer, and H.-G. Wittmann in Tübingen. This

*Lecture delivered April 19, 1979.

TABLE I

Tobacco Mosaic Virus (TMV) Structure and Assembly—A Selected Chronology[a]

1936–1939	Isolation, characterization, and first X-ray studies (Stanley, Bawden, Pirie, Bernal, and Fankuchen)
1947–1955	Isolation of protein subunits and reaggregation into helical rods (Schramm)
1952–1955	Resumption of X-ray work—TMV shown to be a helix (Watson and Franklin)
1955	Self-assembly of infectious particles from separate components (Fraenkel-Conrat and Williams)
1956–1958	First one-dimensional Fourier maps, helical geometry, and general description of structure (Franklin, Caspar, Klug, and Holmes)

Virus
(Holmes and Klug; Cambridge)

1965	First 3D map; 12 Å resolution

(Holmes; Heidelberg)

1975	7 Å resolution
1977	4 Å resolution; RNA:protein contacts

Protein disk (Cambridge)

1966	First X-ray studies, 17-fold symmetry
1971	e.m. image reconstruction; 20 Å resolution
1972	First X-ray 3D map; 15 Å resolution
1975	5 Å resolution; chain traced
1977	2.8 Å resolution; atomic model

Assembly

1958	Physicochemical studies of the protein (Lauffer, Caspar, Paulsen)
1970	"Phase diagram" of protein aggregates
1971	Disk shown to nucleate assembly
1976	Nucleation region of RNA sequenced
1977	Mechanisms of initiation and elongation shown

[a] This table deals mainly with structural determinations and experiments on assembly. It omits the more biochemical and biological parts of the history, e.g., the discovery of the infectivity of the RNA by Gierer and Schramm and by Fraenkel-Conrat; the use of mutants in Melchers' laboratory to study the effects of changes in the protein subunit, and by Wittman to test the genetic code; the sequencing of the protein in Tübingen and Berkeley.

early work (reviewed by Klug and Caspar, 1960; Caspar, 1963) led to an overall understanding of the helical subunit structure of TMV and of the basis of its infectivity. Although subsequent investigations have led to a considerable refinement of this picture, at few points has it had to be basically changed.

II. SELF-ASSEMBLY

The infectivity of a virus resides in its nucleic acid, on which is carried the information for the production of the proteins encoded in the nucleic acid, and also for other specific functions of the nucleic acid such as replication and virus assembly. Tobacco mosaic virus contains a single RNA molecule 6400 nucleotide residues long. It is packaged as a single strand embedded in a helical framework made of 2130 copies of a single protein—the virus "coat-protein" (Fig. 1). The protein is a single polypeptide chain of 158 amino acid residues, and it ultimately

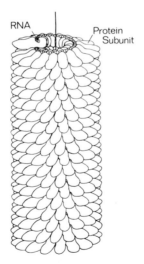

FIG. 1. Diagram summarizing the results of the first stage of structure analysis of tobacco mosaic virus (Klug and Caspar, 1960). The protein subunits form a tight helical array with 16⅓ units per turn, and the RNA is packed in between at a radius of about 40 Å from the helix axis. There are three nucleotides per protein subunit. Only about one-sixth of the length of a complete particle is shown.

determines the architecture of the virus particles, an arrangement of 16⅓ subunits per turn of a rather flat helix with adjacent turns in contact. The RNA is intercalated between these turns with three nucleotide residues per protein subunit. The length is determined by the length of the RNA—the particle grows just long enough to encoat all of the RNA strand—and the rods are about 3000 Å long and 180 Å in diameter. The RNA is situated at a radial distance of 40 Å from the central axis and is therefore isolated from the outside world by the coat protein. The geometry of the protein arrangement forces the RNA backbone into a moderately extended single-strand configuration. Running up the central axis of the virus particle is a cylindrical hole of diameter 40 Å, previously thought to be a trivial consequence of the protein packing, but which now, as we shall see, figures prominently in the story about to be told.

With this simple structure, it is in retrospect not surprising that it was found, in the classic experiments by Fraenkel-Conrat and Williams (1955), that TMV could be reassembled from its isolated protein and nucleic acid components. They showed that, upon simple remixing, infectious virus particles were formed that were structurally indistinguishable from the original virus. Thus all the information necessary to assemble the particle must be contained in its components—the virus "self-assembles." Later experiments showed that the reassembly was fairly specific for the viral RNA, occurring most readily with the RNA homologous to the coat protein or with that from a closely related strain (Fraenkel-Conrat and Singer, 1959). Other natural RNAs were not coated under these conditions, and selectivity was also found between synthetic polyribonucleotides, polyadenylic acid or copolymers containing a high proportion of adenosine being favored (Fraenkel-Conrat and Singer, 1964).

These experiments on the reassembly of TMV *in vitro* had several features resembling the natural assembly process. Reassembly carried out under conditions that were plausibly physiological (i.e., near room temperature and around neutral pH) showed a specificity among natural RNAs that corresponded to the finding that virus isolates contain only the unique viral RNA. But other experiments (Hart and Smith, 1956; Matthews, 1966), which showed that foreign RNAs could be incorporated into virus-like rods, cast doubt on the belief that specificity *in vivo* was actually achieved during the assembly itself. Another feature about reassembly carried out in this way, which suggested to us in Cambridge that there were still missing elements in the story, was its slow rate. Times of 6 hours or more were required to give maximum yields of assembled particles. This seemed to us rather too slow for the assembly of a virus *in vivo*, since the nucleic acid is fully protected only on completion. Our research group in Cambridge had been investigating, in parallel with our structural studies on the protein disk (see below), the properties of the protein isolated on its own. Some of our findings on how the protein associated with itself (Durham *et al.*, 1971; Durham and Klug, 1971; Finch and Klug, 1971) led us to reconsider the process of assembly with the RNA (Butler and Klug, 1971), and the development of this work has led finally to a detailed picture of the assembly process, with which the rest of this lecture is concerned.

III. Protein Polymorphism and Virus Assembly

At first sight, the growth of a helical structure like that of TMV presents no problem of comprehension. Each protein subunit makes identical contacts with its neighbors so that the bonding between them repeats over and over again. Subunits could have a precise built-in surface geometry so that they would assemble only in a unique way. Subunits would simply add, one or a few at a time, onto the "step" at the end of a growing helix, entrapping the RNA that would protrude there and generating a new step, and so on. Such a mode of growth is analogous to the growth of a crystal at a screw dislocation. Moreover, the obvious expectation was that, since both the final TMV particle and its RNA have distinct ends, growth would start at or near one and proceed toward the other. Both of these simple and eminently plausible ideas are now known to be wrong, and, with the benefit of hindsight, we can see good reasons why the virus has adopted what at first appeared to be a puzzlingly more complex strategy.

Assembly of any large aggregate of identical subunits, such as a crystal, can be considered from a physical point of view in two stages: first the nucleation and then the subsequent growth. The process of nucleation—or, crudely, getting started—is frequently more difficult than the growth. In the case of TMV, these phases of the assembly may also be referred to, in more biochemical language, as the initiation and elongation. Now a simple mode of initiation, in which the free RNA interacts with individual protein subunits, does pose problems in getting the helix started. Because of the large number of subunits per turn in the helix (16⅓), at least 17 separate subunits would have to bind to the flexible RNA molecule before the assembling structure could close round on itself and become more than a mere linear aggregate of the protein along the RNA. This difficulty could be avoided if some form of "jig" or "former" were available upon which the first few turns of the viral helix could assemble until it reached a sufficient size to be stable.

It occurred to me that there was a structure to hand that might serve the purpose—the disk aggregate of the virus protein, which Finch and I had shown by image reconstruction from electron microscopy to be a polar two-layer structure, and which thus appeared to be a cylindrical variant of a two-turn segment of the protein helix in the virus. The protein on its own, free of RNA, can aggregate in a number of distinct, yet related, forms, rather than only as a helix. This polymorphism was first considered in some detail by Caspar (1963), who foresaw that some of the aggregation states might give insight into the way the protein functions. Quantitative studies of the aggregation were started by Lauffer and his associates (e.g., Lauffer and Stevens, 1968), but they concentrated upon a rather narrow range of conditions, the main interest being in understanding the forces driving the aggregation. Because of the scattered nature of the earlier observations, my colleagues, Durham and Finch, and I began a systematic survey of the aggregation states, as a result of which the broad outline became clear (reviewed by Butler and Durham, 1977). The results can be summarized as a phase diagram (Fig. 2).

At low or acid pH, the protein alone will form helices of indefinite length that are structurally very similar to the virus except for lack of the RNA. Above neutrality, the protein tends to exist as a mixture of small aggregates, from about trimer upward, in rapid equilibrium with each other, and this mixture is commonly referred to as "A-protein." Near pH 7 and at about room temperature a specific aggregate, the "disk," occurs together with the A-protein and in a relatively slow equilibrium with it. Around physiological conditions the disks comprise as much as 80% of the protein, with the other 20% as A-protein. A disk consists of two layers, each made of a ring of 17 subunits. The subunits in the two rings of a disk face the same way (i.e., the disk is polar) but are differently tilted toward the axis of the disk, giving rise to a "pairing"

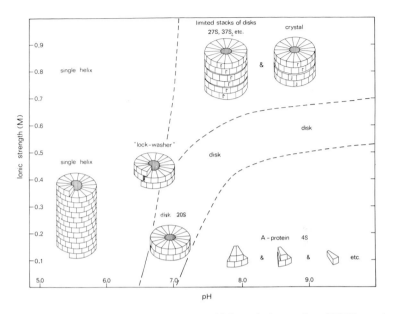

FIG. 2. Diagram showing the ranges over which particular species of TMV protein participate significantly in the equilibrium. This is not a conventional phase diagram: a boundary is drawn where a larger species becomes detectable and does not imply that the smaller species disappears sharply. The "lock washer" indicated on the boundary between the 20 S disk and helix is not well defined and represents a metastable transitory state observed when not enough time is allowed for the transition (Fig. 4). The boundaries are approximately correct for a protein concentration of 5 mg/ml at 20°C, but not all species that have been observed are shown.

between the rings, which limits the polymerization to two layers. Disks do stack to a limited extent, but this happens at rather high salt concentrations, so this further stacking is not biologically relevant.

The dominant factor controlling the state of aggregation of the coat protein is thus the pH. This control is mediated through groups [probably including carboxylic acid residues (Caspar, 1963)] that bind protons abnormally in the helical state, but not in the A-form. Thus the helical structure can be stabilized either by the RNA interaction in the virus or by a pH acid enough to enable these groups to be substantially protonated (Fig. 3). These groups thus act as a "negative switch" ensuring that under physiological conditions the helix is not formed, and thus that

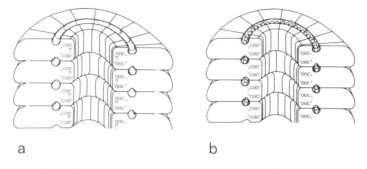

a   b

FIG. 3. Stabilization of the protein helix can occur either (a) by protonation of abnormally titrating groups in the protein subunit, or (b) by interaction with the RNA to give the virus particle. The abnormal group, which has a pK of 7.1, has been shown as a carboxyl–carboxylate pair at a radius of 24 Å from the axis. after a proposal by Caspar (1963). The helical structure can only be attained by the protein alone when it is at a pH acid enough to enable the groups to be substantially protonated. On the other hand, when the RNA is present—and this is the relevant biological process—it provides a stabilizing interaction with its binding sites on the protein to overcome the repulsion of these groups, and so a nucleoprotein helix can be formed even at neutral pH. At pH 7 the abnormal groups will be half protonated, thus partly relieving the unfavorable interaction between them.

These groups thus play an important part in the control of the protein polymerization. In the absence of either RNA or added protons, the stable state of the protein is the disk form, the obligatory aggregate required to nucleate virus assembly. It is noteworthy that, in the disk, the region of the protein closest to the center is disordered or flexible (Fig. 6a), very likely because of the high concentration of negatively charged acidic groups, including the invariant residues Asp 115 and Asp 116.

In the language of allosteric theory, the helical state has a high affinity for the "Caspar" protons, and the disk state a low affinity for them; the helix is the "tense" state because it has a strained environment for the carboxyl groups, as shown by their abnormal pK, while the disk is the "relaxed" state.

enough free protein in the form of disks or A-protein is available to interact with the RNA during virus assembly. One important conversion was clearly demonstrated by some "pH-drop" experiments (Klug and Durham, 1971). These showed (Fig. 4) that an abrupt lowering of the pH would convert disks directly into short helices just over two turns in length, which stack on each other in imperfect register to give "nicked helices." The conversion is an *in situ* one, not requiring dissociation and then reassociation into a different form.

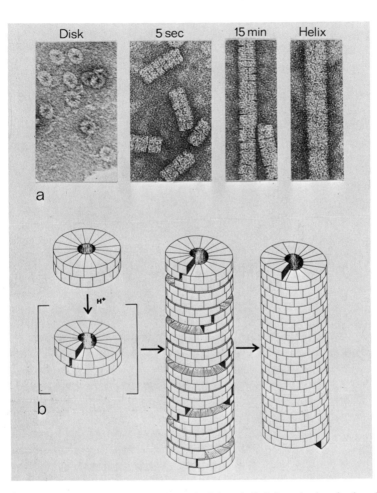

FIG. 4. (a) Direct transformation of protein disks to helix is brought about by dropping
the pH rapidly from pH 7 to pH 5. The disks are "dislocated" into short helices, of just
over two turns, without dissociation into subunits, and these stack together in random
azimuthal orientation to give longer, imperfect or "nicked" helices. The imperfections
anneal over a further period of hours to give continuous helical rods. Samples were
negatively stained with uranyl acetate. The reaction is stopped as soon as the specimen is
stained on the grid, so rapid changes can be followed. Approximately × 500,000.

(b) Schematic diagram of stages observed in the disk-to-helix transformation. The
single dislocated disk or "lock-washer" is shown as a transitory intermediate, since it is
not observed in isolation.

IV. A ROLE FOR THE DISK

The disk aggregate of the protein therefore has a number of significant properties. It is the dominant form of the protein under conditions
that are both plausible for the physiological assembly of a virus and
known to be optimal for *in vitro* reassembly. Its size and structure
suggested that it might be ideal to act as the ''jig'' for the initiation of
virus assembly, and the pH drop experiment had shown that it could be
converted directly into a helical structure similar to that taken up by the
protein subunits in the virus. We therefore thought that it might
well serve as a nucleating center for virus assembly and looked at its
effect upon the reassembly reaction (Butler and Klug, 1971). This
proved to be dramatic. Complete virus particles were formed within 10
minutes rather than over a period of hours, as was the case in the early
reassembly experiments of Fraenkel-Conrat and Williams, in which
protein had been used in the disaggregated form. If disks were required
for the initiation step, much of this long time would have been spent
waiting for sufficient disks to form to start the assembly.

The notion that disks are involved in the natural biological process of
initiation was strengthened by companion experiments in which assembly was carried out with RNAs from different sources. These showed a
preference, by several orders of magnitude, of disks for the viral RNA
over foreign RNAs or synthetic polynucleotides of simple sequences.
Moreover, this specificity for the viral RNA occurs because of the very
different rates of nucleation of different RNAs with disks. The structure
of the disk allows up to a complete turn of RNA to bind to the protein
during the first step, and this clearly allows much greater discrimination
in binding than could be achieved with only three nucleotides binding to
a single protein subunit. Indeed it is clear that it is the disk state of the
protein that is needed to achieve specificity in the interaction with RNA.
In the experiments cited above, in which virus-like rods were made
containing TMV protein and foreign RNAs, the reactions were carried
out at acid pH and under these artificial conditions the protein alone
would be forming helical rods and so could entrap any RNA.

Besides this effect of disks on the rates of initiation, which we had
predicted, we also found to our surprise that they appear to enhance the
rate of elongation, and must therefore be actively involved in growth.
This result has been questioned by some other workers in the field

(Richards and Williams, 1972, 1973; Okada and Ohno, 1972) and was defended by Butler and Klug (1972, 1973). It is still the subject of argument (reviewed by Butler and Durham, 1977), but recent discoveries on the configuration of the RNA during incorporation into a growing particle (discussed later) have made the involvement of disks in the elongation, as well as in nucleation, much more intelligible.

V. INITIATION SEQUENCE ON THE VIRAL RNA ("ORIGIN OF ASSEMBLY")

Specificity in initiation ensures that only the viral RNA is picked out for coating with the viral protein. It is itself brought about by the presence of a unique site on the viral RNA for interaction with the protein disk. No special bases have been found in TMV RNA other than the "cap" at the 5' terminus (Zimmern, 1975; Keith and Fraenkel-Conrat, 1975), so this site must involve a significant stretch of the RNA, to give the very high selectivity found. It seemed likely that this would contain about 50 nucleotides, which could interact together with one turn of the first disk (i.e., 17 protein subunits in a ring times 3 nucleotides per subunit = 51 nucleotides). Zimmern and Butler (1977) and Zimmern (1977) have isolated the nucleation region containing this site by supplying limited quantities of disk protein, sufficient to allow nucleation to proceed, but not subsequent growth, and then digesting away the uncoated ends of the RNA with nuclease. With varying protein:RNA ratios and different digestion conditions, they found that they could isolate a series of RNA fragments, all of which contained a unique common core sequence with variable extents of elongation at either end. These RNA fragments are encoated in short particles with the same RNA:protein ratio as the intact virus, and, after reisolation, they can be rebound to the coat protein. This rebinding reproduces the nucleation with full-length RNA, in that it requires disks rather than A-protein and in having a very high binding constant.

One unexpected feature of the isolated RNA was the length of the fragments. Even when the protein was added at only one disk per RNA molecule (which would be expected to bind only up to 100 nucleotides), the average length of the protected RNA was over 250 nucleotides, and less than half of the RNA molecules had reacted. This "disproportionation" can be explained as a kinetic effect whereby disks react coopera-

A. KLUG

```
Triplet Number:    1   2   3   4   5   6   7   8   9   10  11  12  13  14  15  16  17

Line 2                                                          5' UAU UGU UUA UAG

Line 1             AAA UAA UAU AAA AUU AGG UUU GAG AGA GAA GAU UAC AAA CGU GAG AGA CGG

Line 0         AGG GCC CAU GGA ACU UAC AGA AGA AGU UGU UGA UGA GUU CAU GGA AGA UGU ,

Line -1            CCC UAU GUC GAU CAG GCU UGC AAA GU 3'
```
                                                                              (a)

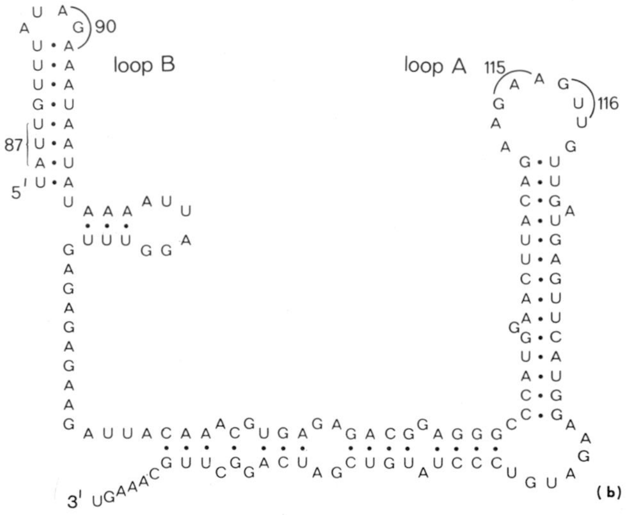

(b)

FIG. 5. (a) Ribonucleic acid sequence around the nucleation region or assembly origin aligned with the coat protein disk showing triplet phase repeats (Zimmern, 1977). Line numbers start at line 0 (the best protected part of the whole assembly nucleation site, which may bind between layers of the initiating disk) and increase in the 5' direction (the major direction of assembly). Lines are 17 triplets long (the number of subunits per turn of the disk). Heavy boxes are AGA-related triplets in line 0; dashed boxes indicate two in-phase repeating hexanucleotides.

(b) Postulated secondary structure of the RNA in the nucleation region (Zimmern, 1977). This gives a weakly bonded double-helical stem with a special sequence, probably the actual origin of assembly, looped out at the top (loop A). This sequence is based on a motif of three bases having G in the middle position and usually A, but sometimes U, in the outer positions. (The very low frequency of C throughout this region is noticeable—in the whole RNA it occurs at a frequency comparable to the other bases.) The sequence in the nucleation region shows a strong homology with that part of the RNA sequence of the neighboring coat protein gene (Fig. 14) that codes for amino acid residues 85–130 of the protein subunit. Some homologous triplets have been marked by the residue number in the protein.

tively with an already nucleated rod, up to some minimum stable size, and therefore more readily than with a free RNA molecule. Among this population of fragments, there are fragments only about 65 nucleotides long—just over the length necessary to bind round a single disk—and these appear to represent the minimum protected core. Because of the strong rebinding of these fragments back to disks, it seems likely that such fragments contain all the information necessary to specify the normal nucleation reaction, and we therefore think that this minimum core contains the origin of assembly for the virus.

The size and relatively low yield of the nucleation region rendered sequencing the RNA technically difficult. However, while Zimmern and Butler in Cambridge had been tackling the isolation and sequencing of this region, Hirth and his colleagues in Strasbourg had started to sequence various fragments of TMV RNA, which they had been able to isolate from partial nuclease digests of the unprotected RNA (Jonard *et al.*, 1977). In this way they could obtain relatively good yields of shorter fragments, and the sequencing was not too difficult. By chance, one of the fragments generated overlapped the part of the nucleation region containing the origin of assembly, and, from the joint Cambridge and Strasbourg results, it was possible to identify and complete this sequence (Fig. 5a).

VI. THE STRUCTURE OF THE PROTEIN DISK

In parallel with these experiments on the assembly of the virus and the determination of the initiation sequence of the RNA, investigations have also been going on into the detailed structure of both the virus and the protein disk, using X-ray diffraction methods. Holmes and his colleagues in Heidelberg have pursued the studies on the virus structure originated by Bernal in Cambridge, continued at Birkbeck College by Franklin (until her untimely death in 1958), and then carried back to Cambridge by Holmes and Klug in 1961 and continued until 1968. Virus specimens for X-ray work can be prepared in the form of gels in which the particles are oriented parallel to each other, but randomly rotated about their long axes. These gels diffract X-rays well, but, because of the nature of the gels, the three-dimensional X-ray data are scrambled into two dimensions. Unscrambling these data to reconstruct the three-dimensional structure has proved to be a major undertaking

(Barrett *et al.*, 1971), and it is only recently that the analysis has reached a resolution approaching 4 Å in the best regions of the electron density map, but falling off significantly in other parts (Stubbs *et al.*, 1977). At this resolution it is not possible to identify individual amino acid residues with any certainty, and the ambiguities are too great to build a unique atomic model. However, the overall packing of the subunits and the general nature of the contacts with the viral RNA can be readily discerned.

In parallel to the X-ray work on the virus, our group in Cambridge has been investigating the structure of the two-layer protein disk. This study of the disk was begun before its relevance to virus assembly had been established (Finch *et al.*, 1966). Disks will form true three-dimensional crystals, and so the X-ray analysis is more akin to ordinary protein crystallography, except for the exceptionally large size of the asymmetric unit—the complete disk containing 34 protein subunits, with a molecular weight of about 600,000. This was the first very large structure ever to be tackled in detail by X-rays and it has taken about a dozen years to carry the analysis through to high resolution (Bloomer *et al.*, 1978). The formidable technical problems were overcome only after the development in the MRC Laboratory of more powerful X-ray tubes and of special apparatus (cameras, computer-linked densitometers) for the crystallographic analysis of structures of this magnitude. The 17-fold rotational symmetry of the disk gives rise to redundant information in the X-ray data, which was exploited in the analysis (Bricogne, 1977) to improve and extend the resolution of a map based originally on only one heavy atom derivative (Gilbert and Klug, 1974). The map at 2.8 Å resolution has been interpreted in terms of a detailed atomic model for the protein (Figs. 6 and 7), although the individual interactions upon RNA binding have yet to be deduced.

This is the first protein of a molecular assembly that can be described in clear detail, and while much of its conformation is similar to that described for other proteins, it does have a number of unusual features. The central part of each subunit comprises four α-helices, which are aligned to form a supercoiled bundle in which the helices are alternately parallel and antiparallel. The ends of the helices nearest to the central axis of the disk are joined in pairs by a rigid hairpin bend and by a flexible loop of about 24 amino acids (Fig. 6a). This loop is mobile without any defined conformation, but it becomes less mobile on bind-

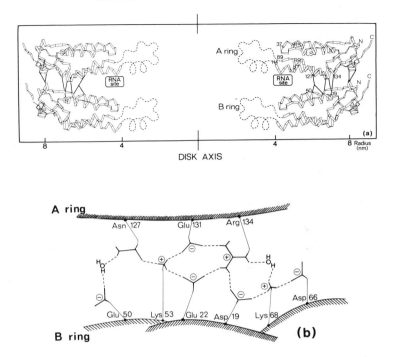

FIG. 6. (a) Section through a disk along its axis reconstructed from the results of X-ray analysis to a resolution of 2.8 Å (Bloomer *et al.*, 1978). The ribbons show the path of the polypeptide chain of the protein subunits. Subunits of the two rings can be seen touching over a small area toward the outside of the disk (where all the side-chain contacts that occur between the rings have been drawn in as solid lines) but opening up into the "jaws" toward the center. The dashed lines at low radius indicate schematically the mobile portion of the subunits in the disk, extending in from near the RNA binding site (between the rings around 40 Å radius as shown) to the edge of the central hole, which has a radius of 20 Å. LS and RS = left and right slewed helices, RR and LR = right and left radial.

(b) The extended salt bridge system linking subunits in the two rings of the disk presented schematically in a side view. It lies between a radius of 60 Å and 70 Å in (a).

ing of oligonucleotides to the disk (Graham and Butler, 1979), and adopts a definite conformation in the virus in the presence of RNA. The flexibility of this loop enables it, as described below, to be poised for interaction with, and intercalation of, RNA between the two layers of the disk. The distal ends of the four α-helices are braced together by a narrow strip of β-sheet (Fig. 7b), beyond which lies an extended cluster

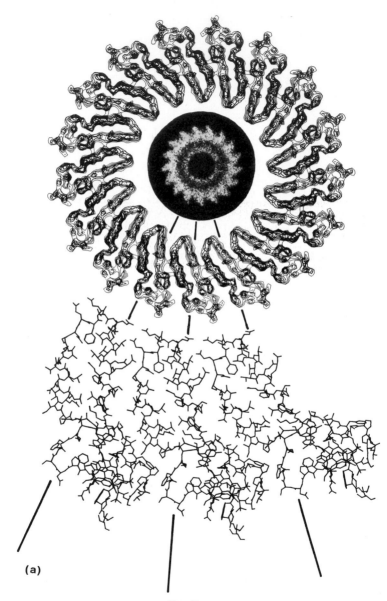

FIG. 7a.

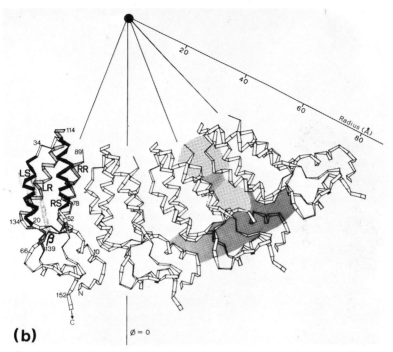

(b)

FIG. 7. (a) The disk viewed from above at successive stages of resolution. From the center outward there follow (i) a rotationally filtered electron microscope image at about 25 Å resolution (Crowther and Amos, 1971); (ii) a slice through the 5 Å electron density map of the disk obtained by X-ray analysis (Champness *et al.*, 1976); and (iii) part of the atomic model built from the 2.8 Å map (Bloomer *et al.*, 1978).

(b) The lateral interactions between subunits in the disk. Four adjacent subunits within a ring are shown viewed from above. The N and C termini of the chain are marked together with the four main helices, left and right slewed (LS and RS) in the upper half of the molecule with the right and left radial (RR and LR) below, and the β sheet, which connects all four helices at their higher radius ends. The interface contains alternating patches of polar residues, indicated by stippling, and of hydrophobic residues, indicated by solid shading. The hydrophobic patch at higher radius is continuous with the hydrophobic girdle, which extends circumferentially across the whole width of a subunit and across the interface, forming a continuous belt around the ring.

of aromatic residues. These form part of a continuous girdle of hydrophobic residues encircling each ring of the disk.

The interactions between subunits can be considered in two classes: the contacts between rings or layers, which are completely changed during the disk to helix transition; and the contacts within a ring, which are maintained with only minor modification. Contacts between the two layers are found only at high radius and at only three places: they are of unequal length so that the A and B subunits are connected, as it were, by an irregular tripod, leading to the relative inclination of their long axes by an angle of about 10° (Fig. 6a). There is a small patch of polar interactions at a radius of about 80 Å; nearer in there is one of hydrophobic interactions; and, third, there is an extended salt-bridge system of interactions (Fig. 6b) involving two lysines, an arginine, four acidic residues, and two water molecules. Almost all the possible hydrogen-bonding capabilities are utilized in this complex three-dimensional network. Within a ring (Fig. 7b) the lateral subunit interface has four alternating patches of polar and hydrophobic interactions, both of the polar patches involving simple salt bridges. The general nature of all these patches of subunit interactions is conserved in different strains of TMV, but the boundaries between the patches show some variation.

VII. The Interaction of the Protein Disk with the Initiation Sequence on the RNA

Although the structure of the disk is now known in the detail just described, it was an earlier stage in the X-ray analysis that gave the clue as to how the disk might interact with the RNA. At 5 Å resolution (Champness *et al.*, 1976) the course of the polypeptide chains could be traced and the basic design of the disk established. The subunits of the upper ring of the disk lie in a plane perpendicular to the disk, while those of the lower ring are tilted downward toward the center, so that the two rings touch only toward the outside of the disk and are opened apart onto the central hole, like a "pair of jaws" (Fig. 6a), which could, as it were, "bite" a stretch of RNA entering through the central hole. The possibility of this happening is further accentuated by the flexibility observed in the inner region of the protein, from around the RNA binding site inward (residues 90–114 in Fig. 6a), where it is found to be disordered and not tightly packed into a regular structure. Upon transformation into the helix, these inner regions of the subunits must pack tightly together, becoming stabilized into a definite inner wall which completely encloses and protects the RNA. This structural transition (Fig. 8) thus "closes the jaws," with the RNA inside. It looked very

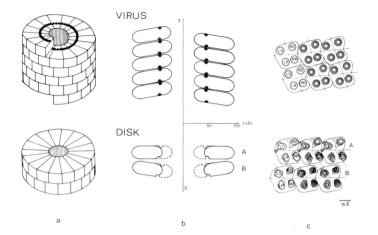

FIG. 8. Packing of subunits in the tobacco mosaic virus protein disk (below) and in the virus (above). (a) The disk contains 34 subunits in two rings of 17; the virus, 16⅓ subunits per turn of the helix. RNA is present in the virus particle, sandwiched between the helically arranged subunits as shown. (b) Subunits in the A (top) and B (bottom) layers of the disk have different tilts with respect to the axis, and subunits in the virus have a still different tilt. The innermost part of the subunit appears to be disordered in the disk (dashed outline), perhaps to facilitate incorporation of RNA in the disk-to-helix transition that occurs during assembly. (c) Cylindrical sections through subunits in the disk and in the virus, viewed end-on. The disk sections are taken from the electron density map; the virus section is schematic. The major part of each subunit consists of four α-helical rods, running in a roughly radial direction, and denoted RS, LS, RR, LR; the sections have been taken through these rods. The figure shows that in the transition from a 17-fold disk to a 16⅓-fold helix, subunits slide over each other by about 10 Å. Because of the change in subunit tilt, lateral contacts will be bent somewhat, but not completely shifted like the axial bonds.

much as though the disk was designed to permit the RNA to enter through the central hole, effectively enlarged by the flexibility of the inner loop of protein, and intercalated between the two layers of the disk.

At this point the results on the RNA sequencing and the structure of the disk, hitherto pursued spearately, drew together. With the identification and sequencing of the nucleation region (Zimmern, 1977) it became possible to locate it positively upon the viral RNA, and, again, the obvious expectation that it would be near one end turned out to be wrong. Zimmern and Wilson (1976) showed that nucleation occurs about one-sixth of the way along the RNA, so that over 5000 nucleotides have to be coated in the major direction of elongation, i.e., from the 3'-OH end to the 5' end, and 1000 have to be coated in the opposite direction (see Fig. 14). This confounding of the expectation that nucleation would occur at one end of the RNA gave rise to a conundrum. Growing rods seen in the electron microscope were always found to have RNA only at one end (see Fig. 11a), and yet we knew that the nucleation of the rod was occurring well away from either end of the RNA and that there must therefore be two RNA tails on the particles. Why then were rods never seen with a tail at each end?

The resolution of this puzzle came from considering the structures of the protein disk and the nucleation region of the RNA, and how they might interact to trigger the assembly. The smallest RNA fragment that is protected during nucleation has a base sequence suggesting that it would consist of a weakly paired double-helical stem with a loop at the top (a "hairpin," Fig. 5b) (Zimmern, 1977). The loop and the top of the stem has a very unusual sequence, based on a motif of three nucleotides, with guanosine (G) always occupying one specific position and usually adenosine (A) or sometimes uridine (U) in the other two. Since there are three nucleotide binding sites per protein subunit, such a triplet repeat pattern will place a specific nucleotide in any one particular binding site and could well lead to the recognition of the exposed RNA loop by the disk during the nucleation.

VIII. Nucleation and Growth

These observations led us to propose a hypothesis for the nucleation in which this special RNA hairpin would insert through the central hole of the disk into the jaws formed by the two layers of protein subunits (Butler *et al.*, 1976). The dimensions are quite suitable for this to occur, and the open loop could then bind to the RNA binding sites on the protein (Fig. 9). More of the double-helical stem would then unpair and be opened out as more of the RNA was bound within the jaws of the nucleating disk. Some, as yet unknown, feature of this interaction would cause the disk to "dislocate" into a short helical segment, entrapping the RNA, and further disks would rapidly add, up to the minimum stable size from where normal elongation could occur.

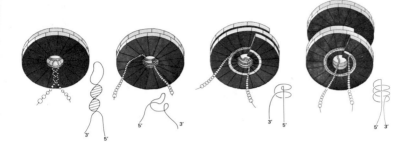

FIG. 9. Nucleation of virus assembly is believed to occur by the insertion of a hairpin of RNA (loop A in Fig. 5b) into the central hole of the protein disk and between the two layers of subunits. This loop formed by the nucleation region of the RNA binds round the first turn, opening up the base-paired stem as it does so, and causes the disk to dislocate into a short helix. This "closes the jaws," entraining the RNA between the turns of protein subunits, and gives a start to the nucleoprotein helix (which can then elongate rapidly to some minimum stable size).

Such a mode of nucleation has an interesting consequence for the growth of the nucleoprotein rod. The special configuration generated during the insertion of the loop into the middle of the disk can be repeated during subsequent addition of disks, as further RNA could be pulled up the central hole of the growing rod to perpetuate this loop (Fig. 10). Thus, elongation could occur by a substantially similar mechanism to nucleation, only now, rather than requiring the specific nucleation loop of the RNA, it occurs by means of a "traveling loop," which is constantly replenished by further RNA moving up the central hole of the growing rod. A loop is thus always present at the growing end of the particle, and this is inserted into the center of the next incoming disk, to cause its transformation and continue the growth. In the growth regime, there is no obvious requirement for special nucleotide sequences, and indeed the protein must be able to coat any sequence of bases that occurs in the RNA. These could be reinforced by purine-rich tracts farther along the RNA, but only the full sequence of the viral RNA will show if this is so. However, the geometry of the growing particle would now facilitate the dislocation of the next incoming disk, and the traveling loop is self-perpetuating all along the major RNA tail. Ultimately, when all of the longer 5' tail has been coated, elongation must also occur along the shorter 3' tail to produce the complete particle, but as yet little is known

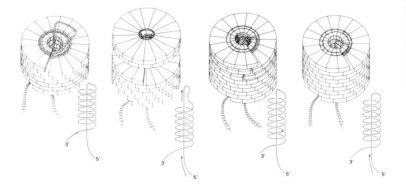

Fig. 10. Picture of rod elongation in the major (3′→5′) direction by the addition of protein disks on to a "traveling loop" of RNA. The longer RNA tail, which runs through the central hole of the growing rod, protrudes from the top as a loop. This special configuration of the RNA chain in a growing rod is a consequence of the mode of nucleation described in Fig. 9. The RNA loop can both bind round on the top surface of the rod and also insert into the center of an incoming disk to reach the RNA binding sites between the two turns. If this disk is then transformed into a short segment of helix, it can add onto the top of the preexisting nucleoprotein helix, entrapping the RNA loop and refolding it into further helix. During or after the incorporation of the disk, the traveling loop is perpetuated by pulling more RNA up the central hole, ready for the initial steps to recur. If no disk were immediately available, smaller numbers of subunits could of course add—the elongation differing in this form from the nucleation that absolutely requires disks.

about this process. The first experiments (Lomonossoff and Butler, 1979) show that the coating of the shorter tail begins before the end of the longer tail has reached its final position in the completed virus. The protein species involved, whether disks or A-protein or both, is not yet known, but it seems likely to be A-protein. (See note added in proof.)

IX. Experimental Confirmation

Our hypothesis for the mechanism of nucleation leads to two predictions that can be tested experimentally. If a loop is inserted into the center of the first disk, and this is then transformed into the beginning of the nucleoprotein helix, *both* tails of the RNA would be left at the same end of the nucleoprotein rod formed from this first disk, with one of the tails projecting directly and the other one doubled back all the way from

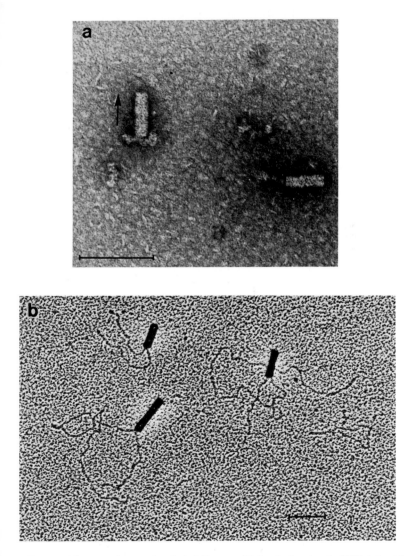

FIG. 11. Electron micrographs of partially assembled rods showing the RNA tails. (a) Using negative staining to show up the particles (Butler and Klug, 1971). The arrow points in what we now know to be the major direction of elongation (Butler *et al.*, 1977).

(b) The RNA was spread by partial denaturation and then shadowed before electron microscopy; this procedure shows the two tails (From Lebeurier *et al.*, 1977). The bar lines represent distances of 100 Å.

164   A. KLUG

the active growing point down the central hole of the growing rod. If
this looped-back structure has a major significance for the elongation
process, then it may be expected that it will be the longer RNA tail
(containing the 5′ end) that runs through the hole, as it is along this that
most of the elongation must occur.

Both of these predictions have now been confirmed. The group in
Strasbourg have obtained electron micrographs of the RNA tails spread
by partial denaturation from the end of the growing rods, and they find
two tails on many of the particles (Lebeurier *et al.*, 1977) (Fig. 11b). In
Cambridge, my colleagues have used high resolution electron microscopy, with which the two ends of the particles can be identified by their
shapes, to confirm that it is indeed the longer tail that is doubled back
through the growing rod (Butler *et al.*, 1977). They also prepared rods
with only one RNA tail free, containing the 5′ end, by stripping protein
from one end of the virus particle with alkali, thus exposing the RNA

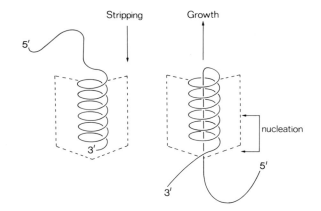

Fig. 12. Ribonucleic acid configurations in rods formed by partial assembly or by
stripping of intact virus particles. The solid line represents the course of the RNA chain
and the broken line outlines the shape of the rodlet, showing the morphologically distinct
ends as observed in the electron microscope (cf. Fig. 8b). The partially assembled rods are
obtained by allowing reassembly with only limited amounts of protein disks, while the
partially stripped rods are produced by alkaline degradation of TMV. The directions of
stripping and of the major elongation are indicated, as also is the site of the first disk,
which was involved in the nucleation reaction. This is nearer to the 3′-hydroxyl end of the
RNA, resulting in a minor tail at this 3′ end and the major tail at the 5′ end. From Butler *et
al.* (1977).

freely at that end, and not looped back down the middle (Fig. 12). The rods with this simple tail of RNA grow at less than a tenth of the rate of the partially assembled rods, showing the substantial effect of the special RNA configuration on assembly.

The involvement of a traveling loop overcomes the main difficulty in understanding how a complete disk of protein subunits could add together onto the growing helix. Apart from the results on the rate of growth of the virus particles, there is now direct evidence for growth mainly by incorporation of whole disks rather than addition of individual subunits—the subject of the longstanding controversy referred to previously. Addition of a whole block of subunits like the disk, would lead to the incorporation of a considerable length of RNA at each step, rather than a gradual increase in length of RNA incorporated. In some very recent experiments, Butler and Lomonosoff (1978) examined the lengths of the RNA protected against nuclease digestion in partially assembled rods and found that this is the case. The RNA is protected in discrete steps which are 50 to 100 bases long, corresponding to one or two turns of RNA in the helix (Fig. 13). When growth is well established, the step size in the RNA tends to be 100 bases, corresponding to the incorporation of a protein disk. This points firmly toward the conclusion that the disk aggregate is used during growth as well as during initiation.

It would seem that earlier conceptual difficulty in visualizing how disks could be incorporated had prevented general acceptance of this idea. Such acceptance frequently depends upon the promulgation of a suitable mechanism to explain how the necessary process can come about. A parallel at a rather different level in contemporary science is the idea of continental drift. Although this was proposed early this century, and the geological data were strong, acceptance came only when sea floor spreading was discovered, revealing a mechanism by which the continents could move apart.

X. Design and Construction: Physical and Biological Requirements

We have seen that the special properties of the protein disk are the key to the mechanism of the assembly of TMV. Indeed one might say that the protein subunit is designed to form not an endless helix, but a

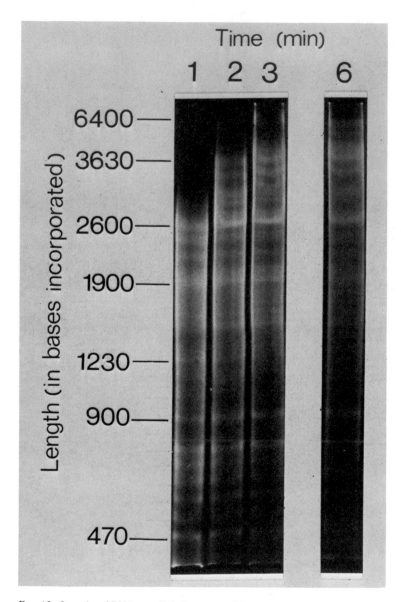

FIG. 13. Lengths of RNA coated during reassembly as shown by electrophoretic separation of the protected pieces upon agarose-polyacrylamide gels. Reassembly was carried

closed two-layer ring variant of it, the disk, which is stable, but can be converted to the lockwasher or helix-going form. The disk therefore represents an intermediate subassembly by means of which the entropically difficult problem of nucleating helical growth is overcome. At the same time the disk subassembly furnishes a mechanism for recognition of the homologous viral RNA (and rejection of foreign RNAs) by providing a long stretch of sites for interacting with a special sequence of bases on it. The disk is thus an obligatory intermediate in the assembly of the virus, which simultaneously fulfills the physical requirement for nucleating the growth of the helical particle and the biological requirement for specific recognition of the viral RNA.

Moreover, the disks are also used in the subsequent growth of the nucleoprotein rod along the main direction of elongation. Apart from the obvious kinetic advantage for growth of delivering a package of 34 subunits at a time, rather than single protein subunits, this mode of coating the RNA will not be affected by any unfavorable nucleotide sequences appearing along the length of the RNA to the same extent that addition of single protein subunits would be. It seems that, with the development of the disk form of the protein and a hairpin configuration in the RNA to go with it for nucleation, this was too good a system to abandon in favor of subsequent elongation by addition of single subunits at a helical step.

On the other hand, the disassembly of the virus particle that is necessary to liberate free RNA during infection might well take place by simple removal of subunits sequentially from an end, and this under conditions not far removed from those under which assembly of the progeny virus will occur. Thus, a biological assembly process like this

---

out with excess protein disks and stopped at the times indicated; the RNA tails were removed from the growing rods by nuclease digestion, and the protected fragments of RNA were reisolated. The number of nucleotides in the major short fragments is indicated alongside the picture, and it is noticeable that these tend to increase in steps of approximately 50 or 100, corresponding to one or two complete turns of the helix at a time. (Because of this variation, a simple division of the length difference by the number of bands does *not* give a meaningful step size.) This result would be expected from the addition of protein subunits directly from a whole disk aggregate, but not if subunits were added singly or a few at a time. The gel patterns also show that the first completed virus particles, containing 6400 bases, appear within 6 minutes. From Lomonossoff and Butler (1978).

is not left to the driving power of an unbalanced biochemical equilibrium, as would be the case if assembly and disassembly were simple reversals of each other.

Another general conclusion derived from the story of TMV assembly is that one must distinguish between the design of a structure and the construction process used to achieve it. In the TMV structure all protein subunits (except the few at the ends of the particle) make the same noncovalent contacts with each other, and this specific bonding pattern repeated many times leads to a symmetrical final structure. There is nothing in the design of the completed structure that gives a hint that different bonding patterns, and nonequivalent ones at that, are required during the process of assembly. This is unlike the case of the spherical viruses, where the design itself calls for departures from precise identity of subunit packing (Caspar and Klug, 1962). So, while TMV looks like a "helical crystal," and its design lends itself to a process of simple addition of units, its construction takes place with a very high degree of determination following a path that is highly controlled.

The moral of all this is that not merely does nature once again confound our obvious preconceptions. A most intricate structural mechanism has been evolved to give the process an efficiency and purposefulness whose basis we now understand.

XI. EVOLUTION OF THE RNA NUCLEATION SEQUENCE AND THE COAT PROTEIN

We may now ask how the special RNA sequence developed for initiation of TMV assembly is related to the rest of the RNA. It is believed that the viral RNA codes for four proteins, and the genetic map (Hunter *et al.*, 1976) is shown in Fig. 14. The 5′ end codes for two large proteins, which are probably components of the viral replicase. The larger product is generated by partial readthrough of an amber (UAG) termination codon (Pelham, 1978). The next gene is for a 28,000–30,000 dalton protein (Beachy *et al.*, 1976), whose function is unknown. The assembly origin maps within the 28,000 dalton protein gene, so that the sequence has a dual function in assembly nucleation and as coding sequence. Then, to the right of the assembly origin, comes the coat protein gene, which is at the 3′ end of the TMV RNA (Richards *et al.*, 1975). There are extensive homologies in sequence, between the assembly ori-

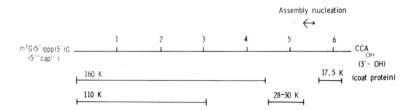

FIG. 14. A genetic map of TMV RNA (adapted from Hunter *et al.*, 1976; Beachy *et al.*, 1976). Distances from the 5' terminus are shown in kilobases. The position of the assembly nucleation region (Zimmern and Wilson, 1976) is marked by a double-headed arrow, to indicate the major and minor directions of elongation. It should be noted that the synthesis of the coat protein and of the 30,000 dalton (30 K) protein are directed not by the viral RNA itself, but by subgenomic mRNAs derived from it.

gin and the coat protein gene (Zimmern, 1977; Jonard *et al.*, 1977), and both pieces of RNA bind strongly to the protein disk, although the stretch of coat protein gene does not act as an alternative origin of assembly which produces dislocation of the disk and promotes helix growth.

Still more remarkable (Zimmern, 1977) than the resemblance of sequence in these two parts of the RNA is the fact that the sequence in the coat protein gene that shows this homology codes for amino acids that are conserved in all strains and mutants of TMV, including the conserved arginine residues, 90 and 92, which form part of the nucleotide binding site. Thus one has a nucleotide sequence that codes for a protein that binds back to itself, clearly a requirement for the primitive virus. One therefore imagines that, as the virus evolved, there was a gene duplication that allowed a separation of the coding and the binding functions, so that the latter could then develop independently to give the sophisticated assembly mechanism now present.

Indeed by considering the sequence of the assembly origin in terms of the three-dimensional structure of the protein sequences coded for by the homologous part of coat protein gene, one can perhaps get a glimpse of how the assembly mechanism evolved. One imagines that the original protein subunit lacked the flexible loop (residues 95–120, approximately) but possessed binding sites at arginine residues 90 and 92, which lie at the inner ends of the lower two helices in the protein subunit (Fig. 6a). This binding site would be coded for by the RNA sequence drawn as loop B in Fig. 5b. Now this is not the loop which, we believe, is nowadays first inserted into the central hole of the disk—during nucleation this role is played by loop A. What this loop A, in the homologous region of the coat protein gene, codes for is the unstructured loop of the protein (residues 110–120), right on the inside of the protein subunit, whose flexibility effectively enlarges the central hole of the disk. This region of the protein contains the invariant pair of acid residues Asp 115 and Asp 116, which are probably two of the "Caspar" residues responsible for preventing helix formation by the isolated protein and favoring the disk state instead (Durham and Klug, 1971). It also contains the invariant residue Arg 113, probably involved in RNA binding in the helix, but not the disk. It would thus appear very likely that loop A on the RNA and the flexible loop 110–120 on the protein developed together.

Whether this particular explanation is correct or not (and how shall we ever tell?), there is little doubt that the coevolution of the viral RNA and the viral protein must have imposed particular constraints, since at all stages the RNA and protein had to be able to interact physically. This may account for the fact that in the virus structure there are three nucleotides associated with each protein subunit, and for the large amount of quasi-repetition in the RNA sequence on a period of three bases (Zimmern, 1977). This would allow a protein subunit to have extra amino acids added in the course of evolution (by inserting an RNA triplet) and yet allow the existing RNA–protein interaction to be maintained.

Apart from these considerations, there is further evidence for evolution within the coat protein gene, involving the helical regions. We have already noted that there is a local dyad axis in the protein subunit, running roughly radially through it and relating the four α-helices in pairs. This internal symmetry has been analyzed in detail by McLachlan et al. (1980), who have proposed that the present subunit arose by a process of gene duplication beginning from a primitive protein consisting of two helices; they have also produced an ingenious extension of this idea to account for the development of the "jaws" mechanisms by which the RNA becomes sandwiched between two layers of helices. It is hoped that, as further information becomes available on the RNA sequences and structures of other strains of the virus, these ideas can be extended and refined.

ACKNOWLEDGMENTS

I would like to acknowledge the contributions of my students and colleagues to the studies described here, especially A. C. H. Durham, J. T. Finch, K. C. Holmes, P. F. C. Gilbert, J. C. Champness, A. C. Bloomer, G. Bricogne, D. Zimmern, and P. J. G. Butler. I wish to thank P. J. G. Butler for his help with the manuscript and for many helpful suggestions. I have benefited over the years from the advice and criticism of D. L. D. Caspar. I wish also to take the opportunity of paying tribute to the pioneers in the X-ray study of TMV, the late J. D. Bernal and I. Fankuchen, and to the late Rosalind Franklin, who introduced me to the subject and whose skill and single-mindedness opened the era of quantitative analysis.

REFERENCES

Barrett, A. N., Barrington Leigh, J., Holmes, K. C., Leberman, R., Vonsengbusch, P., and Klug, A. (1971). *Cold Spring Harbor Symp. Quant. Biol.* **36,** 433–448.
Beachy, R. N., Zaitlin, M., Bruening, G., and Israel, H. W. (1976). *Virology* **73,** 498–507.
Bloomer, A. C., Champness, J. N., Bricogne, G., Staden, R., and Klug, A. (1978). *Nature (London)* **276,** 362–368.
Bricogne, G. (1976). *Acta Crystallogr., Sect. A* **32,** 832–847.
Butler, P. J. G., and Durham, A. C. H. (1977). *Adv. Protein Chem.* **31,** 187–251.
Butler, P. J. G., and Klug, A. (1971). *Nature (London), New Biol.* **229,** 47–50.
Butler, P. J. G., and Klug, A. (1972). *Proc. Natl. Acad. Sci. U.S.A.* **69,** 2950–2953.
Butler, P. J. G., and Klug, A. (1973). *Mol. Gen. Genet.* **120,** 91–93.
Butler, P. J. G., and Lomonossoff, G. P. (1978). *J. Mol. Biol.* **126,** 877–882.
Butler, P. J. G., Bloomer, A. C., Bricogne, G., Champness, J. N., Graham, J., Guilley, H., Klug, A., and Zimmern, D. (1976). *In* "Structure–Function Relationships of Proteins" (R. Markham and R. W. Horne, eds.), 3rd. John Innes Symp., pp. 101–110. North-Holland/Elsevier, Amsterdam.
Butler, P. J. G., Finch, J. T., and Zimmern, D. (1977). *Nature (London)* **265,** 217–219.
Caspar, D. L. D. (1963). *Adv. Protein Chem.* **18,** 37–121.
Caspar, D. L. D., and Klug, A. (1962). *Cold Spring Harbor Symp. Quant. Biol.* **27,** 1–24.
Champness, J. N., Bloomer, A. C., Bricogne, G., Butler, P. J. G. and Klug, A. (1976). *Nature (London)* **259,** 20–24.
Crowther, R. C., and Amos, L. A. (1971). *J. Mol. Biol.* **60,** 123–130.
Durham, A. C. H., and Klug, A. (1971). *Nature (London), New Biol.* **229,** 42–46.
Durham, A. C. H., Finch, J. T., and Klug, A. (1971). *Nature (London), New Biol.* **229,** 37–42.
Finch, J. T., and Klug, A. (1971). *Philos. Trans. R. Soc. London Ser. B* **261,** 211–216.
Finch, J. T., Leberman, R., Chang, Y.-S., and Klug, A. (1966). *Nature (London)* **212,** 349–350.
Fraenkel-Conrat, H., and Singer, B. (1959). *Biochim. Biophys. Acta* **33,** 359–370.
Fraenkel-Conrat, H., and Singer, B. (1964). *Virology* **23,** 354–362.

Fraenkel, Conrat, H., and Williams, R. C. (1955). *Proc. Natl. Acad. Sci. U.S.A.* **41,** 690–698.

Gilbert, P. F. C., and Klug, A. (1974). *J. Mol. Biol.* **86,** 193–207.

Graham, J., and Butler, P. J. G. (1979). *Eur. J. Biochem.* **93,** 333–337.

Hart, R. G., and Smith, J. D. (1956). *Nature (London)* **178,** 739–740.

Hunter, T. R., Hunt, T., Knowland, J., and Zimmern, D. (1976). *Nature (London)* **260,** 759–764.

Jonard, G., Richards, K. E., Guilley, H., and Hirth, L. (1977). *Cell* **11,** 483–493.

Keith, J., and Fraenkel-Conrat, H. (1975). *FEBS Lett.* **57,** 31–33.

Klug, A., and Caspar, D. L. D. (1960). *Adv. Virus Res.* **7,** 225–325.

Klug, A., and Durham, A. C. H. (1971). *Cold Spring Harbor Symp. Quant. Biol.* **36,** 449–460.

Lauffer, M. A., and Stevens, C. L. (1968). *Adv. Virus Res.* **13,** 1–63.

Lebeurier, G., Nicolaieff, A., and Richards, K. E. (1977). *Proc. Natl. Acad. Sci. U.S.A.* **74,** 149–153.

Lomonossoff, G. P., and Butler, P. J. G. (1979). *Eur. J. Biochem.* **93,** 157–164.

McLachlan, A. D., Bloomer, A. C., and Butler, P. J. G. (1980). *J. Mol. Biol.* **136,** 203–224.

Matthews, R. E. F. (1966). *Virology* **30,** 82–96.

Okada, Y., and Ohno, T. (1972). *Mol. Gen. Genet.* **114,** 205–213.

Pelham, H. R. B. (1978). *Nature (London)* **272,** 469–471.

Richards, K. E., and Williams, R. C. (1972). *Proc. Natl. Acad. Sci. U.S.A.* **69,** 1121–1124.

Richards, K. E., and Williams, R. C. (1973). *Biochemistry* **12,** 4574–4581.

Richards, K. E., Morel, M. C., Nicolaieff, A., Lebeurier, G., and Hirth, L. (1975). *Biochimie* **57,** 749–755.

Stubbs, G., Warren, S., and Holmes, K. (1977). *Nature (London)* **267,** 216–221.

Zimmern, D. (1975). *Nucl. Acids Res.* **2,** 1189–1201.

Zimmern, D. (1977). *Cell* **11,** 463–482.

Zimmern, D., and Butler, P. J. G. (1977). *Cell* **11,** 455–462.

Zimmern, D., and Wilson, T. M. A. (1976). *FEBS Lett.* **71,** 294–298.

NOTE ADDED IN PROOF. The kinetics of elongation in the minor direction, i.e., toward the 3′ terminus, have now been studied by Lomonossoff and Butler (*FEBS Lett.* **113,** 271–274, 1980). They find that assembly in this direction is more rapid when the protein is supplied in the form of A-protein than when a disk preparation is used. The direct addition of disks cannot be ruled out entirely but addition of a component from the A-protein seems more likely, particularly in view of the absence of a special configuration at the 3′ tail of the RNA. This is in contrast to the situation found for the major (5′) tail where the "traveling loop" of RNA would seem specifically adapted to the addition of disks.

THE TRANSPLANTATION AND MANIPULATION OF GENES IN MICROORGANISMS*

STANLEY N. COHEN

Departments of Genetics and Medicine,
Stanford University,
Stanford, California

I. INTRODUCTION

U UNTIL this decade, genetics has been largely a descriptive science: our knowledge of genes and their actions has been derived mostly from observing the consequences of natural biological processes such as mutation and recombination. Certainly, the ability to introduce new genetic information into bacterial cells by the manipulative processes of transduction, transformation, or conjugation has advanced knowledge of the biology of prokaryotic organisms in major ways, and concurrent progress in biochemistry and molecular biology has enabled the structural and functional study of the individual genes and gene products of prokaryotes. However, the complexity of the chromosomes of higher organisms and the inability to isolate particular segments of these DNA molecules has until recently precluded detailed molecular analysis of eukaryotic genes.

Development of the concepts and methods of "recombinant DNA" now enables the manipulation of DNA molecules *in vitro* and the cloning of new genetic combinations in microorganisms. This has permitted the investigation of prokaryotic genes at a level that was not previously possible and has allowed for the first time the analysis of individual eukaryotic genes and study of the organization of genetic information in higher organisms. The advances that laid the foundations for genetic manipulation in microorganisms were made in a number of different laboratories in the late 1960s and early 1970s. There are four general requirements: (*a*) a replicon (cloning vehicle or vector) able to propa-

*Lecture delivered May 17, 1979.

gate itself in the recipient organism; (*b*) a method of joining another DNA segment to the cloning vector; (*c*) a procedure for introducing the composite molecule into a biologically functional recipient cell; and (*d*) a means of selecting those microorganisms that have acquired the hybrid DNA species.

II. Historical Background and the Development of DNA Cloning Methods

A. *Plasmids and Plasmid DNA Transformation*

The studies reviewed here grew out of experiments aimed at elucidating the molecular nature of a class of genetic elements responsible for antibiotic resistance in bacteria. It has been known for some years that many bacterial species contain autonomously replicating extra-chromosomal elements called *plasmids*. Most simply, plasmids can be considered as primitive bacteriophages that carry a function that allows the unit to be replicated autonomously (the replication system), but that lack the genetic information required for a complex life cycle or existence in an extracellular state (Cohen, 1976). Circular plasmid DNA molecules (Fig. 1) are physically separate from the bacterial chromosome, and they can encode a variety of genetic traits that are not essential for growth of the host cell but that commonly provide a biological advantage to cells carrying the plasmids; antibiotic resistance is one of these properties. Examples of other traits carried by plasmids are shown in Table I.

Plasmids commonly are present in multiple copies within each cell, and plasmid DNA preparations isolated from bacterial cultures contain a heterogeneous population of DNA molecules. To employ classical genetic methods for the study of plasmid mutants, and to investigate the organization of genetic information on plasmid DNA, it was therefore necessary to establish a method for the cloning of individual plasmid DNA molecules. Procedures for transforming bacteria for chromosomally encoded traits had been developed for *Pneumococcus, Haemophilus, Bacillus,* and certain other organisms (Avery *et al.,* 1944; Hotchkiss and Gabor, 1970), but transformation had not been shown for *Escherichia coli* or the other enteric bacteria with which we were working. It was known that treatment of *E. coli* cells with calcium

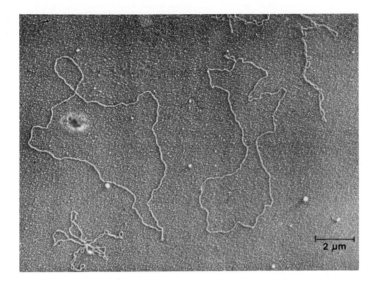

Fig. 1. Electron photomicrograph showing twisted "supercoiled" and "open" circular molecules of the antibiotic resistance plasmid, R1. From Cohen and Miller (1969).

TABLE I

Some Properties Encoded by Naturally Ocurring Plasmids[a]

Antibiotic resistance
Fertility (ability to transfer genetic material by conjugation)
Production of bacteriocins
Antibiotic production
Heavy-metal resistance (Cd^{2+}, Hg^{2+})
Ultraviolet resistance
Enterotoxin
Virulence factors, hemolysin, K 88 antigen
Metabolism of camphor, octane, and other polycyclic hydrocarbons
Tumorigenicity in plants
Restriction/modification

[a] Modified from Cohen (1976).

176   STANLEY N. COHEN

chloride enabled them to take up DNA of the bacteriophage λ, and that viable viral particles were produced in such CaCl₂-treated bacteria; however, attempts to generate clones that had acquired new genetic properties from the transformed DNA had not been successful (Mandel and Higa, 1970).

In 1972, my colleagues and I found, using a modification of the previously described CaCl₂ procedure, that *E. coli* could take up circular plasmid DNA molecules (Fig. 2), and that a line of transformed cells that phenotypically express genetic information carried by the incoming plasmid DNA could be produced (Cohen *et al.*, 1972). While this was an inefficient process (approximately one in 10^6 cells were transformed), transformants could readily be identified and selected by utilizing the antibiotic resistance genes carried by the plasmids we were studying. Plasmid-transformed cells reproduced themselves normally, and acquired a DNA species having the same genetic and molecular properties as the parent plasmid. Since each cell in the resulting clone contains a replica of the single plasmid DNA molecule that was taken up

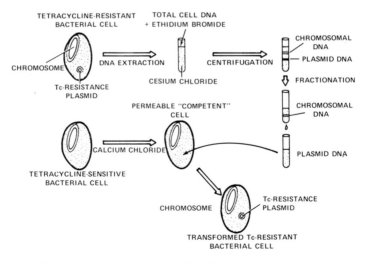

FIG. 2. Schematic presentation of plasmid DNA transformation procedure. Purified plasmid DNA separated from chromosomal DNA by cesium chloride–ethidium bromide gradient centrifugation is introduced into bacteria made permeable to DNA by treatment with calcium chloride. Antibiotic resistance genes carried by the plasmid are used in the selection of transformed bacterial cells.

by the originally transformed bacterium, the procedure made it possible to clone (and thus separate and purify biologically) genetically distinct plasmids present in a heterogeneous population. We could now apply to the study of plasmids a variety of genetic and biochemical methods that previously were restricted to bacteriophages, which could be cloned because of their plaque-forming properties.

To determine the genetic and molecular properties of specific regions of the DNA of large antibiotic resistance plasmids (R-plasmids), we began to take these plasmids apart by shearing the molecules mechanically and then introducing the resulting DNA fragments into $CaCl_2$-treated *E. coli* cells by transformation (Cohen and Chang, 1973). However, work being carried out with restriction endonucleases in other laboratories (Smith and Wilcox, 1970; Kelly and Smith, 1970; Danna and Nathans, 1971) suggested that these enzymes would be highly useful in our analysis. It had been discovered that restriction endonucleases, which are produced by many different species of bacterial cells, can recognize specific nucleotide sequences within DNA and can cleave DNA molecules at these recognition sites (Smith and Wilcox, 1970; Kelly and Smith, 1970). The cell's own DNA is protected from cleavage by modification enzymes (methylases) that add methyl groups to certain nucleotides within the recognition sequence, rendering the site resistant to cleavage by the companion endonuclease (Arber, 1965; Meselson and Yuan, 1968; Nathans and Smith, 1975). Thus, restriction endonucleases could be used to generate reproducibly a characteristic set of cleavage fragments for each plasmid; for most of our experiments, this would be preferable to generating a random series of plasmid DNA fragments by mechanical shearing. Moreover, the fragments produced by restriction enzyme cleavage could be analyzed and characterized by electrophoresis on gels; such methods had already been used effectively by Nathans and his collaborators for analysis of the SV40 animal virus genome (Danna and Nathans, 1971; Nathans and Danna, 1972).

B. The Joining of Separate DNA Fragments in Vitro

The conceptual and experimental basis for linking DNA segments by means of projecting single-strand ends having complementary nucleotides can be found in the work of Khorana and his collaborators, who in the late 1960s showed that short segments of synthetic DNA could be joined by the addition of overlapping complementary single-stranded segments (Khorana, 1968; Agarwal *et al.*, 1970). The construction of such complementary DNA sequences by the addition of single nucleotides was laborious, however. Jensen *et al.* (1971) first reported the use of the enzyme terminal transferase to add homopolymeric stretches of deoxyadenosine (dA) or deoxythymidine (dT) to the ends of DNA fragments in an attempt to link the fragments covalently *in vitro* by (*a*) hydrogen bonding of the complentary nucleotides; (*b*) subsequent closure of the resulting single-strand breaks by DNA ligation. In these conceptually sound, but only partially successful experiments, a series of DNA molecules were joined together end-to-end by dA-dT "tails" to form catenated structures; however, Jensen *et al.* did not achieve the final step (i.e., ligation) necessary to accomplish covalent DNA linkage. It is now known that *in vitro* ligation is not required for the covalent joining of separate DNA segments that contain homopolymeric additions; ligation of such segments occurs *in vivo* when the hydrogen-bonded segments are introduced into bacterial cells by transformation (Wensink *et al.*, 1974).

The problem of *in vitro* ligation of DNA fragments that have homopolymeric extensions at their ends was solved by the discovery by Lobban and Kaiser (1973) that such covalent joining could be achieved by the use of exonuclease III, and this finding was employed by Jackson *et al.* (1972) in linking the tumor virus SV40 to DNA molecules of bacteriophage λdv. It has been of some historical interest that concern about possible biohazards related to the SV40 component of the hybrid λdv-SV40 molecule that Jackson *et al.* had constructed led Berg and his colleagues to decide not to try to clone the molecule in *E. coli* (Wade, 1974). Ironically, however, with regard to the biosafety controversy that ensued (Berg *et al.*, 1975), we can reasonably assume that no bacterial clones carrying the composite molecule would have resulted if the experiment had been tried: the λdv cleavage site at which the two DNA segments were joined is located within a gene essential for replication of λdv, and interruption of the continuity of this gene by an inserted DNA fragment prevents the bacteriophage DNA molecule from functioning as a replicon (Helling *et al.*, 1974; Streek and Hobom, 1975; Mukai *et al.*, 1976).

The subsequent discovery that restriction endonucleases could generate in one step DNA termini having projecting single-strand ends, and that these could be linked to a complementary nucleotide sequence on another endonuclease-generated DNA fragment, made the joining of DNA segments much simpler. The nucleotide sequences that constitute the cleavage sites for several endonucleases were identified in the early 1970s; in every instance, cleavage occurred at or near an axis of bidirectional rotational symmetry: that is, the endonuclease recognition site consists of a sequence that reads the same on both DNA strands in the 5′ to 3′ direction. Often, restriction endonucleases cleave both DNA strands at precisely the same location, yielding blunt-ended DNA fragments (for review, see Nathans and Smith, 1975). Certain of these endonucleases, however (for example, the *Eco*RI enzyme), introduce breaks that are several nucleotides apart in the two DNA strands (Fig. 3). Because of the bidirectional rotational symmetry of the nucleotide sequence in the region of cleavage, cleavage of the two DNA strands at separated points within this region yields fragments that have protruding complementary nucleotide sequences at their ends. Such termini, which resemble mortise and tenon type joints, can be linked together by hydrogen bonding. Since all DNA termini generated by the enzyme are

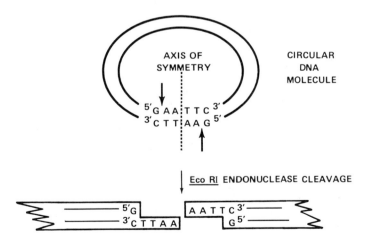

FIG. 3. The six-nucleotide-long recognition sequence cleaved by the *Eco*RI endonuclease is shown. Because of the bidirectional rotational symmetry of the nucleotide sequence in the region of the cleavage, the two DNA strands are cut at separate points, yielding fragments that have protruding complementary single-strand ends.

identical, fragments derived from different DNA molecules can be spliced together.

The finding that the DNA fragments generated by the *Eco*RI restriction endonuclease have projecting single strands at their termini was reported simultaneously in 1972 by Sgaramella (1972) and by Mertz and Davis (1972). Sgaramella found that molecules of the bacterial virus P22 cleaved with the *Eco*RI enzyme can form catenated DNA segments equal in length to two or more viral DNA molecules. Mertz and Davis observed that closed-loop SV40 DNA molecules cleaved by *Eco*RI could re-form themselves into circular molecules by hydrogen bonding and could be sealed covalently with DNA ligase; furthermore, the reconstituted molecules were infectious in animal cells growing in tissue culture. While this property of the *Eco*RI enzyme and certain other restriction endonucleases was of great importance in the development of recombinant DNA methods, it is now appreciated that cohesive DNA termini are not essential for the linkage of DNA termini. Sgaramella *et al.* (1970) had reported that even blunt-ended DNA fragments can be joined together by use of the bacteriophage T4 ligase; such blunt-ended joining has found widespread use in the linking together of DNA fragments generated by restriction endonucleases that do not yield projecting single-strand ends (Sgaramella *et al.*, 1977), and for the joining of DNA fragments that have been made blunt-ended by the S1 nuclease or DNA polymerase I (Bolivar *et al.*, 1977; Chang and Cohen, 1978).

The discovery of DNA ligases (Gellert, 1967; Weiss and Richardson, 1967; Gefter *et al.*, 1967; Olivera and Lehman, 1967; Cozzarelli *et al.*, 1967) also has had a major role in the development of recombinant DNA methods. These enzymes, which can form phosphodiester bonds between adjacent DNA nucleotides, are required for the *in vitro* joining of DNA molecules. However, as noted above it is now known that *in vitro* ligation is not necessary to join DNA fragments that are being held together by extended homopolymeric terminal additions (Wensink *et al.*, 1974). Fragments that have protruding single-strand ends generated by restriction endonucleases can also be linked together *in vivo* by the *intracellular* action of DNA ligase (Mertz and Davis, 1972; Cohen *et al.*, 1973), and such linkage can fully and accurately reconstitute the genetic continuity of the DNA sequence (Chang and Cohen, 1977).

C. Construction of Biologically Functional Bacterial Plasmids in Vitro

To determine whether large and complex plasmid DNA molecules could be reduced in size or restructured entirely by cleaving them into multiple fragments with a restriction endonuclease and joining together the resulting fragments in a different arrangement, A. C. Y. Chang, H. W. Boyer, R. B. Helling, and I studied the large antibiotic resistance plasmid R6-5 (Cohen *et al.*, 1973). We established that this plasmid (Silver and Cohen, 1972), which consists of almost 100,000 nucleotide base pairs and contains several genes encoding several different antibiotic resistances, was cleaved into 11 separate DNA fragments by the *Eco*RI endonuclease; hopefully the location of the cleavage sites would leave the replication machinery of the plasmid and one or more of its antibiotic resistance genes intact. R6-5 DNA was treated with the *Eco*RI enzyme and was introduced by transformation into $CaCl_2$-treated *E. coli* cells with or without prior ligation of the DNA. Selection was carried out for transformants that expressed one or more of the antibiotic resistance determinants located on the parent plasmid.

One such clone, which expressed kanamycin (Km) resistance but none of the other antibiotic resistances of R6-5, was identified and its plasmid DNA was isolated and characterized by *Eco*RI endonuclease digestion and agarose gel electrophoresis (Fig. 4). The digestion pattern showed that a new plasmid replicon containing only 3 of the 11 *Eco*RI fragments of R6-5 had been formed. By selecting for propagation of the Km resistance gene of R6-5, we had been able to clone a specific DNA segment carrying this gene. The Km resistance fragment, which we later showed does not have the capacity for autonomous replication, had become linked to an *Eco*RI-generated DNA fragment carrying the rep-

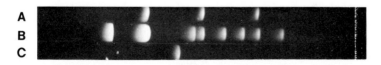

A
B
C

FIG. 4. Agarose gel electrophores of *Eco*RI digest of the pSC102 plasmid (A) containing three of the *Eco*RI-generated fragments comprising the R6-5 plasmid (B). The pSC101 plasmid is cleaved by the *Eco*RI endonuclease only once to yield a single linear DNA fragment (C). From Cohen *et al.* (1973).

lication region of R6–5, and this enabled its propagation in transformed bacteria (Cohen *et al.*, 1973). These findings demonstrated that a plasmid DNA segment carrying replication functions could serve as a cloning vehicle or "vector" for the cloning of other restriction endonuclease-generated DNA fragments. Ideally, a plasmid vector suitable for the cloning of nonreplicating *Eco*RI-generated DNA fragments would contain replication machinery plus a selectable antibiotic resistance gene on the same *Eco*RI fragment. We searched for such a vector among the antibiotic resistance plasmids we had been studying.

In our collection at Stanford was a small plasmid, 9000 base pairs in length, that carried a gene conferring resistance to the antibiotic tetracycline (Tc). When we subjected the DNA of this plasmid (pSC101) (Cohen and Chang, 1973, 1977) to cleavage by *Eco*RI endonuclease and analyzed the products by gel electrophoresis, we found that the enzyme had cut the DNA molecule at only a single location. This indicated that the pSC101 plasmid could be used as a directly selectable cloning vector if a fragment of foreign DNA could be inserted at its *Eco*RI cleavage site without interfering with either the replication functions or expression of the Tc resistance gene carried by the plasmid.

We mixed the DNA of the pSC101 plasmid with the previously constructed R6–5-derived plasmid carrying a Km resistance gene on an *Eco*RI-generated fragment, cleaved the mixture with *Eco*RI endonuclease, and treated the resulting DNA with ligase. The DNA was introduced into *E. coli* by transformation, and bacteria that expressed both the R6–5-derived Km resistance determinant and the Tc resistance gene of pSC101 were selected. A plasmid from one of the resulting clones was found to contain the entire pSC101 vector plus one of the three fragments of the Km-resistance plasmid (Fig. 5). Thus, pSC101 could at least be used to propagate a nonreplicating segment of another *Eco*RI DNA plasmid. In similar experiments, we showed that the pSC101 plasmid could be joined *in vitro* to a second *Eco*RI-cleaved replicon carrying a gene for streptomycin resistance. The procedure is summarized schematically in Fig. 6.

Chang and I proceeded to determine whether the procedure we had used to clone fragments of *E. coli* plasmids could be used to propagate and genetically express DNA from an unrelated bacterial species (Chang and Cohen, 1974). It was possible that the way genetic information was arranged on totally foreign DNA molecules or another yet unknown

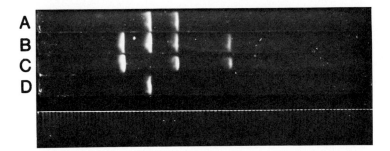

Fig. 5. Agarose gel electrophoresis of *Eco*RI digest of newly constructed plasmid DNA species. A new plasmid (A) consisting of the pSC101 vector (D) plus the kanamycin resistance (middle) fragment of pSC102. (C) has been constructed by *Eco*RI cleavage of the parental DNA molecules plus ligation and transformation. (B) shows a mixture of the *Eco*RI-cleaved plasmid DNA preparations. From Cohen *et al.* (1973).

factor might produce an aberrant situation that would prevent the survival of such hybrid molecules in a new host. [It is now known that the DNA sequence arrangement on some DNA fragments impedes their cloning or stability, or both, as part of recombinant DNA molecules (Heyneker *et al.*, 1976; Timmis *et al.*, 1978b)]. Even if DNA from a very different bacterial species, such as *Staphylococcus aureus*, could be replicated in *E. coli* by joining it to the pSC101 vector, the foreign genes might not be expressed phenotypically in a heterospecific environment. [There is now evidence that some genes derived from foreign bacterial species can be expressed phenotypically in *E. coli*, but others cannot (Chakrabarty *et al.*, 1978); we made a fortunate choice in selecting a gene that was expressed.]

*Eco*RI-cleaved pSC101 plasmid DNA and DNA from the *S. aureus* plasmid pI258, which carries a gene that encodes the enzyme β-lactamase and specifies resistance to penicillin and ampicillin (Ap), were mixed, treated with DNA ligase, and introduced into *E. coli* by transformation. Transformant cells that expressed the penicillin resistance of the *S. aureus* plasmid as well as the Tc resistance of *E. coli* were isolated; these were found to contain a new DNA species consisting of the entire pSC101 plasmid plus an *Eco*RI-generated *S. aureus* DNA fragment that contained the Ap resistance gene derived from the pI258 plasmid (Fig. 7).

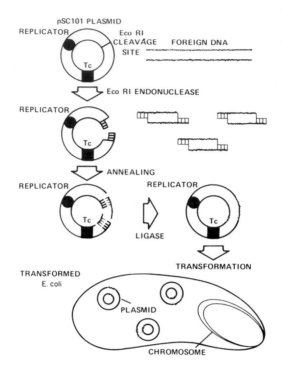

Fig. 6. Schematic representation of the procedure used in the initial DNA cloning experiments. Fragments of *Eco*RI endonuclease-cleaved DNA were joined to the similarly cleaved pSC101 plasmid vector by hydrogen bonding of protruding single strands containing complementary base sequences. After covalent joining of the fragments by DNA ligase, they were introduced by transformation into CaCl$_2$-treated bacteria. Cells resistant to tetracycline were selected, and each yielded a bacterial clone containing a plasmid identical to the plasmid DNA molecule taken up by a single transformed cell.

The replication and expression in *E. coli* of genes derived from an organism not known to exchange DNA with *E. coli* suggested that interspecies genetic combinations might be generally obtainable. We reasoned that it might be practical to use these methods to introduce into *E. coli* genes specifying metabolic and synthetic functions indigenous to other biological classes. Potentially, plasmid replicons such as pSC101 might also allow DNA derived from eukaryotic organisms to be introduced into *E. coli*, thus enabling the application of bacterial genetic and biochemical techniques to the study of eukaryotic genes. Moreover, by fragmenting the eukaryotic chromosome and cloning segments of it on individual plasmids, it potentially would be feasible to isolate specific eukaryotic genes and to study the organization of genetic information of higher organisms in ways that were not previously possible.

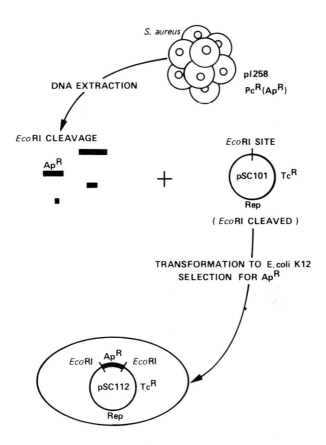

FIG. 7. Chimeric plasmids containing DNA segments derived from *Staphylococcus aureus* and *Escherichia coli* were constructed by joining an *Eco*RI-generated fragment from the *S. aureus* plasmid pI258 to the pSC101 vector and introducing the composite molecule into *E. coli*. The Ap-resistance gene carried by the *S. aureus* plasmid DNA was expressed phenotypically in the unrelated bacterial host.

D. Cloning of Eukaryotic DNA in E. coli

To determine whether eukaryotic DNA could in fact be replicated in bacteria, my colleagues and I undertook the cloning of DNA that encodes the ribosomal RNA of the frog *Xenopus laevis* (Morrow *et al.*, 1974). Although this DNA does not express traits (such as antibiotic resistance) that enable selection of bacteria carrying chimeric plasmids, *X. laevis* ribosomal DNA (rDNA) had been well characterized, and its physical properties would permit the identification of *X. laevis* DNA fragments of bacterial plasmids. The Tc resistance conferred by the pSC101 plasmid allowed us to select for transformed clones, and we could then examine the plasmid DNA isolated from such clones to determine whether any of the plasmids contained DNA fragments having molecular properties of *Xenopus* ribosomal DNA. The foreign DNA fragments being propagated in bacteria could also be tested for nucleotide sequence homology with DNA isolated directly from *X. laevis* oocytes, using electron microscope heteroduplex techniques (Davis and Davidson, 1968; Westmoreland *et al.*, 1969).

Ribosomal DNA from *X. laevis* and the pSC101 plasmid were mixed, cleaved with *Eco*RI endonuclease, and ligated using the procedures we had employed earlier. Fifty-five Tc-resistant transformants were isolated, and DNA obtained from such transformants was analyzed by gel electrophoresis, cesium chloride gradient centrifugation, and/or electron microscopy to determine the presence of an *Eco*RI-generated DNA fragment similar in size and/or buoyant density to similarly generated fragments of bona fide *X. laevis* rDNA. The results of these experiments are summarized in Table II. Fifteen of the Tc-resistance clones contained one or more *Eco*RI-generated fragments having the same size as fragments produced by cleavage of *X. laevis* rDNA. Moreover, the plasmid chimeras isolated from *E. coli* were shown to contain DNA with a buoyant density characteristic of the high $G+C$ base composition of *X. laevis* rDNA. These experiments also produced an unexpected finding that provided an example of the type of new information that DNA cloning procedures could yield about the organization and structure of eukaryotic chromosomes. Variation in size of the *Eco*RI-generated *X. laevis* rDNA fragments present in plasmid chimeras was observed; together with the *Eco*RI cleavage pattern found in the amplified *X. laevis* rDNA isolated from frog oocytes, this finding

TABLE II

Xenopus laevis–Escherichia coli Recombinant Plasmids[a,b]

Plasmid DNA	Molecular weight of *Eco*RI plasmid fragments estimated by gel electrophoresis ($\times 10^{-6}$)	Molecular weight from contour length ($\times 10^{-6}$)	Buoyant density of intact plasmid in CsCl (g/cm^3)
CD4	5.8, 4.2, 3.0	13.6	1.721
CD7	5.8, 4.2	—	—
CD12, CD20, CD45, CD47, CD51	5.8, 3.0	—	—
CD14	5.8, 4.2, 3.0	9.2	1.720
CD18	5.8, 3.9	10.0	1.719
CD35	5.8, 3.9, 3.0	—	—
CD42	5.8, 4.2	10.6	1.720
pSC101	5.8	6.0	1.710

[a] Modified from Morrow *et al.* (1974).

[b] *Eco*RI-cleaved chimeric plasmids containing *X. laevis* rDNA were characterized by buoyant density centrifugation in cesium chloride, electron microscopy, and electrophoresis in agarose gels.

suggested that the amplified repeat unit was heterogeneous in the oocytes (Morrow *et al.,* 1974).

Electron microscope analysis (Fig. 8) of a heteroduplex formed between *X. laevis* rDNA and one of the plasmid chimeras (CD42) demonstrated that this plasmid contains DNA nucleotide sequences homologous with those present in rDNA isolated directly from *X. laevis.* In some instances, segments of two separate chimeric plasmid DNA molecules were seen to form duplex regions with the single strand of *X. laevis* rDNA, consistent with the observation (Dawid *et al.,* 1970; Wensink and Brown, 1971) that the rDNA sequences of amplified *X. laevis* are tandomly repeated.

The plasmid chimeras containing both *E. coli* and *X. laevis* rDNA were found to replicate stably in bacterial hosts as part of the pSC101 plasmid replicon and could be recovered from transformed *E. coli* by procedures commonly employed for the isolation of bacterial plasmids. Tritium-labeled RNA isolated from bacteria harboring these plasmids

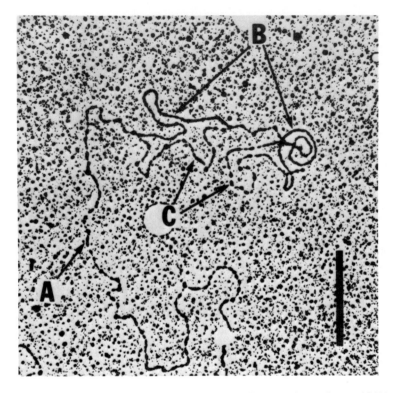

FIG. 8. Electron photomicrograph of a heteroduplex of *Xenopus laevis* ribosomal DNA and two separate molecules of a tetracycline resistance plasmid chimera (CD42) isolated from *E. coli* and containing a cloned DNA fragment derived from *X. laevis*. A, Single-strand rDNA *X. laevis;* B, double-strand regions of homology between the plasmid and *X. laevis* rDNA; C, single-strand segments corresponding in length to the DNA segment of the plasmid derived from the pSC101 plasmid vector. From Morrow *et al.* (1974).

hybridized *in vitro* to amplified *X. laevis* rDNA isolated directly from the eukaryotic organism, indicating that RNA synthesis could occur on the eukaryotic DNA transplanted into the prokaryotic host.

III. Some Subsequent Advances

Since these early DNA cloning experiments, major advances made in a number of laboratories have increased the ease and flexibility of gene manipulation, so that segments of DNA molecules can now be taken apart and put together in a variety of different ways. Dozens of site-specific endonucleases that recognize different nucleotide sequences and thus cleave DNA at different sites have been identified and characterized (Roberts, 1976). Synthetic and natural "adaptor" fragments have been used to convert one kind of endonuclease cleavage site to another (Marians *et al.*, 1976; Heyneker *et al.*, 1976; Cohen *et al.*, 1977; Roberts, 1977; Scheller *et al.*, 1977). Additional naturally occurring plasmids suitable as vectors were identified (Hershfield *et al.*, 1974), and recombinant DNA methods have been used to modify these plasmids to yield vectors suitable for specific purposes (Armstrong *et al.*, 1977, Timmis *et al.*, 1978c; Bolivar *et al.*, 1977; Chang and Cohen, 1978). Vectors that utilize the replication and packaging systems of bacteriophage λ (Rambach and Tiollais, 1974; Murray and Murray, 1974; Thomas *et al.*, 1974; Blattner *et al.*, 1977; Leder *et al.*, 1977; Hohn and Murray, 1977) or other bacteriophages (Messing *et al.*, 1977; Hermann *et al.*, 1978). Specific messenger RNA (mRNA) species produced by certain organs or tissues has been used as template for the enzymic synthesis of double-stranded complementary DNA (cDNA) sequences corresponding to the mRNA (Ruogeon *et al.*, 1975; Rabbits, 1976; Eftratiadis *et al.*, 1976). Double-stranded DNA segments that have a nucleotide sequence corresponding to a known amino acid sequence have been synthesized chemically and have been purified and amplified by cloning them as part of a bacterial plasmid (Itakura *et al.*, 1977; Goeddel *et al.*, 1979). Novel methods of detecting plasmids that include specifically desired gene sequences have been developed using subculture cloning procedures (Kedes *et al.*, 1975) or *in situ* hybridization procedures (Grunstein and Hogness, 1975). Cotransformation procedures that enable introduction of nonselectable segments of DNA into bacteria (Kretschmer *et al.*, 1975) or mammalian cells (Wigler *et al.*, 1977) have been devised.

Although the site-specific endonucleases used for gene manipulation *in vitro* are commonly called "restriction enzymes," some of the bacterial species that encode such endonucleases show no detectable restriction of foreign DNA *in vivo,* and it has been speculated that the primary function of such enzymes may be DNA recombination (Kornberg, 1974; Nathans and Smith, 1975; Roberts, 1976). It seems highly likely that DNA cleavage by at least some restriction endonucleases also oc-

curs *in vivo:* the transforming ability of infecting phage DNA is restricted by several orders of magnitude in cells that produce the *Eco*RI
enzyme (Takano *et al.,* 1968a,b), implying that most of the entering
DNA molecules are cleaved *in vivo* before they can be methylated by
the modification enzyme associated with the *Eco*RI restriction–
modification system. There is evidence that the combined actions of the
*Eco*RI endonuclease and DNA ligase can promote site-specific recombination *in vivo,* with results similar to the effects of these enzymes
in vitro (Chang and Cohen, 1977). Moreover, "transposons," which
can operate *in vivo* to join DNA segments having no ancestral relationship, can accomplish a result that is analogous to *in vitro* site-specific
recombination (Cohen, 1976).

IV. Use of DNA Cloning as a Tool for the Study of
Prokaryotic and Eukaryotic Biology

A. Studies of Plasmid Biology

The wish to study bacterial plasmids themselves was the motive that
initially prompted our development of DNA cloning methods, and during the past 6 years my laboratory has used these methods extensively in
such studies. DNA cloning has made possible elucidation of the structure and control of plasmid genes and has yielded much information
about the replication of plasmid DNA. Using nonreplicating DNA
fragments that contain antibiotic resistance genes as biological "probes,"
it has been possible to isolate and study DNA fragments carrying the
replication functions of large and structurally complex plasmids (for
example, Timmis *et al.,* 1975; Lovett and Helinski, 1976; Taylor and
Cohen, 1979), as well as those of small plasmids (Chang and Cohen,
1978) (Fig. 9).

Using hybrid replicons formed by the fusion of two functionally
different types of replication systems, we have investigated the relationship of plasmid replication and incompatibility (Timmis *et al.,* 1974;
Cabello *et al.,* 1976; Meacock and Cohen, 1979) and have studied
replication control in plasmids. A DNA sequence that accomplishes
active partitioning of plasmids in dividing cell populations and that is
functionally equivalent to the centromere of eukaryotic cells has been

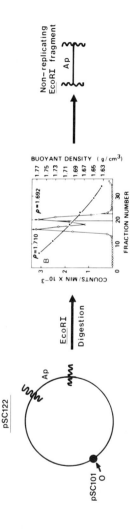

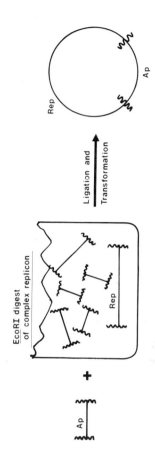

FIG. 9. Scheme for isolation of replication regions of complex plasmids. In the experiment shown, a plasmid carrying a nonreplicating Ap-resistance segment was cleaved by the *Eco*RI restriction endonuclease, and the Ap-resistance "probe" fragment was separated from its vector. The probe was then added to a mixture of DNA fragments produced by *Eco*RI cleavage of a large plasmid, and ligation and transformation were carried out. Since the probe fragment is incapable of replication, its propagation in transformants requires linkage to a DNA segment carrying replication functions. From Timmis *et al.* (1978c).

discovered and characterized using DNA cloning methods (P. Meacock and S. N. Cohen, unpublished data). The genes carried by large antibiotic resistance plasmids have been assigned to specific loci on plasmid DNA by the cloning of endonuclease-generated DNA fragments, and maps of complex plasmid genomes have been constructed (for example, see Timmis *et al.*, 1978a). Natural evolutionary variations in plasmid structure have been identified and have led to the concept that plasmid DNA is in a constant state of flux undergoing both macro- and micro-evolution (Chang *et al.*, 1975; Brutlag *et al.*, 1976; Cohen *et al.*, 1978; Timmis *et al.*, 1978b). Genes within transposable genetic elements have been studied, and their functional interactions have been elucidated.

B. Study of Organization of the Eukaryotic Genetic Sequence Encoding Pro-opiocortin

We and others have also used DNA cloning methods for the study of gene organization, evolution, and expression in eukaryotes. Of particular recent interest to my laboratory has been the genetic sequence that encodes the pituitary hormones ACTH and β-lipotropin (β-LPH). These peptide hormones are known each to include smaller peptides having distinct biological activities: α-melanotropin (α-MSH) and corticotropin-like intermediate lobe peptide (CLIP) are derived from ACTH; β-melanotropin (β-MSH), endorphins, and methionine enkephalin are included within β-LPH (Scott *et al.*, 1973; Li and Chung, 1976; Ling *et al.*, 1976; Li *et al.*, 1977) (Fig. 10). The intracellular level of the mRNA encoding the common precursor protein (pro-opiocortin) is known to be depressed by glucocorticoids, which seem to act at the transcriptional level by means of a glucocorticoid receptor (Nakanishi *et al.*, 1977; Nakamura *et al.*, 1978). The various component peptides are liberated from pro-opiocortin and secreted from pituitary cells by processing mechanisms.

Although the general positions of ACTH and β-LPH on the pro-opiocortin peptide have been known for several years, earlier studies had provided no information about the precise relationships of these peptides and the nature of the processing that the precursor molecule undergoes to yield its two major components. Moreover, ACTH and β-LPH account for only one-third to one-half of the molecular weight of

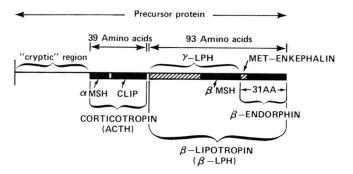

Fig. 10. Map of pro-opiocortin (corticotropin-β-lipotropin) precursor protein showing peptide components previously identified by amino acid analysis and "cryptic" region. Corticotropin (ACTH) and β-lipotropin (β-LPH) were positioned on pro-opiocortin by analysis of cloned cDNA derived from mRNA encoding the precursor protein. The length shown for β-LPH (93 amino acids) has been assigned from the nucleotide sequence of a cloned cDNA insert and differs from the commonly accepted 91 amino acid sequence for β-LPH determined by amino acid analysis (Li *et al.*, 1977).

the precursor protein; thus there has been considerable interest in, and speculation about, the primary structure and possible biological functions of the peptides encoded by the remaining "cryptic" portion. Our recent studies of the genetic sequence encoding pro-opiocortin provide an example of the application of DNA cloning methods for the investigation of gene organization in eukaryotes.

The cloning of complementary DNA (cDNA) (Nakanishi *et al.*, 1977) corresponding to the sequence encoding mRNA the ACTH-β-LPH precursor protein was carried out utilizing mRNA purified from the neurointermediate lobe of bovine pituitaries (Kita *et al.*, 1979). Avian myeloblastosis virus (AMV) reverse transcriptase was used for the sequential synthesis of the two strands of cDNA, homopolymeric dC "tails" were added, and complementary poly(dG) extensions were added to *Pst*I endonuclease cleaved-DNA of the Tc resistance plasmid vector pBR322 (Bolivar, 1977). These steps are summarized in Fig. 11. Following transformation of *E. coli* cells with the dG-dC tailed pro-opiocortin cDNA, Tc-resistant transformants were isolated, and bacterial clones that contained cDNA inserts were identified by a colony hybridization procedure (Grunstein and Hogness, 1975) using ^{32}P-labeled pituitary mRNA as a probe.

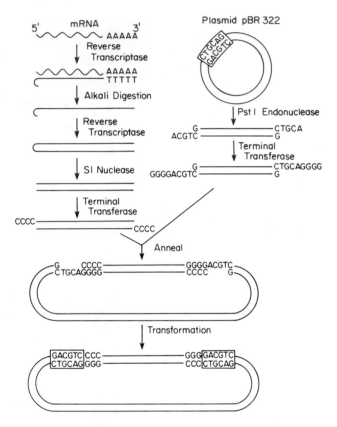

Fig. 11. Outline for protocol used for cloning of pro-opiocortin mRNA. For details, see text and Nakanishi *et al.* (1979). The Tc resistance gene on plasmid pBR322 was used for selection of transformants. As shown in the figure, the recognition sequence for *Pst*I endonuclease is regenerated at the plasmid/cDNA junction by the "tailing" procedure used.

The plasmid present in one of these clones (pSNAC20) was selected for further study. By determining the entire 1091 base pair nucleotide sequence (Maxam and Gilbert, 1978) of the cDNA insert of the pSNAC20 plasmid, we were able to infer certain important features of the protein encoded by the pro-opiocortin mRNA. Since the amino acid composition of ACTH and β-LPH are known (Scott *et al.*, 1973; Li and Chung, 1976; Ling *et al.*, 1976, Li *et al.*, 1977), the translational reading frame of the cDNA sequence could be determined, and an amino acid sequence could thus be assigned for the previously cryptic segment of the pro-opiocortin protein. A probable translational initiation codon (AUG) for the precursor protein was identified from the translational reading frame and the previously known approximate length of pro-opiocortin. The first 20 amino acid residues following the putative initiative methionine were found to include a large proportion of hydrophobic amino acids (13 nonpolar residues, including 7 leucines), consistent with a putative role for the amino-terminal segment of pro-opiocortin as a "signal" peptide (Blobel and Dobberstein, 1975a,b) involved in secretion of the protein. This assignment has been verified recently by analysis of peptide fragments derived from the previously cryptic segment of the protein (Nakamura *et al.*, 1979; Keutmann *et al.*, 1979; E. Herbert, personal communication).

Computer analysis of amino acids assigned from the DNA sequence of the cryptic portion of the precursor protein showed that the pro-opiocortin protein contains a sequence of amino acids strikingly similar to the amino acid sequences of the previously identified hormones α-MSH and β-MSH. As in the case of α- and β-MSH, this peptide segment (which was named γ-MSH, Nakanishi *et al.*, 1979) is flanked by pairs of the basic amino acids lysine and/or arginine, suggesting that it could be liberated from pro-opiocortin by proteolytic processing. A second peptide segment located within the putative signal peptide segment of pro-opiocortin was found to have less extensive structural similarity to the MSHs; the presence of several largely homologous units within the same precursor molecule (Fig. 12) suggests that the gene for pro-opiocortin may have been formed by a series of structural duplications. The previously "cryptic" part of the pro-opiocortin molecule was also found to contain a number of amino acids in positions equivalent to those found in the hormone calcitonin, which is believed to have biological functions quite unrelated to those of the other components of molecule (Chang *et al.*, 1979).

Recently, we have isolated plasmids that include *genomic* DNA sequences encoding for *human* pro-opiocortin. Comparison of the DNA sequence of such clones with the cDNA sequence for the bovine hormone should provide information about the extent of interspecies variation within the cryptic part of the molecule and may yield data relating the ACTH and β-LPH coding sequences on the human chromosome to

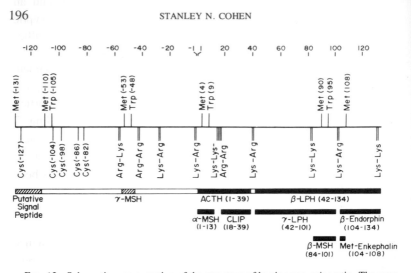

FIG. 12. Schematic representation of the structure of bovine pro-opiocortin. The numbering of the amino acid residues is as described in Nakanishi *et al.* (1979). Filled bars represent the region for which the amino acid sequence was known independently, and the open and hatched bars represent the regions for which the amino acid sequence was predicted from the nucleotide sequence of the pro-opiocortin mRNA. The Lys-Arg residues at sites of possible processing of the precursor protein into its peptide components, the positions of amino acids relevant to the MSH-like subunits of the protein, and certain other structural features are indicated. From Nakanishi *et al.* (1979).

the genes encoding calcitonin and other hormones. It should also provide insight into the relationship of intervening sequences to the protein-encoding sequences comprising the various structural and functional domains of the precursor protein.

C. *Expression of Mammalian DNA Sequences in Bacterial Cells*

Since the initial propagation of eukaryotic DNA in bacteria (Morrow *et al.,* 1974), several systems have been used to study expression in *E. coli* of DNA derived from higher organisms. Our early studies with cloned *X. laevis* ribosomal DNA genes indicated that the nucleotide sequences of the eukaryotic DNA could be faithfully transcribed in *E. coli* (Morrow *et al.,* 1974). However, these experiments did not show whether such RNA synthesis resulted from read-through transcription from the bacterial component of the chimeric plasmids or from initiation of RNA synthesis on the eukaryotic DNA fragment. Subsequent investigations with plasmids containing the intact mouse mitochondrial DNA genome (Chang *et al.*, 1975) indicated that the transcriptional and translational control signals located on at least this eukaryotic cell-derived DNA did not function in bacteria to yield bona fide eukaryotic proteins.

Biological activity of genes from the lower eukaryotes *Saccharomyces cerevisiae* and *Neurospora crassa* was demonstrated subsequently using phenotypic selection for functions that complement mutationally inactivated homologous bacterial genes (Struhl *et al.*, 1976; Ratzkin and Carbon, 1977; Vapnek *et al.*, 1977). Later, immunological activity with antibody against the human hormones somatostatin and insulin was shown for peptide fragments cleaved *in vitro* from hybrid "fusion" proteins encoded in part by bacterial DNA and in part by chemically synthesized somatostatin or insulin DNA sequences (Itakura *et al.*, 1977; Goeddel *et al.*, 1978). In another instance, a hybrid protein containing the amino acids of proinsulin was shown to be made by bacteria that carry a double-stranded cDNA transcript of preproinsulin mRNA (Villa-Kamaroff *et al.*, 1978). Antigenic determinants for the bacterial β-lactamase and the eukaryotic gene product were detected on fused peptides and on the peptide fragments cleaved from such fused proteins; however, biological activity of the mammalian components of such immunologically reactive hybrid proteins was not shown.

Our approach to the study of mammalian gene expression in bacteria was to generate a heterogeneous population of clones carrying a DNA sequence that encodes for a selectable mammalian gene product, and then to select directly those bacteria in the population that phenotypically express the genetic sequence (Chang *et al.*, 1978). The mammalian enzyme dihydrofolate reductase (DHFR), which catalyzes the conversion of dihydrofolic acid to tetrahydrofolic acid, was especially suitable for this purpose: the mammalian DHFR has a much lower affinity for the antimetabolic drug, trimethoprim (Tp) than does the corresponding bacterial enzyme (Burchall and Hitching, 1965). Thus, bacterial cells that biologically express mammalian DHFR activity are resistant to the levels of Tp that ordinarily would inhibit their growth. The primary DNA sequence of plasmids that showed phenotypic expression of the mammalian gene product in bacteria could then be analyzed to determine the specific sequence arrangement that accomplishes expression. Moreover, differences in the level of expression in various clones could be correlated with the primary sequence of the clone.

198   STANLEY N. COHEN

Figure 13 summarizes the experimental plan used in these investigations. Partially purified mRNA containing DHFR sequences from mouse cells resistant to the DHFR-inhibiting drug methotrexate (Buell *et al.*, 1978) served as a template for the preparation of double-stranded cDNA using reverse transcriptase and DNA polymerase I. As in the case of the experiments described above for the ACTH-β-LPH mRNA, homopolymeric dC "tails" were added to the unfractionated cDNA by terminal deoxynucleotidyltransferase and homopolymeric dG tails were added to the termini generated by *Pst*I endonuclease cleavage within the β-lactamase of the pBR322 plasmid. Constructed plasmids were introduced into *E. coli* by transformation, and plasmid DNA isolated from Tp-resistant colonies was isolated and subjected to fragmentation analysis by various restriction endonculeases and to DNA sequence analysis.

As shown in Table III, the nucleotide sequence in the region of the vector-cDNA junction nearest the 5' end of the DHFR mRNA was

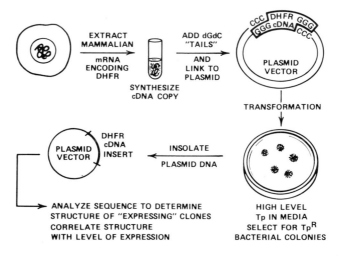

Fɪɢ. 13. Strategy used to obtain phenotypic expression of a mammalian genetic sequence in *Escherichia coli*. A heterogeneous population of clones carrying a DNA sequence that encodes for a mammalian gene product, dihydrofolate reductase (DHFR), that produces a selectable trait [high level trimethoprim resistance (Tp^R)] was generated, and those bacteria in the population that phenotypically expressed the gene were selected directly.

TABLE III
Properties of pDHFR Chimeric Plasmids[a]

Plasmid	Nucleotide sequence[b]	Orientation of cDNA	Base pairs (bp) from A of ATG to center of 5-bp sequence	DHFR specific activity (units/mg protein)	MIC of Tp (μg/ml)	Relative DHFR activity	Reading frame of DHFR
pDHFR 7	Ala −13 −1 +1 TGCAG|GGGGGGGGGGGATGGTT	A	12	2	>1000	1	+1
pDHFR 12	−28 TGC AG|GGGGGGGGGGGGGAGCTGCCATCATGGTT	A	10	4.2	>1000	2.1	+1
pDHRF 13	−22 TGCAG|GGGGGGGGGGGGCCATCATGGTT	A	11	2	>1000	1	+1
pDHFR 26	−102 −38 TGCAG|G GTGA AGGCTGGTAGGATTTTATCCCGCTGCCATCATGGTT	A	20	ND	75	0.075	+2
pDHFR 27	−13 TGCAG|GGGGGGGGGGGGATGGTT	A	12	—	250	0.250	+1
pDHFR 28	−27 TGCAG|GGGGGGGGGGGGGGGCTGCCATCATGGTT	A	11	ND	150	0.150	+2
pDHFR 29	TGC AG|GGGGGGGGGGGTCATGGTT	A	5 or 15	1	500	0.500	+1
pDHFR 23	−39 TGCAG|GGGGGG						

[a] DHFR, dihydrofolate reductase; MIC, mean inhibitory concentration; Tp, trimethoprim; ND, not detected.

[b] The black dots below nucleotides indicate homology with the nucleotide sequence at the 3′-OH terminus of 16 S rRNA (i.e., 3′-AUUCCUCCACUAGG-5′).

correlated with other properties of pDHFR chimeric plasmids, including the level of DHFR expression. In each instance, bacteria that expressed DHFR activity phenotypically were found to synthesize a protein that has the enzymic properties, immunological reactivity, and molecular size of the mouse DHFR (Chang *et al.*, 1978; Erlich *et al.*, 1979). Moreover, the DHFR cDNA segment in such clones was found to be in a different translational reading frame from the bacterial β-lactamase gene into which it had been inserted, suggesting that the biologically active DHFR being produced was not made as part of a fused protein.

Together, these findings implied that initiation of translation was occurring at the translational start codon (AUG) normally used for the synthesis of mouse DHFR in its original host. Thus, initiation of a structurally discrete and biologically functional eukaryotic peptide was occurring in bacteria on a fused (polycistronic) mRNA molecule. One structural feature important in accomplishing such translation "re-starts" is the presence of a ribosomal binding site at an appropriate distance from the translational start codon; the efficiency of expression was found to be strongly influenced by the extent of homology of this region of the mRNA with the $3'$-OH end of 16 S ribosomal RNA (Shine and Dalgarno, 1974; Steitz and Steege, 1977; Steege, 1977), as well as the distance between the AUG codon and the ribosomal binding sequence of the mRNA. The sequence configuration found to accomplish phenotypic expression of the mouse DHFR genetic sequence in bacterial cells has been used for expression of other eukaryotic proteins in *E. coli,* and it seems to be generally applicable to the production of a wide variety of structurally discrete biologically functional heterospecific proteins in bacterial cells.

ACKNOWLEDGMENTS

It is a pleasure to acknowledge the collaboration of students, postdoctoral research fellows, and research assistants in my own laboratory, and the collaboration of additional colleagues in other laboratories at Stanford and elsewhere in the studies I have reported here. Special acknowledgment is due to A. C. Y. Chang for her continuing involvement in much of this work. The studies were supported by funds from the National Institutes of Health, the American Cancer Society, and the National Science Foundation.

REFERENCES

Agarwal, K. L., Buchi, H., Caruthers, M. H., Gupta, N. Khorana, H. G., Kleppe, K., Kumar, A., Ohtsuka, E., Rajbhandary, U. L., Van De Sande, J. H., Sgaramella, V., Weber, H., and Yamada, T. (1970). *Nature (London)* 277, 27.

Arber, W. (1965). *Annu. Rev. Microbiol.* **19,** 365.

Armstrong, K. A., Hershfield, V., and Helinski, D. R. (1977). *Science* **196,** 172.

Avery, O. T., Macleod, C. M., and McCarthy, M. (1944). *J. Exp. Med.* **79,** 137.

Berg, P., Baltimore, D., Brenner, S., Roblin, R. O., III, and Singer, M. F. (1975). *Proc. Natl. Acad. Sci. U.S.A.* **72,** 1981.

Blattner, F. R., Williams, B. G., Blechl, A. E., Denniston-Thompson, K., Faber, H. E., Furlong, L., Grunwald, D. J., Kiefer, D. O., Moore, D. D., Schumm, J. W., Sheldon, E. L., and Smithies, O. (1977). *Science* **196,** 161.

Blobel, A., and Dobberstein, B. (1975a). *J. Cell Biol.* **67,** 835.

Blobel, A., and Dobberstein, B. (1975b). *J. Cell Biol.* **67,** 852.

Bolivar, F., Rodriquez, R. L., Greene, P. J., Betlach, M. C., Heyneker, H. L., and Boyer, H. (1977). *Gene* **2,** 95.

Brutlag, D., Fry, K., Nelson, T., and Hung, P. (1977). *Cell* **10,** 509.

Buell, G. N., Wickens, M. P., Payvar, F., and Schimke, R. T. (1978). *J. Biol. Chem.* **253,** 2471.

Burchall, J. J., and Hitching, G. H. (1965). *Mol. Pharmacol.* **1,** 126.

Cabello, F., Timmis, K., and Cohen, S. N. (1976). *Nature (London)* **259,** 285.

Chakrabarty, A. M., Friello, D. A., and Bopp, L. H. (1978). *Proc. Natl. Acad. Sci. U.S.A.* **75,** 3109.

Chang, A. C. Y., and Cohen, S. N. (1974). *Proc. Natl. Acad. Sci. U.S.A.* **71,** 1030.

Chang, A. C. Y., and Cohen, S. N. (1978). *J. Bacteriol.* **134,** 1141.

Chang, A. C. Y., Lansman, R. A., Clayton, D. A., and Cohen, S. N. (1975). *Cell* **6,** 231.

Chang, A. C. Y., Nunberg, J. N., Kaufman, R. J., Erlich, H. A., Schimke, R. T., and Cohen, S. N. (1978). *Nature (London)* **275,** 617.

Chang, A. C. Y., Cohen, S. N., Nakanishi, S., Inoue, A., Kita, T., Nakamura, M., and Numa, S. (1979). *In* "Peptides. Structure and Biological Function. Proceedings of the Sixth American Peptide Symposium" (E. Gross and J. Meienhofer, eds.), p. 957. Pierce Chemical Co., Rockford, Illinois.

Chang, S., and Cohen, S. N. (1977). *Proc. Natl. Acad. Sci. U.S.A.* **74,** 4811.

Cohen, S. N. (1976). *Nature (London)* **263,** 731.

Cohen, S. N., and Chang, A. C. Y. (1973). *Proc. Natl. Acad. Sci. U.S.A.* **70,** 1293.

Cohen, S. N., and Chang, A. C. Y. (1977). *J. Bacteriol.* **132,** 734.

Cohen, S. N., and Miller, C. A. (1968). *Nature (London)* **224,** 1273.

Cohen, S. N., Chang, A. C. Y., and Hsu, L. (1972). *Proc. Natl. Acad. Sci. U.S.A.* **69,** 2110.

Cohen, S. N., Chang, A. C. Y., Boyer, H. W., and Helling, R. B. (1973). *Proc. Natl. Acad. Sci. U.S.A.* **70,** 3240.

Cohen, S. N., Cabello, F., Chang, A. C. Y., and Timmis, K. (1977). *In* "Tenth Miles International Symposium on Recombinant Molecules: Impact on Science and Society (R. F. Beers, Jr., and E. G. Bassett, eds.), p. 91. Raven, New York.

Cohen, S. N., Brevet, J., Cabello, F., Chang, A. C. Y., Chou, J., Kopecko, D. J., Kretschmer, P. J., Nisen, P., and Timmis, K. (1978). *In* "Microbiology (D. Schlessenger, ed.), p. 217. Am. Soc. Microbiol., Washington, D.C.

Cozzarelli, N. R., Melechen, N. E., Jovin, T. M., and Kornberg, A. (1967). *Biochem. Biophys. Res. Commun.* **28,** 578.

Danna, K. J., and Nathans, D. (1971). *Proc. Natl. Acad. Sci. U.S.A.* **68,** 2913.

Davis, R. W., and Davidson, N. (1968). *Proc. Natl. Acad. Sci. U.S.A.* **60,** 243.

Dawid, I. B., Brown, D. D., and Reeder, R. H. (1970). *J. Mol. Biol.* **51,** 341.

Efstratiadis, A., Kafatos, F. C., Maxam, A. M., and Maniatis, T. (1976). *Cell* **7,** 279.

Erlich, H. A., Levinson, J. R., Cohen, S. N., and McDevitt, H. O. (1979). *J. Biol. Chem.* **254,** 12240.

Gefter, M. L., Becker, A., and Hurwitz, J. (1967). *Proc. Natl. Acad. Sci. U.S.A.* **58,** 240.

Gellert, M. (1967). *Proc. Natl. Acad. Sci. U.S.A.* **57,** 148.

Goeddel, D. V., Kleid, D. G., Bolivar, F., Heyneker, H. L., Yansura, D. G., Crea, R., Hirose, T., Kraszewski, A., Itakura, K., and Riggs, A. D. (1979). *Proc. Natl. Acad. Sci. U.S.A.* **76,** 106.

Grunstein, M., and Hogness, D. S. (1975). *Proc. Natl. Acad. Sci. U.S.A.* **72,** 3961.

Helling, R. B., Goodman, H. M., and Boyer, H. W. (1974). *J. Virol.* **14,** 1235.

Herrmann, R., Neugebauer, K., Schaller, H., and Zentgraf, H. (1978). *In* "Single-stranded DNA Phages" (D. T. Denhardt, D. N. Dressler, and D. S. Ray, eds.), p. 473. Cold Spring Harbor Laboratory, Cold Spring Harbor, New York.

Hershfield, V., Boyer, H. W., Yanofsky, C., Lovett, M. A., and Helinski, D. R. (1974). *Proc. Natl. Acad. Sci. U.S.A.* **71,** 3455.

Heyneker, H. L., Shine, J., Goodman, H. M., Boyer, H. W., Rosenberg, J., Dickerson, R. E., Narang, S. A., Itakura, K., Lin, S., and Riggs, A. D. (1976). *Nature (London)* **263,** 748.

Hohn, B., and Murray, K. (1977). *Proc. Natl. Acad. Sci. U.S.A.* **74,** 3259.

Hotchkiss, R. D., and Gabor, M. (1970). *Annu. Rev. Genet.* **4,** 193.

Itakura, K., Hirose, T., Crea, R., and Riggs, A. D. (1977). *Science* **198,** 1056.

Jackson, D. A. Symons, R. H., and Berg, P. (1972). *Proc. Natl. Acad. Sci. U.S.A.* **69,** 2904.

Jensen, R. H., Wodzinski, R. J., and Rogoff, M. H. (1971). *Biochem. Biophys. Res. Commun.* **43,** 384.

Kedes, L. H., Chang, A. C. Y., Housman, D., and Cohen, S. N. (1975). *Nature (London)* **255,** 533.

Kelly, T. J., Jr., and Smith, H. O. (1970). *J. Mol. Biol.* **51,** 393.

Keutmann, H. T., Eipper, B. A., and Mains, R. E. (1979). *J. Biol. Chem.* **254,** 9204.

Khorana, H. G. (1968). *Pure Appl. Chem.* **17,** 349.

Kita, T., Inoue, A., Nakanishi, S., and Numa, S. (1979). *Eur. J. Biochem.* **93,** 213.

Kornberg, A. (1974). "DNA Synthesis." Freeman, San Francisco, California.

Kretschmer, P. J., Chang, A. C. Y., and Cohen, S. N. (1975). *J. Bacteriol.* **124,** 225.

Leder, P., Tiemeier, D., and Enquist, L. (1977). *Science* **196,** 175.

Li, C. H., and Chung, D. (1976). *Proc. Natl. Acad. Sci. U.S.A.* **73,** 1145.

Li, C. H., Tan, L., and Chung, D. (1977). *Biochem. Biophys. Res. Commun.* **77,** 1088.

Ling, N., Burgus, R., and Guillemin, R. (1976). *Proc. Natl. Acad. Sci. U.S.A.* **73,** 3942.

Lobban, P. E., and Kaiser, A. D. (1973). *J. Mol. Biol.* **78,** 453.

Lovett, M. A., and Helinski, D. R. (1976). *J. Bacteriol.* **127,** 982.

Mandel, M., and Higa, A. (1970). *J. Mol. Biol.* **53,** 159.

Marians, K. J., Wu, R., Stawinski, J., Hozumi, T., and Narang, S. A. (1976). *Nature (London)* **263**, 744.

Maxam, A. M., and Gilbert, W. (1977). *Proc. Natl. Acad. Sci. U.S.A.* **74**, 560.

Meacock, P. A., and Cohen, S. N. (1979). *Mol. Gen. Genet.* **174**, 135.

Mertz, J., and Davis, R. W. (1972). *Proc. Natl. Acad. Sci. U.S.A.* **69**, 3370.

Meselson, M., and Yuan, R. (1968). *Nature (London)* **217**, 1110.

Messing, J., Gronenborn, B., Muller-Hill, B., and Hofschneider, P. H. (1977). *Proc. Natl. Acad. Sci. U.S.A.* **74**, 3642.

Morrow, J. F., Cohen, S. N., Chang, A. C. Y., Boyer, H. W., Goodman, H. M., and Helling, R. B. (1974). *Proc. Natl. Acad. Sci. U.S.A.* **71**, 1743.

Mukai, T., Matsubara, K., and Takagi, Y. (1976). *Mol. Gen. Genet.* **146**, 269.

Murray, N. E., and Murray, L. (1974). *Nature (London)* **251**, 476.

Nakamura, M., Nakanishi, S., Sueoka, S., Imura, H., and Numa, S. (1978). *Eur. J. Biochem.* **86**, 61.

Nakamura, M., Inoue, A., Nakanishi, S., and Numa, S. (1979). *FEBS Lett.* **105**, 357.

Nakanishi, S., Kita, T., Taii, S., Imura, H., and Numa, S. (1977). *Proc. Natl. Acad. Sci. U.S.A.* **74**, 3283.

Nakanishi, S., Inoue, A., Kita, T., Numa, S., Chang, A. C. Y., Cohen, S. N., Nunberg, J., and Schimke, R. T. (1978). *Proc. Natl. Acad. Sci. U.S.A.* **75**, 6021.

Nakanishi, S., Inoue, A., Kita, T., Nakamura, M., Chang, A. C. Y., Cohen, S. N., and Numa, S. (1979). *Nature (London)* **278**, 423.

Nathans, D., and Danna, K. J. (1972). *J. Mol. Biol.* **64**, 515.

Nathans, D., and Smith, H. O. (1975). *Annu. Rev. Biochem.* **4**, 273.

Olivera, B. M., and Lehman, I. R. (1967). *Proc. Natl. Acad. Sci. U.S.A.* **57**, 1426.

Rabbits, T. H. (1976). *Nature (London)* **260**, 221.

Rambach, A., and Tiollais, P. (1974). *Proc. Natl. Acad. Sci. U.S.A.* **71**, 3927.

Ratzkin, G., and Carbon, J. (1977). *Proc. Natl. Acad. Sci. U.S.A.* **74**, 487.

Roberts, R. J. (1976). *Crit. Rev. Biochem.* **4**, 123.

Roberts, R. J. (1977). *In* "Tenth Miles International Symposium on Recombinant Molecules: Impact on Science and Society (R. F. Beers, Jr., and E. G. Bassett, eds.), p. 21. Raven, New York.

Ruogeon, F., Kourilsky, P., and Mach, B. (1975). *Nucl. Acids Res.* **2**, 2365.

Scheller, R. H., Dickerson, R. E., Boyer, H. W., Riggs, A. D., and Itakura, K. (1977). *Science* **196**, 177.

Scott, A. P., Ratcliffe, J. G., Rees, L. H., Landon, J., Bennett, H. P. J., Lowry, P. J., and McMartin, C. (1973). *Nature (London), New Biol.* **244**, 65.

Sgaramella, V. (1972). *Proc. Natl. Acad. Sci. U.S.A.* **69**, 3348.

Sgaramella, V., van de Sande, J. H., and Khorana, H. G. (1970). *Proc. Natl. Acad. Sci. U.S.A.* **67**, 1468.

Sgaramella, V., Bursztyn-Pettegrew, H., and Ehrlich, S. D. (1977). *In* "Tenth Miles International Symposium on Recombinant Molecules: Impact on Science and Society (R. F. Beers, Jr., and E. G. Bassett, eds.), p. 57. Raven, New York.

Shine, J., and Dalgarno, L. (1974). *Proc. Natl. Acad. Sci. U.S.A.* **71**, 1342.

Silver, R. P., and Cohen, S. N. (1972). *J. Bacteriol.* **110**, 1082.

Smith, H. O., and Wilcox, K. W. (1970). *J. Mol. Biol.* **51,** 371.

Steege, D. A. (1977). *Proc. Natl. Acad. Sci. U.S.A.* **74,** 4163.

Steitz, J. A., and Steege, D. A. (1977). *J. Mol. Biol.* **114,** 545.

Streek, R. E., and Hobom, G. (1975). *Eur. J. Biochem.* **57,** 595.

Struhl, K., Cameron, J. R., and Davis, R. W. (1976). *Proc. Natl. Acad. Sci. U.S.A.* **73,** 1471.

Takano, T., Watanabe, T., and Fukasawa, T. (1968a). *Virology* **34,** 290.

Takano, T., Watanabe, T., and Fukasawa, T. (1968b). *Biochem. Biophys. Res. Commun.* **25,** 192.

Taylor, D. P., and Cohen, S. N. (1979). *J. Bacteriol.* **137,** 92.

Thomas, M., Cameron, J. R., and Davis, R. W. (1974). *Proc. Natl. Acad. Sci. U.S.A.* **71,** 4579.

Timmis, K., Cabello, F., and Cohen, S. N. (1974). *Proc. Natl. Acad. Sci. U.S.A.* **71,** 4556.

Timmis, K., Cabello, F., and Cohen, S. N. (1975). *Proc. Natl. Acad. Sci. U.S.A.* **72,** 2242.

Timmis, K., Cabello, F., and Cohen, S. N. (1978a). *Mol. Gen. Genet.* **162,** 121.

Timmis, K. N., Cabello, F., Andres, I., Nordheim, A., Burkhardt, H. J., and Cohen, S. N. (1978b). *Mol. Gen. Genet.* **167,** 11.

Timmis, K. N., Cohen, S. N., and Cabello, F. C. (1978c). *In*: "Progress in Molecular and Subcellular Biology" (F. E. Hahn, ed.), Vol. 6, p. 1. Springer-Verlag, Berlin and New York.

Vapnek, D., Hautala, J. A., Jacobson, J. W., Giles, N. H., and Kushner, S. (1977). *Proc. Natl. Acad. Sci. U.S.A.* **74,** 3508.

Villa-Kamaroff, L., Efstratiadis, A., Broome, S., Lomedico, P., Tizard, R., Naber, S. P., Chick, W. L., and Gilbert, W. (1978). *Proc. Natl. Acad. Sci. U.S.A.* **75,** 3727.

Wade, N. (1974). *Science* **195,** 332.

Weiss, B., and Richardson, C. C. (1967). *Proc. Natl. Acad. Sci. U.S.A.* **57,** 1021.

Wensink, P. C., and Brown, D. D. (1971). *J. Mol. Biol.* **60,** 235.

Wensink, P. C., Finnegan, D. J., Donelson, J. E., and Hogness, D. S. (1974). *Cell* **3,** 315.

Westmoreland, B. C., Szybalski, W., and Ris, H. (1969). *Science* **163,** 1343.

Wigler, M., Silverstein, S., Lee, L-S., Pellicer, A., Ching, Y.-C., and Axel, R. (1977). *Cell* **11,** 223.

FORMER OFFICERS OF THE HARVEY SOCIETY

1905–1906

President: GRAHAM LUSK
Vice-President: SIMON FLEXNER
Treasurer: FREDERIC S. LEE
Secretary: GEORGE B. WALLACE

Council:
  C. A. HERTER
  S. J. MELTZER
  EDWARD K. DUNHAM

1906–1907

President: GRAHAM LUSK
Vice-President: SIMON FLEXNER
Treasurer: FREDERIC S. LEE
Secretary: GEORGE B. WALLACE

Council:
  C. A. HERTER
  S. J. MELTZER
  JAMES EWING

1907–1908

President: GRAHAM LUSK
Vice-President: JAMES EWING
Treasurer: EDWARD K. DUNHAM
Secretary: GEORGE B. WALLACE

Council:
  SIMON FLEXNER
  THEO. C. JANEWAY
  PHILIP H. HISS, JR.

1908–1909

President: JAMES EWING
Vice-President: SIMON FLEXNER
Treasurer: EDWARD K. DUNHAM
Secretary: FRANCIS C. WOOD

Council:
  GRAHAM LUSK
  S. J. MELTZER
  ADOLPH MEYER

1909–1910*

President: JAMES EWING
Vice-President: THEO. C. JANEWAY
Treasurer: EDWARD K. DUNHAM
Secretary: FRANCIS C. WOOD

Council:
  GRAHAM LUSK
  S. J. MELTZER
  W. J. GIES

1910–1911

President: SIMON FLEXNER
Vice-President: JOHN HOWLAND
Treasurer: EDWARD K. DUNHAM
Secretary: HAVEN EMERSON

Council:
  GRAHAM LUSK
  S. J. MELTZER
  JAMES EWING

---

* At the Annual Meeting of May 18, 1909, these officers were elected. In publishing the 1909–1910 volume their names were omitted, possibly because in that volume the custom of publishing the names of the incumbents of the current year was changed to publishing the names of the officers selected for the ensuing year.

1911–1912

President: S. J. MELTZER
Vice-President: FREDERIC S. LEE
Treasurer: EDWARD K. DUNHAM
Secretary: HAVEN EMERSON

Council:
  GRAHAM LUSK
  JAMES EWING
  SIMON FLEXNER

1912–1913

President: FREDERIC S. LEE
Vice-President: WM. H. PARK
Treasurer: EDWARD K. DUNHAM
Secretary: HAVEN EMERSON

Council:
  GRAHAM LUSK
  S. J. MELTZER
  WM. G. MACCALLUM

1913–1914

President: FREDERIC S. LEE
Vice-President: WM. G. MACCALLUM
Treasurer: EDWARD K. DUNHAM
Secretary: AUGUSTUS B. WADSWORTH

Council:
  GRAHAM LUSK
  WM. H. PARK
  GEORGE B. WALLACE

1914–1915

President: WM. G. MACCALLUM
Vice-President: RUFUS I. COLE
Treasurer: EDWARD K. DUNHAM
Secretary: JOHN A. MANDEL

Council:
  GRAHAM LUSK
  FREDERIC S. LEE
  W. T. LONGCOPE

1915–1916

President: GEORGE B. WALLACE*
Treasurer: EDWARD K. DUNHAM
Secretary: ROBERT A. LAMBERT

Council:
  GRAHAM LUSK
  RUFUS I. COLE
  NELLIS B. FOSTER

1916–1917

President: GEORGE B. WALLACE
Vice-President: RUFUS I. COLE
Treasurer: EDWARD K. DUNHAM
Secretary: ROBERT A. LAMBERT

Council:
  GRAHAM LUSK†
  W. T. LONGCOPE
  S. R. BENEDICT
  HANS ZINSSER

1917–1918

President: EDWARD K. DUNHAM
Vice-President: RUFUS I. COLE
Treasurer: F. H. PIKE
Secretary: A. M. PAPPENHEIMER

Council:
  GRAHAM LUSK
  GEORGE B. WALLACE
  FREDERIC S. LEE
  PEYTON ROUS

* Dr. William G. MacCallum resigned after election. On Doctor Lusk's motion Doctor George B. Wallace was made President—no Vice-President was appointed.
† Doctor Lusk was made Honorary permanent Counsellor.

1918–1919

President: GRAHAM LUSK
Vice-President: RUFUS I. COLE
Treasurer: F. H. PIKE
Secretary: K. M. VOGEL

Council:
GRAHAM LUSK
JAMES W. JOBLING
FREDERIC S. LEE
JOHN AUER

1919–1920

President: WARFIELD T. LONGCOPE
Vice-President: S. R. BENEDICT
Treasurer: F. H. PIKE
Secretary: K. M. VOGEL

Council:
GRAHAM LUSK
HANS ZINSSER
FREDERIC S. LEE
GEORGE B. WALLACE

1920–1921*

President: WARFIELD T. LONGCOPE
Vice-President: S. R. BENEDICT
Treasurer: A. M. PAPPENHEIMER
Secretary: HOMER F. SWIFT

Council:
GRAHAM LUSK
FREDERIC S. LEE
HANS ZINSSER
GEORGE B. WALLACE

1921–1922

President: RUFUS I. COLE
Vice-President: S. R. BENEDICT
Treasurer: A. M. PAPPENHEIMER
Secretary: HOMER F. SWIFT

Council:
GRAHAM LUSK
HANS ZINSSER
H. C. JACKSON
W. T. LONGCOPE

1922–1923

President: RUFUS I. COLE
Vice-President: HANS ZINSSER
Treasurer: CHARLES C. LIEB
Secretary: HOMER F. SWIFT

Council:
GRAHAM LUSK
W. T. LONGCOPE
H. C. JACKSON
S. R. BENEDICT

1923–1924

President: EUGENE F. DuBOIS
Vice-President: HOMER F. SWIFT
Treasurer: CHARLES C. LIEB
Secretary: GEORGE M. MACKENZIE

Council:
GRAHAM LUSK
ALPHONSE R. DOCHEZ
DAVID MARINE
PEYTON ROUS

---

* These officers were elected at the Annual Meeting of May 21, 1920 but were
omitted in the publication of the 1919–1920 volume.

1924–1925

President: EUGENE F. DUBOIS
Vice-President: PEYTON ROUS
Treasurer: CHARLES C. LIEB
Secretary: GEORGE M. MACKENZIE

Council:
GRAHAM LUSK
RUFUS COLE
HAVEN EMERSON
WM. H. PARK

1925–1926

President: HOMER F. SWIFT
Vice-President: H. B. WILLIAMS
Treasurer: HAVEN EMERSON
Secretary: GEORGE M. MACKENZIE

Council:
GRAHAM LUSK
EUGENE F. DUBOIS
WALTER W. PALMER
H. D. SENIOR

1926–1927

President: WALTER W. PALMER
Vice-President: WM. H. PARK
Treasurer: HAVEN EMERSON
Secretary: GEORGE M. MACKENZIE

Council:
GRAHAM LUSK
HOMER F. SWIFT
A. R. DOCHEZ
ROBERT CHAMBERS

1927–1928

President: DONALD D. VAN SLYKE
Vice-President: JAMES W. JOBLING
Treasurer: HAVEN EMERSON
Secretary: CARL A. L. BINGER

Council:
GRAHAM LUSK
RUSSEL L. CECIL
WARD J. MACNEAL
DAVID MARINE

1928–1929

President: PEYTON ROUS
Vice-President: HORATIO B. WILLIAMS
Treasurer: HAVEN EMERSON
Secretary: PHILIP D. MCMASTER

Council:
GRAHAM LUSK
ROBERT CHAMBERS
ALFRED F. HESS
H. D. SENIOR

1929–1930

President: G. CANBY ROBINSON
Vice-President: ALFRED F. HESS
Treasurer: HAVEN EMERSON
Secretary: DAYTON J. EDWARDS

Council:
GRAHAM LUSK
ALFRED E. COHN
A. M. PAPPENHEIMER
H. D. SENIOR

1930–1931

President: ALFRED E. COHN
Vice-President: J. G. HOPKINS
Treasurer: HAVEN EMERSON
Secretary: DAYTON J. EDWARDS

Council
GRAHAM LUSK
O. T. AVERY
A. M. PAPPENHEIMER
S. R. DETWILER

1931–1932

President: J. W. JOBLING
Vice-President: HOMER W. SMITH
Treasurer: HAVEN EMERSON
Secretary: DAYTON J. EDWARDS

Council:
GRAHAM LUSK
S. R. DETWILER
THOMAS M. RIVERS
RANDOLPH WEST

1932–1933

President: ALFRED F. HESS
Vice-President: HAVEN EMERSON
Treasurer: THOMAS M. RIVERS
Secretary: EDGAR STILLMAN

Council:
GRAHAM LUSK
HANS T. CLARKE
WALTER W. PALMER
HOMER W. SMITH

1933–1934

President: ALFRED HESS*
Vice-President: ROBERT K. CANNAN
Treasurer: THOMAS M. RIVERS
Secretary: EDGAR STILLMAN

Council:
STANLEY R. BENEDICT
ROBERT F. LOEB
WADE H. BROWN

1934–1935

President: ROBERT K. CANNAN
Vice-President: EUGENE L. OPIE
Treasurer: THOMAS M. RIVERS
Secretary: RANDOLPH H. WEST

Council:
HERBERT S. GASSER
B. S. OPPENHEIMER
PHILIP E. SMITH

1935–1936

President: ROBERT K. CANNAN
Vice-President: EUGENE L. OPIE
Treasurer: THOMAS M. RIVERS
Secretary: RANDOLPH H. WEST

Council:
ROBERT F. LOEB
HOMER W. SMITH
DAVID MARINE

1936–1937

President: EUGENE L. OPIE
Vice-President: PHILIP E. SMITH
Treasurer: THOMAS M. RIVERS
Secretary: McKEEN CATTELL

Council:
GEORGE B. WALLACE
MARTIN H. DAWSON
JAMES B. MURPHY

1937–1938

President: EUGENE L. OPIE
Vice-President: PHILIP E. SMITH
Treasurer: THOMAS M. RIVERS
Secretary: McKEEN CATTELL

Council:
GEORGE B. WALLACE
MARTIN H. DAWSON
HERBERT S. GASSER

---

*Dr. Hess died December 5, 1933.

1938–1939

President: PHILIP E. SMITH
Vice-President: HERBERT S. GASSER
Treasurer: KENNETH GOODNER
Secretary: MCKEEN CATTELL

Council:
  HANS T. CLARKE
  JAMES D. HARDY
  WILLIAM S. TILLETT

1939–1940

President: PHILIP E. SMITH
Vice-President: HERBERT S. GASSER
Treasurer: KENNETH GOODNER
Secretary: THOMAS FRANCIS, JR.

Council:
  HANS T. CLARKE
  N. CHANDLER FOOT
  WILLIAM S. TILLETT

1940–1941

President: HERBERT S. GASSER
Vice-President: HOMER W. SMITH
Treasurer: KENNETH GOODNER
Secretary: THOMAS FRANCIS, JR.

Council:
  N. CHANDLER FOOT
  VINCENT DU VIGNEAUD
  MICHAEL HEIDELBERGER

1941–1942

President: HERBERT S. GASSER
Vice-President: HOMER W. SMITH
Treasurer: KENNETH GOODNER
Secretary: JOSEPH C. HINSEY

Council:
  HARRY S. MUSTARD
  HAROLD G. WOLFF
  MICHAEL HEIDELBERGER

1942–1943

President: HANS T. CLARKE
Vice-President: THOMAS M. RIVERS
Treasurer: KENNETH GOODNER
Secretary: JOSEPH C. HINSEY

Council:
  ROBERT F. LOEB
  HAROLD G. WOLFF
  WILLIAM C. VON GLAHN

1943–1944

President: HANS T. CLARKE
Vice-President: THOMAS M. RIVERS
Treasurer: COLIN M. MACLEOD
Secretary: JOSEPH C. HINSEY

Council:
  ROBERT F. LOEB
  WILLIAM C. VON GLAHN
  WADE W. OLIVER

1944–1945

President: ROBERT CHAMBERS
Vice-President: VINCENT DU VIGNEAUD
Treasurer: COLIN M. MACLEOD
Secretary: JOSEPH C. HINSEY

Council:
  WADE W. OLIVER
  MICHAEL HEIDELBERGER
  PHILIP D. MCMASTER

1945–1946

President: ROBERT CHAMBERS
Vice-President: VINCENT DU VIGNEAUD
Treasurer: COLIN M. MACLEOD
Secretary: EDGAR G. MILLER, JR.

Council:
  PHILIP D. MCMASTER
  EARL T. ENGLE
  FRED W. STEWART

1946–1947

President: VINCENT DU VIGNEAUD
Vice-President: WADE W. OLIVER
Treasurer: COLIN M. MACLEOD
Secretary: EDGAR G. MILLER, JR.

Council:
    EARL T. ENGLE
    HAROLD G. WOLFF
    L. EMMETT HOLT, JR.

1947–1948

President: VINCENT DU VIGNEAUD
Vice-President: WADE W. OLIVER
Treasurer: HARRY B. VAN DYKE
Secretary: MACLYN MCCARTY

Council:
    PAUL KLEMPERER
    L. EMMETT HOLT, JR.
    HAROLD G. WOLFF

1948–1949

President: WADE W. OLIVER
Vice-President: ROBERT F. LOEB
Treasurer: HARRY B. VAN DYKE
Secretary: MACLYN MCCARTY

Council:
    PAUL KLEMPERER
    SEVERO OCHOA
    HAROLD L. TEMPLE

1949–1950

President: WADE W. OLIVER
Vice-President: ROBERT F. LOEB
Treasurer: JAMES B. HAMILTON
Secretary: MACLYN MCCARTY

Council:
    WILLIAM S. TILLETT
    SEVERO OCHOA
    HAROLD L. TEMPLE

1950–1951

President: ROBERT F. LOEB
Vice-President: MICHAEL HEIDELBERGER
Treasurer: JAMES B. HAMILTON
Secretary: LUDWIG W. EICHNA

Council:
    WILLIAM S. TILLETT
    A. M. PAPPENHEIMER, JR.
    DAVID P. BARR

1951–1952

President: RENÉ J. DUBOS
Vice-President: MICHAEL HEIDELBERGER
Treasurer: JAMES B. HAMILTON
Secretary: LUDWIG W. EICHNA

Council:
    DAVID P. BARR
    ROBERT F. PITTS
    A. M. PAPPENHEIMER, JR.

1952–1953

President: MICHAEL HEIDELBERGER
Vice-President: SEVERO OCHOA
Treasurer: CHANDLER McC. BROOKS
Secretary: HENRY D. LAUSON

Council:
    ROBERT F. PITTS
    JEAN OLIVER
    ALEXANDER B. GUTMAN

1953–1954

President: SEVERO OCHOA
Vice-President: DAVID P. BARR
Treasurer: CHANDLER McC. BROOKS
Secretary: HENRY D. LAUSON

Council:
    JEAN OLIVER
    ALEXANDER B. GUTMAN
    ROLLIN D. HOTCHKISS

1954–1955

President: DAVID P. BARR
Vice-President: COLIN M. MACLEOD
Treasurer: CHANDLER McC. BROOKS
Secretary: HENRY D. LAUSON

Council:
  ALEXANDER B. GUTMAN
  ROLLIN D. HOTCHKISS
  DAVID SHEMIN

1955–1956

President: COLIN M. MACLEOD
Vice-President: FRANK L. HORSFALL, JR.
Treasurer: CHANDLER McC. BROOKS
Secretary: RULON W. RAWSON

Council:
  ROLLIN D. HOTCHKISS
  DAVID SHEMIN
  ROBERT F. WATSON

1956–1957

President: Frank L. HORSFALL, JR.
Vice-President: WILLIAM S. TILLETT
Treasurer: CHANDLER McC. BROOKS
Secretary: RULON W. RAWSON

Council:
  DAVID SHEMIN
  ROBERT F. WATSON
  ABRAHAM WHITE

1957–1958

President: WILLIAM S. TILLETT
Vice-President: ROLLIN D. HOTCHKISS
Treasurer: CHANDLER McC. BROOKS
Secretary: H. SHERWOOD LAWRENCE

Council:
  ROBERT F. WATSON
  ABRAHAM WHITE
  JOHN V. TAGGART

1958–1959

President: ROLLIN D. HOTCHKISS
Vice-President: ANDRE COURNAND
Treasurer: CHANDLER McC. BROOKS
Secretary: H. SHERWOOD LAWRENCE

Council:
  ABRAHAM WHITE
  JOHN V. TAGGART
  WALSH McDERMOTT

1959–1960

President: ANDRE COURNAND
Vice-President: ROBERT F. PITTS
Treasurer: EDWARD J. HEHRE
Secretary: H. SHERWOOD LAWRENCE

Council:
  JOHN V. TAGGART
  WALSH McDERMOTT
  ROBERT F. FURCHGOTT

1960–1961

President: ROBERT F. PITTS
Vice-President: DICKINSON W. RICHARDS
Treasurer: EDWARD J. HEHRE
Secretary: ALEXANDER G. BEARN

Council:
  WALSH McDERMOTT
  ROBERT F. FURCHGOTT
  LUDWIG W. EICHNA

1961–1962

President: DICKINSON W. RICHARDS
Vice-President: PAUL WEISS
Treasurer: I. HERBERT SCHEINBERG
Secretary: ALEXANDER G. BEARN

Council:
  ROBERT F. FURCHGOTT
  LUDWIG W. EICHNA
  EFRAIM RACKER

1962–1963

President: PAUL WEISS
Vice-President: ALEXANDER B. GUTMAN
Treasurer: I. HERBERT SCHEINBERG
Secretary: ALEXANDER G. BEARN

Council:
LUDWIG W. EICHNA
EFRAIM RACKER
ROGER L. GREIF

1963–1964

President: ALEXANDER B. GUTMAN
Vice-President: EDWARD L. TATUM
Treasurer: SAUL J. FARBER
Secretary: ALEXANDER G. BEARN

Council:
EFRAIM RACKER
ROGER L. GREIF
IRVING M. LONDON

1964–1965

President: EDWARD TATUM
Vice-President: CHANDLER McC. BROOKS
Treasurer: SAUL J. FARBER
Secretary: RALPH L. ENGLE, JR.

Council:
ROGER L. GREIF
LEWIS THOMAS
IRVING M. LONDON

1965–1966

President: CHANDLER McC. BROOKS
Vice-President: ABRAHAM WHITE
Treasurer: SAUL J. FARBER
Secretary: RALPH L. ENGLE, JR.

Council:
IRVING M. LONDON
LEWIS THOMAS
GEORGE K. HIRST

1966–1967

President: ABRAHAM WHITE
Vice-President: RACHMIEL LEVINE
Treasurer: SAUL J. FARBER
Secretary: RALPH L. ENGLE. JR.

Council:
LEWIS THOMAS
GEORGE K. HIRST
DAVID NACHMANSOHN

1967–1968

President: RACHMIEL LEVINE
Vice-President: SAUL J. FARBER
Treasurer: PAUL A. MARKS
Secretary: RALPH L. ENGLE, JR.

Council:
GEORGE K. HIRST
DAVID NACHMANSOHN
MARTIN SONENBERG

1968–1969

President: SAUL J. FARBER
Vice-President: JOHN V. TAGGART
Treasurer: PAUL A. MARKS
Secretary: ELLIOTT F. OSSERMAN

Council:
DAVID NACHMANSOHN
MARTIN SONENBERG
HOWARD A. EDER

1969–1970

President: JOHN V. TAGGART
Vice-President: BERNARD L. HORECKER
Treasurer: PAUL A. MARKS
Secretary: ELLIOTT F. OSSERMAN

Council:
MARTIN SONENBERG
HOWARD A. EDER
SAUL J. FARBER

1970–1971

President: BERNARD L. HORECKER
Vice-President: MACLYN MCCARTY
Treasurer: EDWARD C. FRANKLIN
Secretary: ELLIOTT F. OSSERMAN

Council:
   HOWARD A. EDER
   SAUL J. FARBER
   SOLOMON A. BERSON

1971–1972

President: MACLYN MCCARTY
Vice-President: ALEXANDER G. BEARN
Treasurer: EDWARD C. FRANKLIN
Secretary: ELLIOTT F. OSSERMAN

Council:
   SAUL J. FARBER
   SOLOMON A. BERSON
   HARRY EAGLE

1972–1973

President: ALEXANDER G. BEARN
Vice-President: PAUL A. MARKS
Treasurer: EDWARD C. FRANKLIN
Secretary: JOHN ZABRISKIE

Council:
   HARRY EAGLE
   JERARD HURWITZ

1973–1974

President: PAUL A. MARKS
Vice-President: IGOR TAMM
Treasurer: EDWARD C. FRANKLIN
Secretary: JOHN B. ZABRISKIE

Council:
   HARRY EAGLE
   CHARLOTTE FRIEND
   JERARD HURWITZ

1974–1975

President: IGOR TAMM
Vice-President: GERALD M. EDELMAN
Treasurer: STEPHEN I. MORSE
Secretary: JOHN B. ZABRISKIE

Council:
   JERARD HURWITZ
   H. SHERWOOD LAWRENCE
   CHARLOTTE FRIEND

1975–1976

President: GERALD M. EDELMAN
Vice-President: ELVIN A. KABAT
Treasurer: STEPHEN I. MORSE
Secretary: JOHN B. ZABRISKIE

Council:
   PAUL A. MARKS
   H. SHERWOOD LAWRENCE
   CHARLOTTE FRIEND

1976–1977

President: ELVIN A. KABAT
Vice-President: FRED PLUM
Treasurer: STEPHEN I. MORSE
Secretary: DONALD M. MARCUS

Council:
   H. SHERWOOD LAWRENCE
   PAUL A. MARKS
   BRUCE CUNNINGHAM

1977–1978

President: FRED PLUM
Vice-President: CHARLOTTE FRIEND
Treasurer: STEPHEN I. MORSE
Secretary: DONALD M. MARCUS

Council:
PAUL A. MARKS
BRUCE CUNNINGHAM
VITTORIO DEFENDI

CUMULATIVE AUTHOR INDEX*

DR. JOHN J. ABEL, 1923–24 (d)
PROF. J. D. ADAMI, 1906–07 (d)
DR. ROGER ADAMS, 1941–42 (d)
DR. THOMAS ADDIS, 1927–28 (d)
DR. JULIUS ADLER, 1976–77 (h)
DR. E. D. ADRIAN, 1931–32 (h)
DR. FULLER ALBRIGHT, 1942–43 (h)
DR. FRANZ ALEXANDER, 1930–31 (h)
DR. FREDERICK ALLEN, 1916–17 (a)
DR. JOHN F. ANDERSON, 1908–09 (d)
DR. R. J. ANDERSON, 1939–40 (d)
DR. CHRISTOPHER H. ANDREWS, 1961–62 (h)
DR. CHRISTIAN B. ANFINSEN, 1965–66 (h)
PROF. G. V. ANREP, 1934–35 (h)
DR. CHARLES ARMSTRONG, 1940–41 (d)
DR. LUDWIG ASCHOFF, 1923–24 (d)
DR. LEON ASHER, 1922–23 (h)
DR. W. T. ASTBURY, 1950–51 (h)
DR. EDWIN ASTWOOD, 1944–45 (h)
DR. JOSEPH C. AUB, 1928–29 (d)
DR. K. FRANK AUSTEN, 1977–78 (h)
DR. JULIUS AXELROD, 1971–72 (h)
DR. E. R. BALDWIN, 1914–15 (d)
DR. DAVID BALTIMORE, 1974–75 (h)
PROF. JOSEPH BARCROFT, 1921–22 (d)
DR. PHILIP BARD, 1921–22 (h)
DR. H. A. BARKER, 1949–50 (h)
PROF. LEWELLYS BARKER, 1905–06 (d)
DR. JULIUS BAUER, 1932–33 (d)
PROF. WILLIAM M. BAYLISS, 1921–22 (d)
DR. FRANK BEACH, 1947–48 (h)
DR. GEORGE W. BEADLE, 1944–45 (h)
DR. ALEXANDER G. BEARN, 1974–75 (a)
DR. ALBERT BEHNKE, 1941–42 (h)
DR. BARUJ BENACERRAF, 1971–72 (a)

PROF. F. G. BENEDICT, 1906–07 (d)
DR. STANLEY BENEDICT, 1915–16 (d)
DR. D. BENNETT, 1978–79 (a)
PROF. R. R. BENSLEY, 1914–15 (d)
DR. SEYMOUR BENZER, 1960–61 (h)
DR. PAUL BERG, 1971–72 (h)
DR. MAX BERGMANN, 1935–36 (d)
DR. SUNE BERGSTRÖM, 1974–75 (h)
DR. ROBERT W. BERLINER, 1958–59 (h)
DR. SOLOMON A. BERSON, 1966–67 (a)
DR. MARCEL C. BESSIS, 1962–63 (h)
DR. C. H. BEST, 1940–41 (h)
DR. A. BIEDL, 1923–24 (h)
DR. RUPERT E. BILLINGHAM, 1966–67 (h)
DR. RICHARD J. BING, 1954–55 (a)
DR. JOHN J. BITTNER, 1946–47 (d)
PROF. FRANCIS G. BLAKE, 1934–35 (d)
DR. ALFRED BLALOCK, 1945–46 (d)
DR. KONRAD BLOCH, 1952–53 (a)
DR. WALTER R. BLOOR, 1923–24 (d)
DR. DAVID BODIAN, 1956–57 (h)
DR. WALTER F. BODMER, 1976–77 (h)
DR. JAMES BONNER, 1952–53 (h)
DR. JULES BORDET, 1920–21 (h)
DR. WILLIAM T. BOVIE, 1922–23 (d)
DR. EDWARD A. BOYSE, 1971–72, 1975–76 (h)
DR. STANLEY E. BRADLEY, 1959–60 (a)
DR. ARMIN C. BRAUN, 1960–61 (h)
DR. EUGENE BRAUNWALD, 1975–76 (h)
PROF. F. BREMER, (h)†
PROF. T. G. BRODIE, 1909–10 (d)
DR. DETLEV W. BRONK, 1933–34 (d)
DR. B. BROUWER, 1925–26 (d)
DR. MICHAEL S. BROWN, 1977–78 (h)
DR. WADE H. BROWN, 1928–29 (d)

---

*(h), honorary; (a), active; (d) deceased.

†Did not present lecture because of World War II.

217

Dr. John M. Buchanan, 1959–60 (h)
Dr. John Cairns, 1970–1971 (h)
Prof. A. Calmette, 1908–09 (d)
Dr. Melvin Calvin, 1950–51 (h)
Prof. Walter B. Cannon, 1911–12 (d)
Prof. A. J. Carlson, 1915–16 (d)
Dr. William B. Castle, 1934–35 (h)
Prof. W. E. Castle, 1910–11 (d)
Dr. I. L. Chaikoff, 1951–52 (d)
Dr. Robert Chambers, 1926–27 (d)
Dr. B. Chance, 1953–54 (h)
Dr. Charles V. Chapin, 1913–14 (d)
Dr. Erwin Chargaff, 1956–57 (h)
Dr. Merrill W. Chase, 1965–66 (a)
Dr. Alan M. Chesney, 1929–30 (d)
Prof. Hans Chiari, 1910–11 (d)
Dr. C.M. Child 1928–29 (d)
Prof. Russell H. Chittenden, 1911–12 (d)
Prof. Henry A. Christian, 1915–16 (d)
Dr. W. Mansfield Clark; 1933–34 (d)
Dr. Albert Claude, 1947–48 (a)
Dr. Samuel W. Clausen, 1942–43 (d)
Dr. Phillip P. Cohen, 1964–65 (h)
Dr. Stanley N. Cohen, 1978–79 (a)
Dr. Alfred E. Cohn, 1927–28 (d)
Dr. Edwin F. Cohn, 1927–28, 1938–39 (d)
Prof. Otto Cohnheim, 1909–10 (d)
Dr. Rufus Cole, 1913–14, 1929–30 (d)
Dr. J. B. Collip, 1925–26 (h)
Dr. Edgar L. Collis, 1926–27 (d)
Dr. Julius H. Comroe, Jr., 1952–53 (h)
Dr. James B. Conant, 1932–33 (h)
Prof. Edwin G. Conklin, 1912–13 (d)
Dr. Jerome W. Conn, 1966–67 (h)
Dr. Albert H. Coons, 1957–58 (d)
Dr. Carl F. Cori, 1927–28, 1945–46 (h)

Dr. Gerty T. Cori, 1952–53 (d)
Dr. George W. Corner, 1932–33 (h)
Dr. George C. Cotzias, 1972–73 (d)
Prof. W. T. Councilman, 1906–07 (d)
Dr. Andre Cournand, 1950–51 (a)
Dr. E. V. Cowdry, 1922–23 (d)
Dr. Lyman C. Craig, 1949–50 (d)
Dr. George Crile, 1907–08 (d)
Dr. S. J. Crowe, 1931–32 (d)
Dr. Harvey Cushing, 1910–11, 1932–33 (d)
Prof. Arthur R. Cushny, 1910–11 (d)
Sir Henry Dale, 1919–20, 1936–37 (h)
Dr. I. deBurgh Daly, 1935–36 (d)
Dr. C. H. Danforth, 1938–39 (d)
Dr. James F. Danielli, 1962–63 (h)
Dr. James E. Darnell, Jr., 1973–74 (a)
Dr. C. B. Davenport, 1908–09 (d)
Dr. Bernard D. Davis, 1954–55 (a)
Dr. Christian deDuve, 1963–64 (h)
Dr. Max Delbruck, 1945–46 (h)
Dr. F. D'Herelle, 1928–29 (d)
Dr. John H. Dingle, 1956–57 (d)
Dr. Frank J. Dixon, 1962–63 (h)
Dr. A. R. Dochez, 1924–25 (d)
Dr. E. C. Dodds, 1934–35 (h)
Dr. E. A. Doisy, 1933–34 (d)
Dr. Vincent P. Dole, 1971–72 (h)
Prof. Henry H. Donaldson, 1916–17 (d)
Dr. Paul Doty, 1958–59 (h)
Prof. Georges Dreyer, 1919–20 (d)
Dr. Cecil K. Drinker, 1937–38 (d)
Dr. J. C. Drummond, 1932–33 (d)
Dr. Lewis I. Dublin, 1922–23 (h)
Dr. Eugene F. DuBois, 1915–16, 1938–39, 1946–47 (d)
Dr. René J. Dubos, 1939–40 (a)
Dr. Renato Dulbecco, 1967–68 (h)
Dr. E. K. Dunham, 1917–19 (d)
Dr. L. C. Dunn, 1939–40 (d)

DR. VINCENT DU VIGNEAUD, 1942–43, 1954–55 (a)

DR. R. E. DYER, 1933–34 (h)

DR. HARRY EAGLE, 1959–60 (a)

DR. E. M. EAST, 1930–31 (d)

DR. J. C. ECCLES, 1955–56 (h)

DR. GERALD M. EDELMAN, 1972–73 (a)

PROF. R. S. EDGAR, 1967–68 (h)

DR. DAVID L. EDSALL, 1907–08 (d)

DR. JOHN T. EDSALL, 1966–67 (h)

DR. WILLIAM EINTHOVEN, 1924–25 (d)

DR. HERMAN N. EISEN, 1964–65 (h)

DR. JOEL ELKES, 1961–62 (h)

DR. C. A. ELVEHJEM, 1939–40 (d)

DR. HAVEN EMERSON, 1954–55 (d)

DR. JOHN F. ENDERS, 1947–48, 1963–64 (h)

DR. BORIS EPHRUSSI, 1950–51 (h)

DR. JOSEPH ERLANGER, 1912–13, 1926–27 (h)

DR. EARL A. EVANS, JR., 1943–44 (h)

DR. HERBERT M. EVANS, 1923–24 (h)

DR. JAMES EWING, 1907–08 (d)

DR. KNUD FABER, 1925–26 (d)

DR. W. FALTA, 1908–09 (d)

DR. W. O. FENN, 1927–28 (d)

DR. FRANK FENNER, 1956–57 (h)

DR. H. O. L. FISCHER, 1944–45 (d)

DR. L. B. FLEXNER, 1951–52 (h)

DR. SIMON FLEXNER, 1911–12 (d)

DR. OTTO FOLIN, 1907–08, 1919–20 (d)

PROF. JOHN A. FORDYCE, 1914–15 (d)

DR. NELLIS B. FOSTER, 1920–21 (d)

DR. EDWARD FRANCIS, 1927–28 (d)

DR. THOMAS FRANCIS, JR., 1941–42 (d)

DR. H. FRAENKEL-CONRAT, 1956–57 (h)

DR. ROBERT T. FRANK, 1930–31 (d)

DR. DONALD S. FREDRICKSON, 1972–73 (h)

DR. CHARLOTTE FRIEND, 1976–77 (a)

DR. C. FROMAGEOT, 1953–54 (h)

DR. JOSEPH S. FRUTON, 1955–56 (a)

DR. JOHN F. FULTON, 1935–36 (d)

DR. JACOB FURTH, 1967–68 (a)

DR. D. CARLETON GADJUSEK, 1976–77 (h)

DR. ERNEST F. GALE, 1955–56 (h)

DR. JOSEPH G. GALL, 1975–76 (h)

DR. T. F. GALLAGHER, 1956–57 (a)

DR. JAMES L GAMBLE, 1946–47 (d)

DR. HERBERT S. GASSER, 1936–37 (d)

DR. FREDERICK P. GAY, 1914–15, 1930–31 (d)

DR. EUGENE M. K. GEILING, 1941–42 (d)

DR. ISIDORE GERSH, 1949–50 (h)

DR. GEORGE O. GEY, 1954–55 (d)

DR. JOHN H. GIBBON, 1957–58 (d)

DR. HARRY GOLDBLATT, 1937–38 (h)

DR. JOSEPH L. GOLDSTEIN, 1977–78 (h)

DR. ROBERT A. GOOD, 1971–72 (a)

DR. EARNEST W. GOODPASTURE, 1929–30 (d)

DR. CARL W. GOTTSCHALK, 1962–63 (h)

DR. J. GOUGH, 1957–58 (h)

PROF. J. I. GOWANS, 1968–69 (h)

DR. EVARTS A. GRAHAM, 1923–24, 1933–34 (d)

DR. S. GRANICK, 1948–49 (h)

DR. DAVID E. GREEN, 1956–57 (h)

DR. HOWARD GREEN, 1978–79 (a)

PROF. R. A. GREGORY, 1968–69 (h)

DR. DONALD R. GRIFFIN, 1975–76 (h)

DR. JEROME GROSS, 1972–73 (h)

DR. ROGER GUILLEMIN, 1975–76 (h)

DR. I. C. GUNSALUS, 1949–50 (h)

DR. JOHN B. GURDON, 1973–74 (h)

DR. ALEXANDER B. GUTMAN, 1964–65 (a)

DR. J. S. HALDANE, 1916–17 (d)

DR. WILLIAM S. HALSTED, 1913–14 (d)

DR. H. J. HAMBURGER, 1922–23 (d)

DR. J. D. HARDY, 1953–54 (a)

SIR WILLIAM HARDY, 1930–31 (d)

PROF. HENRY HARRIS, 1969–70 (h)

DR. ROSS G. HARRISON, 1907–08, 1933–34 (d)

220   CUMULATIVE AUTHOR INDEX

Dr. H. K. Hartline, 1941–42 (h)
Dr. E. Newton Harvey, 1944–45 (h)
Dr. A. Baird Hastings, 1940–41 (a)
Dr. Selig Hecht, 1937–38 (d)
Prof. Sven H. Hedin, 1913–14 (d)
Dr. Michael Heidelberger, 1932–33 (a)
Prof. Ludvig Hektoen, 1909–10 (d)
Prof. L. J. Henderson, 1914–15 (d)
Dr. Yandell Henderson, 1917–19 (d)
Dr. James B. Herrick, 1930–31 (d)
Dr. A. D. Hershey, 1955–56 (h)
Prof. Christian Herter, 1906–07 (d)
Dr. Alfred F. Hess, 1920–21 (d)
Dr. A. V. Hill, 1924–25 (h)
Dr. George Hirst, 1948–49 (a)
Dr. Philip H. Hiss, 1908–09 (d)
Dr. Dorothy C. Hodgkin, 1965–66 (h)
Dr. Alan F. Hofmann, 1978–79 (a)
Dr. Klaus Hofmann, 1963–64 (h)
Prof. F. Gowland Hopkins, 1920–21 (d)
Dr. Bernard L. Horecker, 1961–62 (a)
Dr. Frank Horsfall, Jr., 1952–53 (d)
Dr. R. D. Hotchkiss, 1953–54 (a)
Dr. B. A. Houssay, 1935–36 (h)
Prof. W. H. Howell, 1905–06, 1916–17 (d)
Dr. John Howland, 1912–13, 1922–23 (d)
Dr. David H. Hubel, 1976–77 (h)
Prof. G. Carl Huber, 1909–10 (d)
Dr. Robert J. Huebner, 1960–61 (h)
Dr. Charles Huggins, 1946–47 (h)
Dr. David M. Hume, 1968–69 (d)
Prof. George Huntington, 1906–07 (d)
Dr. Jerard Hurwitz, 1968–69 (a)
Dr. Hugh Huxley, 1964–65 (h)
Dr. Vernon M. Ingram, 1965–66 (h)
Dr. Kurt J. Isselbacher, 1973–74 (h)

Dr. A. C. Ivy, 1931–32 (d)
Dr. Francois Jacob, 1959–60 (h)
Dr. Merkel Jacobs, 1926–27 (d)
Dr. Walter A. Jacobs, 1923–24 (a)
Prof. Theodore C. Janeway, 1912–13 (d)
Dr. Joseph Jastro, 1907–08 (d)
Prof. H. S. Jennings, 1911–12 (d)
Dr. Niels K. Jerne, 1974–75 (h)
Dr. J. W. Jobling, 1916–17 (d)
Dr. Edwin O. Jordan, 1907–08 (d)
Prof. Elliott P. Joslin, 1914–15 (d)
Dr. Alfred Jost, 1958–59 (h)
Dr. Elvin A. Kabat, 1950–51 (a)
Prof. Herman M. Kalckar, 1949–50 (h)
Dr. Eric R. Kandel, 1977–78 (a)
Dr. Henry S. Kaplan, 1968–69 (h)
Dr. Nathan O. Kaplan, 1970–71 (h)
Dr. Ephraim Katchalski, 1963–64 (h)
Prof. E. C. Kendall, 1919–20 (h)
Dr. Eugene P. Kennedy, 1961–62 (h)
Dr. Seymour S. Kety, 1975–76 (h)
Dr. H. Gobind Khorana, 1966–67 (h)
Dr. Edwin D. Kilbourne, 1977–78 (a)
Dr. A. Klug, 1978–79 (a)
Dr. George Klein, 1973–74 (h)
Dr. P. Klemperer, 1953–54 (d)
Dr. B. C. J. G. Knight, 1947–48 (h)
Prof. Franz Knoop, 1912–13 (d)
Dr. F. C. Koch, 1937–38 (d)
Prof. W. Kolle, 1924–25 (d)
Dr. Hilary Koprowski, 1964–65 (h)
Dr. Arthur Kornberg, 1957–58 (a)
Dr. Daniel E. Koshland, Jr., 1969–70 (h)
Prof. Albrecht Kossel, 1911–12 (d)
Dr. Allen K. Krause, 1921–22 (d)
Dr. H. A. Krebs, 1948–49 (h)
Dr. August Krogh, 1922–23 (d)
Dr. Stephen W. Kuffler, 1959–60 (h)
Dr. Henry G. Kunkel, 1963–64 (a)

Dr. L. O. Kunkel, 1932–33 (d)
Dr. Rebecca C. Lancefield, 1940–41 (a)
Dr. Eugene M. Landis, 1936–37 (h)
Dr. Ernst Laquer, 1945–46 (d)
Dr. Henry A. Lardy, 1964–65 (h)
Dr. K. S. Lashley, 1930–31 (d)
Dr. H. Sherwood Lawrence, 1972–73 (a)
Dr. H. A. Lawson, 1927–28 (h)
Dr. J. B. Leathes, 1908–09 (d)
Dr. Philip Leder, 1978–79 (a)
Dr. Joshua Lederberg, 1957–58 (h)
Dr. Frederic S. Lee, 1905–06, 1917–19 (d)
Dr. W. E. LeGros Clark, 1962–63 (h)
Dr. A. L. Lehninger, 1953–54 (h)
Dr. Luis F. Leloir, 1960–61 (h)
Dr. C. Levaditi, 1928–29 (d)
Dr. P. A. Levene, 1905–06 (d)
Dr. Rita Levi-Montalcini, 1964–65 (h)
Dr. Sam Z. Levine, 1946–47 (d)
Dr. Howard B. Lewis, 1940–41 (d)
Dr. Paul A. Lewis, 1916–17 (d)
Prof. Thomas Lewis, 1914–15 (d)
Dr. Warren H. Lewis, 1925–26, 1935–36 (d)
Dr. Richard C. Lewontin, 1974–75 (h)
Dr. Choh Hao Li, 1950–51 (h)
Dr. K. Kindstrom-Lang, 1938–39 (d)
Dr. Karl P. Link, 1943–44 (h)
Dr. Fritz Lipmann, 1948–49 (a)
Dr. C. C. Little, 1921–22 (d)
Prof. Jacques Loeb, 1910–11, 1920–21 (d)
Dr. Leo Loeb, 1940–41 (d)
Dr. Robert F. Loeb, 1941–42 (a)
Prof. A. S. Loevenhart, 1914–15 (d)
Dr. Otto Loewi, 1932–33 (d)
Dr. E. S. London, 1927–28 (h)
Dr. Irving M. London, 1960–61 (a)
Dr. C. N. H. Long, 1936–37 (h)

Dr. Esmond R. Long, 1929–30 (h)
Prof. Warfield T. Longcope, 1915–16 (d)
Dr. Rafael Lorente de Nó, 1946–47 (a)
Prof. Konrad Lorenz, 1959–60 (h)
Dr. William D. Lotspeich, 1960–61 (d)
Dr. Oliver H. Lowry, 1962–63 (a)
Dr. Einar Lundsgaard, 1937–38 (d)
Dr. S. E. Luria, 1964–65 (h)
Dr. Graham Lusk, 1908–09, 1929–30 (d)
Dr. Andre Lwoff, 1954–55 (h)
Dr. Feodor Lynen, 1952–53 (h)
Dr. A. B. Macallum, 1908–09 (d)
Dr. W. G. MacCallum, 1908–09 (d)
Prof. J. J. R. MacLeod, 1913–14 (d)
Dr. William deB. MacNider, 1928–29 (d)
Dr. Thorvald Madsen, 1924–25, 1936–37 (d)
Dr. E. Margoliash, 1970–71 (h)
Prof. A. Magnus-Levy, 1909–10 (d)
Dr. H. W. Magoun, 1951–52 (h)
Dr. F. B. Mallory, 1912–13 (d)
Dr. Frank C. Mann, 1927–28 (d)
Dr. David Marine, 1923–24 (d)
Dr. Clement L. Markert, 1963–64 (h)
Dr. Paul A. Marks, 1970–71 (a)
Dr. Guy Marrian, 1938–39 (h)
Prof. W. McKim Marriott, 1919–20 (d)
Dr. E. K. Marshall, Jr., 1929–30 (d)
Dr. Manfred M. Mayer, 1976–77 (h)
Dr. Daniel Mazia, 1957–58 (h)
Dr. Maclyn McCarty, 1969–70 (a)
Prof. E. V. McCollum, 1916–17 (d)
Dr. Walsh McDermott, 1967–68 (a)
Dr. Harden M. McDonnell (h)
Dr. W. D. McElroy, 1955–56 (h)
Dr. Philip D. McMaster, 1941–42 (a)
Dr. P. B. Medawar, 1956–57 (h)
Dr. Walter J. Meek, 1940–41 (d)

222   CUMULATIVE AUTHOR INDEX

PROF. ALTON MEISTER, 1967–68 (h)
DR. S. J. MELTZER, 1906–07 (d)
PROF. LAFAYETTE B. MENDEL, 1905–06, 1914–15 (d)
DR. R. BRUCE MERRIFIELD, 1971–72 (h)
PROF. ADOLPH MEYER, 1909–10 (d)
PROF. HANS MEYER, 1905–06 (d)
DR. KARL MEYER, 1955–56 (a)
DR. K. F. MEYER, 1939–40 (d)
DR. OTTO MEYERHOF, 1922–23 (d)
DR. LEONOR MICHAELIS, 1926–27 (d)
DR. WILLIAM S. MILLER, 1924–25 (d)
PROF. CHARLES S. MINOT, 1905–06 (d)
DR. GEORGE R. MINOT, 1927–28 (d)
DR. BEATRICE MINTZ, 1975–76 (h)
DR. A. E. MIRSKY, 1950–51 (a)
DR. JACQUES MONOD, 1961–62 (h)
DR. CARL V. MOORE, 1958–59 (h)
DR. FRANCIS D. MOORE, 1956–57 (h)
DR. STANFORD MOORE, 1956–57 (h)
PROF. T. H. MORGAN, 1905–06 (d)
DR. GIUSEPPE MORUZZI, 1962–63 (h)
DR. J. HOWARD MUELLER, 1943–44 (d)
PROF. FRIEDRICH MULLER, 1906–07 (d)
DR. H. J. MULLER, 1947–48 (d)
DR. HANS MÜLLER-EBERHARD, 1970–71 (a)
PROF. JOHN R. MURLIN, 1916–17 (d)
DR. W. P. MURPHY, 1927–28 (d)
DR. DAVID NACHMANSOHN, 1953–54 (a)
DR. F. R. NAGER, 1925–26 (d)
DR. DANIEL NATHANS, 1974–75 (h)
DR. JAMES V. NEEL, 1960–61 (h)
DR. FRED NEUFELD, 1926–27 (d)
SIR ARTHUR NEWSHOLME, 1920–21 (d)
DR. MARSHALL W. NIRENBERG, 1963–64 (h)
DR. HIDEYO NOGUVHI, 1915–16 (d)
DR. JOHN H. NORTHROP, 1925–26, 1934–35 (d)
DR. G. J. V. NOSSAL, 1967–68 (h)
PROF. FREDERICK G. NOVY, 1934–35 (d)

PROF. GEORGE H. F. NUTTALL, 1912–13 (d)
DR. SEVERO OCHOA, 1950–51 (a)
DR. LLOYD J. OLD, 1971–72, 1975–76 (h)
DR. JOHN OLIPHANT, 1943–44 (d)
DR. JEAN OLIVER, 1944–45 (h)
DR. BERT W. O'MALLEY, 1976–77 (h)
DR. J. L. ONCLEY, 1954–55 (h)
DR. EUGENE L. OPIE, 1909–10, 1928–29, 1954–55 (d)
PROF. HENRY F. OSBORN, 1911–12 (d)
DR. THOMAS B. OSBORNE, 1910–11 (d)
DR. WINTHROP J. V. OSTERHOUT, 1921–22, 1929–30 (h)
DR. GEORGE E. PALADE, 1961–62 (a)
DR. A. M. PAPPENHEIMER, JR., 1956–57 (a)
DR. JOHN R. PAPPENHEIMER, 1965–66 (a)
PROF. ARTHUR B. PARDEE, 1969–70 (h)
DR. EDWARDS A. PARK, 1938–39 (d)
PROF. W. H. PARK, 1905–06 (d)
PROF. G. H. PARKER, 1913–14 (d)
DR. STEWART PATON, 1917–19 (d)
DR. JOHN R. PAUL, 1942–43 (d)
DR. L. PAULING, 1953–54 (h)
DR. FRANCIS W. PEABODY, 1916–17 (d)
PROF. RICHARD M. PEARCE, 1909–10 (d)
DR. RAYMOND PEARL, 1921–22 (d)
DR. WILLIAM STANLEY PEART, 1977–78 (h)
DR. WILDER PENFIELD, 1936–37 (d)
DR. M. F. PERUTZ, 1967–68 (h)
DR. JOHN P. PETERS, 1937–38 (d)
DR. W. H. PETERSON, 1946–47 (d)
DR. DAVID C. PHILLIPS, 1970–71 (h)
DR. ERNST P. PICK, 1929–30 (h)
DR. LUDWIG PICK, 1931–32 (d)
DR. GREGORY PINCUS, 1966–67 (d)
DR. CLEMENS PIRQUET, 1921–22 (d)
DR. COLIN PITENDRIGH, 1960–61 (h)

Dr. Robert Pitts, 1952–53 (d)
Dr. A. Policard, 1931–32 (h)
Prof. George J. Popjak, 1969–70 (h)
Dr. Keith R. Porter, 1955–56 (a)
Prof. Rodney R. Porter, 1969–70 (h)
Dr. W. T. Porter, 1906–07, 1917–19 (d)
Dr. Mark Ptashne, 1973–74 (h)
Dr. T. T. Puck, 1958–59 (h)
Dr. J. J. Putnam, 1911–12 (d)
Dr. Efraim Racker, 1955–56 (a)
Dr. Hermann Rahn, 1958–59 (h)
Dr. Charles H. Rammelkamp, Jr., 1955–56 (h)
Dr. S. Walter Ranson, 1936–37 (d)
Dr. Kenneth B. Raper, 1961–62 (h)
Dr. Arnold R. Rich, 1946–47 (d)
Prof. Alfred N. Richards, 1920–21, 1934–35 (a)
Dr. Dickinson W. Richards, 1943–44 (a)
Prof. Theodore W. Richards, 1911–12 (d)
Dr. Curt P. Richter, 1942–43 (h)
Dr. D. Rittenberg, 1948–49 (d)
Dr. Thomas M. Rivers, 1933–34 (d)
Dr. William Robbins, 1942–43 (h)
Dr. O. H. Robertson, 1942–43 (d)
Prof. William C. Rose, 1934–35 (h)
Dr. M. J. Rosenau, 1908–09 (d)
Dr. F. J. W. Roughton, 1943–44 (h)
Dr. Peyton Rous, 1935–36 (d)
Dr. Wallace P. Rowe, 1975–76 (h)
Dr. Harry Rubin, 1965–66 (h)
Prof. Max Rubner, 1912–13 (d)
Dr. Frank H. Ruddle, 1973–74 (h)
Dr. John Runnstrom, 1950–51 (h)
Major Frederick F. Russell, 1912–13 (d)
Dr. F. R. Sabin, 1915–16 (d)
Dr. Leo Sachs, 1972–73 (h)
Dr. Wilbur A. Sawyer, 1934–35 (d)
Dr. Howard Schachman, 1972–73 (h)
Prof. E. A. Schafer, 1907–08 (d)

Dr. Matthew D. Scharff, 1973–74 (a)
Dr. Harold A. Scheraga, 1967–68 (h)
Dr. Bela Schick, 1922–23 (h)
Dr. Oscar Schloss, 1924–25 (d)
Prof. Adolph Schmidt, 1913–14 (d)
Dr. Carl F. Schmidt, 1948–49 (h)
Dr. Knut Schmidt-Neilsen, 1962–63 (h)
Dr. Francis O. Schmitt, 1944–45 (h)
Dr. R. Schoeneheimer, 1936–37 (d)
Dr. P. F. Scholander, 1961–62 (h)
Dr. Nevin S. Scrimshaw, 1962–63 (h)
Dr. William H. Sebrell, 1943–44 (h)
Prof. W. T. Sedgwick, 1911–12 (d)
Dr. Walter Seegers, 1951–52 (h)
Dr. J. Edwin Seegmiller, 1969–70 (h)
Dr. Michael Sela, 1971–72 (h)
Dr. Philip A. Shaffer, 1922–23 (d)
Dr. James A. Shannon, 1945–46 (a)
Dr. David Shemin, 1954–55 (a)
Dr. Henry C. Sherman, 1917–19 (d)
Dr. Richard Shope, 1935–36 (d)
Dr. Ephraim Shorr, 1954–55 (d)
Dr. Robert L. Sinsheimer, 1968–69 (h)
Dr. E. C. Slater, 1970–71 (h)
Dr. G. Elliot Smith, 1930–31 (d)
Dr. Emil L. Smith, 1966–67 (h)
Dr. Homer W. Smith, 1939–40 (d)
Dr. Philip E. Smith, 1929–30 (d)
Prof. Theobald Smith, 1905–06 (d)
Dr. George D. Snell, 1978–79 (a)
Dr. Solomon H. Snyder, 1977–78 (h)
Dr. T. M. Sonneborn, 1948–49 (h)
Dr. S. P. L. Sorenson, 1924–25 (d)
Dr. Carl C. Speidel, 1940–41 (h)
Dr. Sol Spiegelman, 1968–69 (a)
Dr. Roger W. Sperry, 1966–67 (h)
Dr. William C. Stadie, 1941–42 (d)
Dr. Earl R. Stadtman, 1969–70 (h)
Dr. Roger Stanier, 1959–60 (h)

DR. WENDELL STANLEY, 1937–38 (d)
DR. EARNEST H. STARLING, 1907–08 (d)
DR. ISAAC STARR, 1946–47 (h)
DR. WILLIAM H. STEIN, 1956–57 (a)
DR. P. STETSON, 1927–28
PROF. GEORGE STEWART, 1912–13 (d)
PROF. CH. WARDELL STILES, 1915–16 (d)
DR. C. R. STOCKARD, 1921–22 (d)
DR. WALTER STRAUB, 1928–29 (h)
DR. GEORGE L. STREETER, 1933–34 (h)
DR. JACK L. STROMINGER, 1968–69 (h)
DR. R. P. STRONG, 1913–14 (d)
PROF. EARL W. SUTHERLAND, JR., 1961–62 (d)
PROF. HOMER F. SWIFT, 1919–20 (d)
DR. W. W. SWINGLE, 1931–32 (d)
DR. V. P. SYDENSTRICKER, 1942–43 (h)
DR. ALBERT SZENT-GYORGYI, 1938–39 (h)
DR. W. H. TALIAFERRO, 1931–32 (d)
PROF. ALONZO E. TAYLOR, 1907–08 (d)
DR. HOWARD M. TEMIN, 1973–74 (h)
PROF. W. S. THAYER, 1911–12 (d)
DR. HUGO THEORELL, 1965–66 (h)
DR. LEWIS THOMAS, 1967–68 (a)
DR. WILLIAM S. TILLETT, 1949–50 (a)
DR. ARNE TISELIUS, 1939–40 (h)
DR. A. R. TODD, 1951–52 (h)
DR. GORDON M. TOMKINS, 1972–73 (h)
DR. SIDNEY UDENFRIEND, 1964–65 (a)
COLONEL F. P. UNDERHILL, 1917–19 (d)
DR. HANS USSING, 1963–64 (h)
DR. P. ROY VAGELOS, 1974–75 (h)
DR. DONALD D. VAN SLYKE, 1915–16 (d)
PROF. VICTOR C. VAUGHN, 1913–14 (d)
PROF. MAX VERWORN, 1911–12 (d)
PROF. CARL VOEGTLIN, 1919–20 (d)
DR. U.S. VON EULER, 1958–59 (h)
DR. ALEXANDER VON MURALT, 1947–48 (h)

PROF. CARL VON NOORDEN, 1905–06 (d)
DR. SELMAN A. WAKSMAN, 1944–45 (d)
DR. GEORGE WALD, 1945–46 (h)
DR. JAN WALDENSTROM, 1960–61 (h)
PROF. AUGUSTUS D. WALLER, 1913–14 (d)
DR. JOSEF WARKANY, 1952–53 (h)
COLONEL STAFFORD L. WARREN, 1945–46 (h)
DR. ALFRED S. WARTHIN, 1917–19 (d)
DR. C. J. WATSON, 1948–49 (h)
DR. JOSEPH T. WEARN, 1939–40 (h)
DR. H. H. WEBER, 1953–54 (d)
PROF. J. CLARENCE WEBSTER, 1905–06 (d)
DR. L. T. WEBSTER, 1931–32 (d)
DR. A. ASHLEY WEECH, 1938–39 (h)
DR. SILVIO WEIDMANN, 1965–66 (h)
DR. PAUL WEISS, 1958–59 (a)
DR. WILLIAM H. WELCH, 1915–16 (d)
DR. THOMAS H. WELLER, 1956–57 (h)
PROF. H. GIDEON WELLS, 1910–11 (d)
DR. K. F. WENCKEBACH, 1922–23 (d)
DR. GEORGE H. WHIPPLE, 1921–22 (h)
DR. ABRAHAM WHITE, 1947–48 (a)
DR. CARL J. WIGGERS, 1920–21, 1956–57 (d)
DR. V. B. WIGGLESWORTH, 1959–60 (h)
DR. CARROLL M. WILLIAMS, 1951–52 (h)
DR. LINSLEY R. WILLIAMS, 1917–19 (d)
DR. RICHARD WILLSTATTER, 1926–27 (d)
DR. EDMUND B. WILSON, 1906–07 (d)
DR. EDWIN B. WILSON, 1925–26 (d)
PROF. J. GORDON WILSON, 1917–19 (h)
DR. WILLIAM F. WINDLE, 1944–45 (h)
DR. F. R. WINTON, 1951–52 (h)
DR. MAXWELL M. WINTROBE, 1949–50 (h)
PROF. S. B. WOLBACH, 1920–21 (d)

Dr. Harold G. Wolff, 1943–44 (d)

Dr. Harland G. Wood, 1949–50 (h)

Dr. W. Barry Wood, Jr., 1951–52 (d)

Dr. William B. Wood, 1977–78 (h)

Prof. Sir Michael F. A. Woodruff, 1970–71 (h)

Dr. Robert B. Woodward, 1963–64 (h)

Dr. R. T. Woodyatt, 1915–16 (d)

Dr. D. W. Woolley, 1945–46 (d)

Sir Almroth E. Wright, 1906–07 (d)

Dr. Rosalyn S. Yalow, 1966–67 (h)

Prof. Robert M. Yerkes, 1917–19, 1935–36 (d)

Dr. Paul C. Zamecnik, 1959–60 (h)

Dr. L. Zechmeister, 1951–52 (h)

Dr. Norton D. Zinder, 1966–67 (a)

Prof. Hans Zinsser, 1914–15 (d)

ACTIVE MEMBERS

Dr. Bent Aasted
Dr. Ruth Gail Abramson
Dr. S. A. Acharya
Dr. Frederic J. Agate
Dr. Edward H. Ahrens
Dr. Agop Aintablian
Dr. Philip Aisen
Dr. Salah Al-Askari
Dr. Qais Al-Awqati
Dr. Anthony A. Albanese
Dr. Michael Harris Alderman
Dr. Robert Alexander
Dr. Emma Gates Allen
Dr. Fred H. Allen, Jr.
Dr. Jona Allerhand
Dr. Fred Allison, Jr.
Dr. Norman R. Alpert
Dr. Norman Altszuler
Dr. Burton M. Altura
Dr. J. Burns Amberson*
Dr. Richard P. Ames
Dr. A. F. Anderson*
Dr. Charles Anderson
Dr. Helen M. Anderson
Dr. Karl E. Anderson
Dr. Giuseppe A. Andres
Dr. Muriel M. Andrews
Dr. Alfred Angrist*
Dr. Henry Aranow, Jr.
Dr. Reginald M. Archibald*
Dr. Diana C. Argyros
Dr. Irwin M. Arias
Dr. Donald Armstrong
Dr. Philip B. Armstrong*
Dr. Aaron Arnold
Dr. Robert B. Aronson
Dr. Paul W. Aschner*
Dr. Amir Askari
Dr. Muvaffak A. Atamer
Dr. Dana W. Atchley*
Dr. Kimball Chase Atwood

Dr. Arthur H. Aufses, Jr.
Dr. Joseph T. August
Dr. Peter A. M. Auld
Dr. Felice B. Aull
Dr. Robert Austrian
Dr. Avram Avramides
Dr. Theodore W. Av Ruskin
Dr. D. Robert Axelrod
Dr. Stephen M. Ayres
Dr. L. Fred Ayvazian
Dr. Henry A. Azar
Dr. Rostom Bablanian
Dr. Radoslav Bachvaroff
Dr. Mortimer E. Bader
Dr. Richard A. Bader
Dr. George Baehr*
Dr. Silvio Baez
Dr. John C. Baiardi
Dr. Robert D. Baird*
Mrs. Katherine J. Baker
Dr. Sulamita Balagura
Dr. John C. Balardi*
Dr. David S. Baldwin
Dr. Horace S. Baldwin*
Dr. M. Earl Balis
Dr. Amiya K. Banerjee
Dr. S. Banerjee*
Dr. Arthur Bank
Dr. Norman Bank
Dr. Alvan L. Barach*
Dr. W. H. Barber*
Dr. Marion Barclay
Dr. S. B. Barker*
Dr. Lane Barksdale
Dr. W. A. Barnes
Dr. Harry Baron
Dr. Howard Baron
Dr. Jeremiah A. Barondess
Dr. David P. Barr*
Dr. Bruce A. Barron
Dr. Guy T. Barry

*Life member.

227

Dr. Claudio Basilico
Dr. C. Andrew L. Bassett
Dr. Jeanne Bateman*
Dr. Jack R. Battisto
Dr. Stephen G. Baum
Dr. Leona Baumgartner*
Dr. Eliot F. Beach*
Dr. Joseph W. Beard*
Dr. Alexander G. Bearn
Dr. Carl Becker
Dr. E. Lovell Becker
Dr. Joseph W. Becker
Dr. William H. Becker
Dr. Paul B. Beeson*
Dr. Richard E. Behrman
Dr. Julius Belford
Dr. A. L. Loomis Bell
Dr. Bertrand Bell
Dr. Fritz Karl Beller
Dr. Baruj Benacerraf
Dr. Morris Bender*
Dr. Aaron Bendich
Dr. Bernard Benjamin*
Dr. Bry Benjamin
Dr. Ivan L. Bennett
Dr. Thomas P. Bennett
Dr. Harvey L. Benovitz
Dr. Gordon Benson
Dr. Nicholas Beratis
Dr. Richard Beresford
Dr. Benjamin N. Berg*
Dr. Kare Berg
Dr. Stanley S. Bergen
Dr. Adolph Berger
Dr. Lawrence Berger
Dr. Ingemar Berggard
Dr. Edward H. Bergofsky
Dr. James Berkman
Dr. Alice R. Bernheim*
Dr. Alan W. Bernheimer
Dr. Harriet Bernheimer
Dr. Leslie Bernstein
Dr. Carl A. Berntsen

Dr. George Packer Berry*
Dr. John F. Bertles
Dr. Otto A. Bessey*
Dr. Joseph J. Betheil
Dr. Margaret Bevans
Dr. Sherman Beychok
Dr. Rajesh M. Bhatnagar
Dr. Celso Bianco
Dr. Edward Bien
Dr. John T. Bigger, Jr.
Dr. R. J. Bing*
Dr. Carl A. L. Binger*
Dr. Francis Binkley
Dr. LeClair Bissell
Dr. Mark W. Bitensky
Dr. Ira Black
Dr. William A. Blanc
Dr. Kenneth C. Blanchard*
Dr. David H. Blankenhorn
Dr. Sheldon P. Blau
Dr. Richard W. Blide
Dr. Andrew Blitzer
Dr. Konrad E. Bloch
Dr. Arthur D. Bloom
Dr. Barry Bloom
Dr. Richard S. Bockman
Dr. Oscar Bodansky*
Dr. Diethelm Boehme
Dr. Bruce I. Bogart
Dr. Morton D. Bogdonoff
Dr. Alfred J. Bollet
Dr. Richard J. Bonforte
Dr. Roy W. Bonsnes*
Dr. Robert M. Bookchin
Dr. Ellen Borenfreund
Dr. Frank Boschenstein
Dr. Barbara H. Bowman
Dr. Linn J. Boyd*
Dr. Robert J. Boylan
Dr. Richard C. Bozian
Dr. Robert Brackenbury
Dr. Stanley Bradley*
Dr. Thomas B. Bradley

*Life member.

Dr. Leon Bradlow
Dr. J. Leonard Brandt
Dr. Lawrence J. Brandt
Dr. Jo Anne Brasel
Dr. Thomas A. Brastitus
Dr. Goodwin Breinin
Dr. Esther Breslow
Dr. Robin Briehl
Dr. Stanley A. Briller
Dr. Anne E. Briscoe
Dr. Susan Broder
Dr. Felix Bronner
Dr. Chandler McC. Brooks
Dr. Dana C. Brooks
Dr. D. E. S. Brown*
Dr. John Lyman Brown
Dr. Ted Brown
Dr. Howard C. Bruenn*
Dr. Elmer Brummer
Dr. J. Marion Bryant
Dr. J. Robert Buchanan
Dr. Nancy M. Buckley
Dr. Joseph A. Buda
Dr. Elmer D. Bueker
Dr. George E. Burch*
Dr. Joseph H. Burchenal
Dr. Richard Burger
Dr. Dean Burk*
Dr. Edward R. Burka
Dr. E. A. Burkhardt*
Dr. John J. Burns
Dr. Earl O. Butcher*
Dr. Vincent P. Butler, Jr.
Dr. Joel N. Buxbaum
Dr. Abbie Knowlton Calder
Dr. Peter T. B. Caldwell
Dr. Lawrence A. Caliguiri
Dr. Berry Campbell*
Dr. Robert E. Canfield
Dr. Paul Jude Cannon
Dr. Guilio L. Cantoni
Dr. Charles R. Cantor
Dr. Eric T. Carlson

Dr. Peter Wagner Carmel
Dr. Fred Carpenter
Dr. Malcolm B. Carpenter
Dr. Hugh J. Carroll
Dr. Steven Carson
Dr. Anne C. Carter
Dr. Sidney Carter
Dr. J. Casals-Ariet*
Dr. David B. Case
Dr. Robert B. Case
Dr. Albert E. Casey*
Dr. Joan I. Casey
Dr. William D. Cash
Dr. McKeen Cattell*
Dr. William Caveness*
Dr. Peter P. Cervoni
Dr. Raju S. K. Chaganti
Dr. R. W. Chambers
Dr. Philip C. Chan
Dr. W. Y. Chan
Dr. J. P. Chandler*
Dr. Merrill W. Chase*
Dr. Norman E. Chase
Dr. Herbert Chasis*
Dr. Kirk C. S. Chen
Dr. Tehodore Chenkin
Dr. Norman L. Chernik
Dr. David S. Chi
Dr. Marie T. Chiao
Dr. Shu Chien
Dr. C. Gardner Child
Dr. Francis P. Chinard
Dr. Herman Chmel
Dr. Yong Sung Choi
Dr. Purnell W. Choppin
Dr. Charles L. Christian
Dr. Ronald V. Christie*
Dr. Judith K. Christman
Dr. Nicholas P. Christy
Dr. Jacob Churg
Dr. Louis J. Cizek
Dr. Duncan W. Clark*
Dr. Delphine H. Clarke

*Life member.

Dr. Frank H. Clarke
Dr. Albert Claude*
Dr. Hartwig Cleve
Dr. Leighton E. Cluff
Dr. Jaime B. Coelho
Dr. Bernard Cohen
Dr. Michael I. Cohen
Dr. Cal K. Cohn
Dr. Mildred Cohn
Dr. Zanvil A. Cohn
Dr. Henry Colcher
Dr. Morton Coleman
Dr. John E. Coligan
Dr. Neville Colman
Dr. Spencer L. Commerford
Dr. Richard M. Compans
Dr. Neal J. Conan, Jr.
Dr. Lawrence A. Cone
Dr. Stephen C. Connolly
Dr. James H. Conover
Dr. Jean L. Cook
Dr. John S. Cook
Dr. Stuart D. Cook
Dr. George Cooper
Dr. Norman S. Cooper
Dr. Jack M. Cooperman
Dr. W. M. Copenhaver*
Dr. George N. Cornell
Dr. James S. Cornell
Dr. George Corner*
Dr. Armand F. Cortese
Dr. Thomas Costantino
Dr. Richard Costello
Dr. Lucien J. Cote
Dr. Andre Cournand*
Dr. David Cowen
Dr. Herold R. Cox*
Dr. Rody P. Cox
Dr. George Craft
Dr. John P. Craig
Dr. B. B. Crohn*
Dr. Richard J. Cross
Dr. Bruce Cunningham

Dr. Dorothy J. Cunningham
Dr. Edward C. Curnen*
Dr. Mary G. McCrea Curnen
Dr. T. J. Curphey*
Dr. Samuel W. Cushman
Dr. Samuel Dales
Dr. Marie Maynard Daly
Dr. Joseph Dancis
Dr. John A. Dancus
Dr. Betty S. Danes
Dr. Farrington Daniels, Jr.
Dr. R. C. Darling*
Dr. James E. Darnell, Jr.
Dr. Fredric Daum
Dr. Fred M. Davenport
Dr. Charles M. David
Dr. John David
Dr. Leo M. Davidoff*
Dr. Murray Davidson
Dr. Nicholas O. Davidson
Dr. Jean Davignon
Dr. Bernard D. Davis
Dr. Robert P. Davis
Dr. Emerson Day
Dr. Noorbibi K. Day
Dr. Stacey B. Day
Dr. Peter G. Dayton
Dr. Norman Deane
Dr. Robert H. De Bellis
Dr. Vittorio Defendi
Dr. Paul F. de Gara*
Dr. Thomas J. Degnan
Dr. A. C. DeGraff*
Dr. John E. Deitrick*
Dr. C. E. de la Chapelle*
Dr. Nicholas Delhias
Dr. R. J. Dellenback
Dr. Felix E. Demartini
Dr. Quentin B. Deming
Dr. Felix de Narvaez
Dr. Miriam de Salegue
Dr. Dickson D. Despommier
Dr. Ralph A. Deterling, Jr.

*Life member.

Dr. Wolf-Dietrich Dettbarn
Dr. Ingrith J. Deyrup
Dr. Elaine Diacumakos
Dr. Herbert S. Diamond
Dr. Leroy S. Dietrich
Dr. George W. Dietz, Jr.
Dr. Mario Di Girolamo
Dr. Alexander B. Dimich
Dr. Peter Dineen
Dr. J. R. Di Palma
Dr. P. A. Di Sant'Agnese
Dr. Zacharias Dische
Dr. Ann M. Dnistrian
Dr. Charles A. Doan*
Dr. William Dock*
Dr. Alvin M. Donnenfeld
Dr. Philip J. Dorman
Dr. Louis B. Dotti*
Dr. Joseph C. Dougherty
Dr. Gordon W. Douglas
Dr. Steven D. Douglas
Dr. Charles V. Dowling
Dr. Peter C. Dowling
Dr. Alan W. Downie*
Dr. Cora Downs*
Dr. Arnold Drapkin
Dr. Paul Driezen
Dr. David T. Dresdale
Dr. Lewis M. Drusin
Dr. Ronald E. Drusin
Dr. René J. Dubos*
Dr. Allan Dumont
Dr. Bo Dupont
Dr. Vincent Du Vigneaud*
Dr. Murray Dworetzky
Dr. D. Dziewiatkowski
Dr. Harry Eagle
Dr. Lila W. Easley
Dr. John C. Eccles*
Dr. Gerald M. Edelman
Dr. Norman Edelman
Dr. Howard A. Eder
Dr. Adrian L. E. Edwards

Dr. Richard M. Effros
Dr. Hans J. Eggers
Dr. Kathryn H. Ehlers
Dr. Klaus Eichmann
Dr. Ludwig W. Eichna*
Dr. Max Eisenberg
Dr. Moises Eisenberg
Dr. William J. Eisenmenger
Dr. Robert P. Eisinger
Dr. Stuart D. Elliott
Dr. John T. Ellis
Dr. Rose-Ruth Tarr Ellison
Dr. Peter Elsbach
Dr. Samuel K. Elster
Dr. Charles A. Ely
Dr. Kendall Emerson, Jr.*
Dr. Morris Engelman
Dr. Mary Allen Engle
Dr. Ralph L. Engle, Jr.
Dr. Leonard Epifano
Dr. Joseph A. Epstein
Dr. Bernard F. Erlanger
Dr. Solomon Estren
Dr. Hugh E. Evans
Dr. Henry E. Evert
Dr. Stanley Fahn
Dr. Gordon F. Fairclough, Jr.
Dr. Saul J. Farber
Dr. Mehdi Farhangi
Dr. Peter B. Farnsworth
Dr. John W. Farquhar
Dr. Lee E. Farr*
Dr. Don W. Fawcett
Dr. Aaron Feder*
Dr. Martha E. Fedorko
Dr. Muriel F. Feigelson
Dr. Philip Feigelson
Dr. Maurice Feinstein
Dr. Daniel Feldman
Dr. Colin Fell
Dr. Bernard N. Fields
Dr. Ronald R. Fieve
Dr. Arthur M. Figur

*Life member.

Dr. Howard Fillit
Dr. Laurence Finberg
Dr. Bruno Fingerhut
Dr. Louis M. Fink
Dr. Stanley R. Finke
Dr. John T. Finkenstaedt
Dr. Edward E. Fischel
Dr. Saul H. Fischer*
Dr. Vincent A. Fischetti
Dr. Arthur Fishberg*
Dr. Paul B. Fisher
Dr. Patrick J. Fitzgerald
Dr. Martin FitzPatrick
Dr. Raul Fleischmajer
Dr. Alan R. Fleischman
Dr. Charles Flood*
Dr. Alfred L. Florman*
Dr. Kathleen M. Foley
Dr. Conrad T. O. Fong
Dr. Joseph Fortner
Dr. Arthur C. Fox
Dr. Lewis M. Fraad*
Dr. Tova Francus
Dr. Blas Frangione
Dr. Charles W. Frank
Dr. Harry Meyer Frankel
Dr. Edward C. Franklin
Dr. John E. Franklin, Jr.
Dr. Richard C. Franson
Dr. Andrew G. Frantz
Dr. Carl E. Frasch
Dr. Blair A. Fraser
Dr. Aaron D. Freedman
Dr. Michael L. Freedman
Dr. Alvin Freiman
Dr. Matthew Jay Freund
Dr. Richard H. Freyburg*
Dr. Henry Clay Frick, II
Dr. Arnold J. Friedhof
Dr. Ralph Friedlander*
Dr. Eli A. Friedman
Dr. Charlotte Friend
Dr. George W. Frimpter

Dr. William Frisell
Dr. Joseph S. Fruton*
Dr. Fritz F. Fuchs
Dr. Mildred Fulop
Dr. Robert F. Furchgott*
Dr. Palmer H. Futcher*
Dr. Jacques L. Gabrilove
Dr. Morton Galdston
Dr. W. Einar Gall
Dr. Henry Gans
Dr. G. Gail Garnder
Dr. William A. Gardner*
Dr. Martin Gardy
Dr. Owen W. Garrigan
Dr. Lawrence Gartner
Dr. Nancy E. Gary
Dr. Jerald D. Gass
Dr. Frederick T. Gates, III
Dr. Mario Gaudino
Dr. Gerald E. Gaull
Dr. Malcolm Gefter
Dr. Walton B. Geiger
Dr. Lester M. Geller
Dr. Jeremiah M. Gelles
Dr. Dorothy S. Genghof
Dr. Donald Gerber
Dr. James L. German, III
Dr. Edward L. Gershey
Dr. E. C. Gerst
Dr. Menard Gertler
Dr. Melvin Gertner
Dr. Norman R. Gevirtz
Dr. Nimai Ghosh
Dr. Stanley Giannelli, Jr.
Dr. Allan Gibofsky
Dr. Gerhard H. Giebisch
Dr. Harriet S. Gilbert
Dr. Helena Gilder
Dr. Alfred Gilman
Dr. Sid Gilman
Dr. Charles Gilvarg
Dr. H. Earl Ginn
Dr. James Z. Ginos

*Life member.

Dr. Harold S. Ginsberg
Dr. Isaac F. Gittleman
Dr. Sheldon Glabman
Dr. Philip R. Glade
Dr. Herman Gladstone
Dr. Warren Glaser
Dr. George B. Jerzy Glass
Dr. Ephraim Glassmann*
Dr. Vincent V. Glaviano
Dr. Frank Glenn*
Dr. Marvin L. Gliedman
Dr. David L. Globus
Dr. Martin J. Glynn, Jr.*
Dr. David J. Gocke
Dr. Henry P. Godfrey
Dr. Gabriel C. Godman
Dr. Walther F. Goebel*
Dr. Robert B. Golbey
Dr. Allen M. Gold
Dr. Jonathan W. M. Gold
Dr. Allan R. Goldberg
Dr. Burton Goldberg
Dr. Anna Goldfeder
Dr. Roberta M. Goldring
Dr. William Goldring*
Dr. Edward I. Goldsmith
Dr. Eli D. Goldsmith*
Dr. Jack Goldstein
Dr. Marvin H. Goldstein
Dr. Robert Goldstein
Dr. Julius Golubow
Dr. Robert A. Good
Dr. Robert Goodhart*
Dr. DeWitt S. Goodman
Dr. Laurance D. Goodwin
Dr. Norman L. Gootman
Dr. Albert S. Gordon*
Dr. Alvin J. Gordon
Dr. Harry H. Gordon*
Dr. Irving Gordon*
Dr. Emil Claus Gotschlich
Dr. Eugene Gottfried
Dr. Otto Götze

Dr. Dicran Goulian, Jr.
Dr. Arthur W. Grace*
Dr. R. F. Grady
Dr. Irving Graef*
Dr. William R. Grafe
Dr. Samuel Graff*
Dr. Frank A. Graig
Dr. Lester Grant
Dr. Arthur I. Grayzel
Dr. Jack Peter Green
Dr. Peter H. R. Green
Dr. Robert H. Green
Dr. Saul Green
Dr. Lowell M. Greenbaum
Dr. Elias L. Greene
Dr. Lewis J. Greene
Dr. Olga Greengard
Dr. Ezra M. Greenspan
Dr. Isidor Greenwald*
Dr. Robert A. Greenwald
Dr. Mary R. Greenwood
Dr. John R. Gregg
Dr. Gregory Gregariadis
Dr. Anastasia Gregoriades
Dr. John D. Gregory
Dr. Roger I. Greif
Dr. Ira Greifer
Dr. Joel Grinker
Dr. Arthur Grishman
Dr. David Grob
Dr. Howard S. Grob
Dr. Arthur P. Grollman
Dr. Lionel Grossbard
Dr. Carlo E. S. Grossi
Dr. Melvin Grumbach
Dr. Dezider Grunberger
Dr. Harry Grundfest*
Dr. Alan B. Gruskin
Dr. Richard S. Gubner
Dr. Peter Guida
Dr. Guido Guidotti
Dr. Connie M. Guion*
Dr. Stephen J. Gulotta

*Life member.

Dr. Sidney Gutstein
Dr. Gail S. Habicht
Dr. David V. Habif
Dr. John W. Hadden
Dr. Susan Jane Hadley
Dr. Hanspaul Hagenmaier
Dr. Jack W. C. Hagstrom
Dr. Richard G. Hahn*
Dr. Kathleen A. Haines
Dr. Seymour P. Halbert
Dr. Bernard H. Hall*
Dr. Robert I. Hamby
Dr. James B. Hamilton*
Dr. Leonard Hamilton
Dr. Paul B. Hamilton*
Dr. Warner S. Hammond*
Dr. Chester W. Hampel*
Dr. Eugene S. Handler
Dr. Evelyn E. Handler
Dr. Leonard C. Harber
Dr. James D. Hardy*
Dr. Kendrick Hare*
Dr. Ken Harewood
Dr. Joseph Harkavy*
Dr. Peter Cahners Harpel
Dr. Albert H. Harris*
Dr. Michael B. Harris
Dr. Ruth C. Harris
Dr. Benjamin Harrow*
Dr. Una Hart
Dr. ReJane Harvey
Dr. Rudy Haschemeyer
Dr. George A. Hashim
Dr. Sam A. Hashim
Dr. George M. Hass*
Dr. William K. Hass
Dr. A. Baird Hastings*
Dr. Victor Hatcher
Dr. A. Daniel Hauser
Dr. Richard Hawkins
Dr. Arthur M. Hayes
Dr. Richard M. Hayes
Dr. Michael Heidelberger*

Dr. William Carroll Heird
Dr. Leon Hellman
Dr. Lawrence Helson
Dr. Walter L. Henley
Dr. Philip H. Henneman
Dr. Victor Herbert
Dr. Robert M. Hearbst*
Dr. Morris Herman*
Dr. Frederic P. Herter
Dr. Robert B. Hiatt
Dr. Margaret Hilgartner
Dr. Charles H. Hill
Dr. Lawrence E. Hinkle, Jr.
Dr. Joseph C. Hinsey*
Dr. Christophe H. W. Hirs
Dr. Jacob Hirsch
Dr. James G. Hirsch
Dr. Jules Hirsch
Dr. Robert L. Hirsch
Dr. Kurt Hirschhorn
Dr. George K. Hirst*
Dr. Paul Hochstein
Dr. Paul F. A. Hoefer*
Dr. Thomas I. Hoen*
Dr. Alan F. Hofmann
Dr. Frederick G. Hofmann
Dr. Duncan A. Holiday
Dr. Raymond F. Holden*
Dr. Mary Jean C. Holland
Dr. Charles S. Hollander
Dr. Vincent Hollander
Dr. J. H. Holmes*
Dr. Peter R. Holt
Dr. Donald A. Holub
Dr. Robert S. Holzman
Dr. Edward W. Hook
Dr. Bernard L. Horecker
Dr. William H. Horner
Dr. Marshall S. Horwitz
Dr. Verne D. Hospelhorn
Dr. Rollin D. Hotchkiss*
Dr. S. D. Hotta
Dr. Michael Luray Howe

*Life member.

Dr. Howard H. T. Hsu
Dr. Konrad Chang Hsu
Dr. William N. Hubbard, Jr.
Dr. L. E. Hummel*
Dr. George H. Humphreys*
Dr. Jerard Hurwitz
Dr. Dorris Hutchinson
Dr. Thomas H. Hutteroth
Dr. Michael Iacobellis
Dr. Genevieve S. Incefy
Dr. Laura Inselman
Dr. Harry L. Ioachim
Dr. Henry D. Isenberg
Dr. Raymond S. Jackson
Dr. Richard W. Jackson*
Dr. Jerry C. Jacobs
Dr. Eric A. Jaffe
Dr. Ernst R. Jaffe
Dr. Herbert Jaffe
Dr. S. Jakowska
Dr. George James
Dr. James D. Jamieson
Dr. Aaron Janoff
Dr. Alfonso H. Janoski
Dr. Henry D. Janowitz
Dr. Saul Jarcho*
Dr. Charles I. Jaworski
Dr. Jamshid Javid
Dr. Norman B. Javitt
Dr. Graham H. Jeffries
Dr. Alan J. Johnson
Dr. Dorothy D. Johnson
Dr. Walter D. Johnson, Jr.
Dr. Barbara Johnston
Dr. Kenneth H. Johnston
Dr. Thomas Jones
Dr. Alan S. Josephson
Dr. A. Jost*
Dr. Austin L. Joyner*
Dr. Ronald Kaback
Dr. Elvin A. Kabat*
Dr. Lawrence J. Kagen
Dr. Melvin Kahn

Dr. Thomas Kahn
Dr. Eric R. Kandel
Dr. Sungzong Kang
Dr. Stephen M. Kaplan
Dr. Alfred J. Kaltman
Dr. William Kammerer
Dr. Yoshinobu Kanno
Dr. Thomas G. Kantor
Dr. F. F. Kao
Dr. Barry H. Kaplan
Dr. Attallah Kappas
Dr. Arthur Karanas
Dr. Arthur Karlin
Dr. Maxwell Karshan*
Dr. Stuart S. Kassan
Dr. Arnold M. Katz
Dr. Michael Katz
Dr. Robert Katzman
Dr. George L. Kauer, Jr.*
Dr. Seymour Kaufmann
Dr. Hans Kaunitz
Dr. Herbert J. Kayden
Dr. Donald Kaye
Dr. D. Gordon I. Kaye
Dr. B. H. Kean
Dr. Aaron Kellner
Dr. Stephen Kent
Dr. Alan J. Kenyon
Dr. Muriel Kerr
Dr. Lee Kesner
Dr. Richard H. Kessler
Dr. Gerald T. Keusch
Dr. Andre C. Kibrick*
Dr. John G. Kidd*
Dr. Edwin D. Kilbourne
Dr. Margaret Kilcoyne
Dr. Diana C. Killip
Dr. Thomas Killip
Dr. Charles W. Kim
Dr. Yoon Berm Kim
Dr. Thomas J. Kindt
Dr. Barry G. King*
Dr. Donald West King

*Life member.

Dr. Glenn C. King*
Dr. Mary Elizabeth King
Dr. Lawrence C. Kingsland, Jr.
Dr. David W. Kinne
Dr. John M. Kinney
Dr. R. A. Kinsella*
Dr. Esben Kirk
Dr. D. M. Kirschenbaum
Dr. David Klapper
Dr. Arthur A. Klein
Dr. Bernard Klein
Dr. Herbert Klein
Dr. Robert S. Klein
Dr. David L. Kleinberg
Dr. Abraham M. Kleinman
Dr. A. K. Kleinschmidt
Dr. Percy Klingenstein
Dr. Margarete Knecht
Dr. Jerome L. Knittle
Dr. W. Eugene Knox
Dr. Joseph A. Kochen
Dr. Shaul Kochwa
Dr. Samuel Saburo Koide
Dr. Kiyomi Koizumi
Dr. M. J. Kopac*
Dr. Levy Kopelovich
Dr. Arthur Kornberg
Dr. Peter Kornfeld
Dr. Leonard Korngold
Dr. Irvin M. Korr*
Dr. Charles E. Kossmann*
Dr. Ione A. Kourides
Dr. Arthur Kowalsky
Dr. O. Dhodanand Kowlessar
Dr. Philip Kozinn
Dr. Irwin H. Krakoff
Dr. Lawrence R. Krakoff
Dr. Robert J. Kramer
Dr. Alvan Krasna
Dr. Stephen J. Kraus
Dr. Richard M. Krause
Dr. Norman Kretchmer
Dr. Howard P. Krieger

Dr. Isidore Krimsky
Dr. Robert A. Kritzler
Dr. Robert Schild Krooth
Dr. Stephen Krop*
Dr. Saul Krugman
Dr. Edward J. Kuchinskas
Dr. Friedrich Kueppers
Dr. I. Newton Kugelmass*
Dr. Henry G. Kunkel
Dr. Sherman Kupfer
Dr. Herbert S. Kupperman
Dr. Marvin Kuschner
Dr. Henn Kutt
Dr. David M. Kydd
Dr. John S. LaDue
Dr. Chun-Yen Lai
Dr. Robert G. Lahita
Dr. Michael Lake*
Dr. Michael Lamm
Dr. R. C. Lancefield*
Dr. Robert Landesman
Dr. Frank R. Landsberger
Dr. M. Daniel Lane
Dr. William B. Langan
Dr. Gertrude Lange
Dr. Kurt Lange
Dr. Louis Langman*
Dr. Philip Lanzkowsky
Dr. John H. Laragh
Dr. Daniel L. Larson
Dr. Nicholas F. LaRusso
Dr. Etienne Y. Lasfargues
Dr. Sigmund E. Lasker
Dr. Leonard Laster
Dr. Raffaelle Lattes
Dr. John Lattimer
Dr. Henry D. Lauson
Dr. Leroy S. Lavine
Dr. Christine Lawrence
Dr. H. S. Lawrence
Dr. Walter Lawrence, Jr.
Dr. Richard W. Lawton
Dr. Robert W. Leader

*Life member.

Dr. Stanley L. Lee
Dr. Sylvia Lee-Huang
Dr. Robert S. Lees
Dr. Albert M. Lefkovits
Dr. David Lehr
Dr. Gerard M. Lehrer
Miss Grace Leidy
Dr. Edgar Leifer
Dr. Louis Leiter*
Dr. John Lenard
Dr. Edwin H. Lennette*
Dr. Roger L. Lerner
Dr. E. Carwile LeRoy
Dr. Stephen H. Leslie
Dr. Gerson J. Lesnick
Dr. Gerson T. Lesser
Dr. Harry Le Veen
Dr. Stanley M. Levenson
Dr. Arthur H. Levere
Dr. Ricahrd D. Levere
Dr. Harold A. Levey
Dr. Robert Levi
Dr. Aaron R. Levin
Dr. Louis Levin*
Dr. Philip Levine*
Dr. Rachmiel Levine
Dr. Robert A. Levine
Dr. Cyrus Levinthal
Dr. Marvin F. Levitt
Dr. Barnet M. Levy
Dr. David E. Levy
Dr. Harvey M. Levy
Dr. Lester Levy
Dr. Milton Levy*
Dr. Arthur Lewis
Dr. James L. Lewis
Dr. N. D. C. Lewis*
Dr. Marjorie Lewisohn *
Dr. Allyn B. Ley
Dr. Herbert C. Lichtman
Dr. Charles S. Lieber
Dr. Seymour Lieberman
Dr. Frederick M. Liebman

Dr. Martin R. Liebowitz
Dr. Fannie Liebson
Dr. Philip D. Lief
Dr. Frank Lilly
Dr. Edith M. Lincoln*
Dr. Geoffrey C. Linder*
Dr. Alfred S. C. Ling
Dr. George Lipkin
Dr. Martin Lipkin
Dr. Fritz Lipmann*
Dr. M. B. Lipsett
Dr. Julius Littman*
Dr. Stephen D. Litwin
Dr. George Liu
Dr. Teh-Yung Liu
Dr. Arthur Livermore
Dr. David P. C. Lloyd*
Dr. Joseph LoBue
Dr. Michael D. Lockshin
Dr. John N. Loeb
Dr. Robert F. Loeb*
Dr. Werner R. Loewenstein
Dr. Irving M. London
Dr. Morris London
Dr. L. G. Longsworth*
Dr. R. Lorente de Nó*
Dr. Donald B. Louria
Dr. Barbara W. Low
Dr. Jerome Lowenstein
Dr. Oliver H. Lowry*
Dr. Bertram A. Lowy
Dr. Fred V. Lucas
Dr. Jean M. Lucas-Lenard
Dr. E. Hugh Luckey
Dr. A. Leonard Luhby
Dr. Daniel S. Lukas
Dr. Clara J. Lynch*
Dr. Harold Lyons
Dr. George I. Lythcott
Dr. Kenneth McAlpin*
Dr. Marsh McCall
Dr. W. S. McCann*
Dr. Kenneth S. McCarty

*Life member.

238 ACTIVE MEMBERS

DR. MACLYN MCCARTY
DR. ROBERT MCCLUSKY
DR. DAVID J. MCCONNELL
DR. JAMES E. MCCORMACK
DR. DONOVAN J. MCCUNE*
DR. WALSH MCDERMOTT
DR. FLETCHER MCDOWELL
DR. CURRIER MCEWEN*
DR JOHN C. MCGIFF
DR. ELEANOR MCGOWAN
DR. PAUL R. MCHUGH
DR. RUSTIN MCINTOSH*
DR. COSMO G. MACKENZIE*
DR. ROBERT G. MCKITTRICK
DR. JOHN MACLEOD*
DR. DONALD J. MCNAMARA
DR. JAMES J. MCSHARRY
DR. CHARLES K. MCSHERRY
DR. ROBERT M. MCVIE
DR. THOMAS MAACK
DR. NICHOLAS T. MACRIS
DR. MELVILLE G. MAGIDA*
DR. T. P. MAGILL*
DR. JACOB V. MAIZEL, JR.
DR. OLE J. W. MALM
DR. BENJAMIN MANDEL
DR. WILLIAM M. MANGER
DR. BELUR N. MANJULA
DR. MART MANNIK
DR. JAMES M. MANNING
DR. WLADYSLAW MANSKI
DR. KARL MARAMOROSCH
DR. CARLOS MARCHENA*
DR. AARON J. MARCUS
DR. DONALD M. MARCUS
DR. PHILIP I. MARCUS
DR. NORMAN MARINE
DR. MORTON MARKS
DR. PAUL A. MARKS
DR. DOUGLAS A. MARSLAND*
DR. DANIEL S. MARTIN
DR. RICHARD L. MASLAND
DR. BENTO MASCARENHAS

DR. RICHARD C. MASON*
DR. ARTHUR M. MASTER*
DR. EDMUND B. MASUROVSKY
DR. LEONARD M. MATTES
DR. ROBERT MATZ
DR. PAUL H. MAUER
DR. EVELYN A. MAUSS
DR. MORTON H. MAXWELL
DR. KLAUS MAYER
DR. AUBRE DE L. MAYNARD
DR E. W. MAYNERT
DR. RAJARSHI MAZUMDER
DR. ABRAHAM MAZUR
DR. VALENTINO MAZZIA
DR. EDWARD MEILMAN
DR. HARRIET K. MEISS
DR. GILBERT W. MELLIN
DR. ROBERT B. MELLINS
DR. ISMAEL MENA
DR. MILTON MENDLOWITZ*
DR. WALTER L. MERSHEIMER
DR. EDWARD J. MESSINA
DR. WILLIAM METCALF
DR. KARL MEYER*
DR. LEO M. MEYER*
DR. MORTON A. MEYERS
DR. ALEXANDER J. MICHIE
DR. CATHERINE MICHIE
DR. GARDNER MIDDLEBROOK
DR. G. BURROUGHS MIDER*
DR. PETER O. MILCH
DR. A. T. MILHORAT*
DR. DAVID K. MILLER*
DR. FREDERICK MILLER
DR. JOHN A. P. MILLETT*
DR. C. RICHARD MINICK
DR. GEORGE S. MIRICK*
DR. ORMOND G. MITCHELL
DR. WALTER MODELL*
DR. CARL MONDER
DR. WILLIAM L. MONEY
DR. DAN H. MOORE*
DR. JOHN A. MOORE

*Life member.

Dr. Norman S. Moore*
Dr. Stanford Moore
Dr. Anatol G. Morrell
Dr. Augusto Moreno
Dr. Gilda Morillo-Cucci
Dr. Akiro Morishima
Dr. Thomas Quinlan Morris
Dr. Kevin P. Morrissey
Dr. Alan N. Morrison
Dr. John Morrisson
Dr. Jane H. Morse
Dr. Stephen I. Morse
Dr. Norman Moscowitz
Dr. Michael W. Mosesson
Dr. Melvin L. Moss
Dr. Harry Most*
Dr. Isabel M. Mountain*
Dr. Walter E. Mountcastle
Dr. Arden W. Moyer
Dr. Richard W. Moyer
Dr. R. S. Muckenfuss*
Dr. Stuart Mudd*
Dr. G. H. Mudge
Dr. Meredith Mudgett
Dr. John V. Mueller
Dr. M. G. Mulinos*
Dr. Otto H. Muller
Dr. Hans J. Müller-Eberhard
Dr. Ursula Müller-Eberhard
Dr. George E. Murphy
Dr. James S. Murphy
Dr. M. Lois Murphy
Dr. Henry W. Murray
Dr. Carl Muschenheim*
Dr. W. P. Laird Myers
Dr. Martin S. Nachbar
Dr. Ralph L. Nachman
Dr. David D. Nachmansohn*
Dr. Ronald L. Nagel
Dr. Gabriel G. Nahas
Dr. Tatsuji Namba
Dr. William Nastuk
Dr. Benjamin H. Natelson

Dr. Samuel Natelson
Dr. Gerald Nathenson
Dr. M. Nathenson
Dr. Stanley G. Nathenson
Dr. Clayton L. Natta
Dr. Brian A. Naughton
Dr. Enid A. Neidle
Dr. Norton Nelson
Dr. Harold C. Neu
Dr. Maria M. New
Dr. Walter Newman
Miss Eleanor B. Newton*
Dr. Shih-hsun Ngai
Dr. Warren W. Nichols
Dr. John F. Nicholson
Dr. John L. Nickerson*
Dr. Giorgio L. Nicolis
Dr. Julian Niemetz
Dr. Ross Nigrelli*
Dr. Jerome Nisselbaum
Dr. Charles Noback*
Dr. W. C. Noble*
Dr. M. R. Nocenti
Dr. Angelika Noegel
Dr. John H. Northrop
Dr. Robert A. Norum
Dr. Hymie L. Nossel
Dr. Richard Novick
Dr. Alex B. Novikoff
Dr. Ruth Nussenzweig
Dr. Victor Nussenzweig
Dr. Irwin Nydick
Dr. William B. Ober
Dr. Manuel Ochoa, Jr.
Dr. Severo Ochoa*
Dr. Herbert F. Oettgen
Dr. Michiko Okamoto
Dr. Arthur J. Okinaka
Dr. William M. O'Leary
Dr. Eng Bee Ong
Dr. Stanley Opler
Dr. Peter Orahovats
Dr. Irwin Oreskes

*Life member.

DR. MARIAN ORLOWSKI
DR. ERNEST V. ORSI
DR. LOUIS G. ORTEGA
DR. EDUARDO ORTI
DR. ELLIOTT F. OSSERMAN
DR. ELENA I. R. OTTOLENGHI
DR. ZOLTAN OVARY
DR. M. D. OVERHOLSER*
DR. NORBERT I. A. OVERWEG
DR. IRVINE H. PAGE*
DR. GEORGE PALADE
DR. PHOTINI S. PAPAGEORGIOU
DR. GEORGE D. PAPPAS
DR. A. M. PAPPENHEIMER, JR.
DR. JOHN R. PAPPENHEIMER*
DR. E. M. PAPPER
DR. JEAN PAPPS*
DR. FRANK S. PARKER
DR. RAYMOND C. PARKER*
DR. ROBERT J. PARSONS*
DR. PEDRO PASIK
DR. TAUBA PASIK
DR. MARK W. PASMANTIER
DR. GAVRIL W. PASTERNAK
DR. PIERLUIGI PATRIARCA
DR. PHILIP Y. PATTERSON
DR. MARY ANN PAYNE
DR. O. H. PEARSON
DR. EDMUND D. PELLEGRINO
DR. ABRAHAM PENNER
DR. JAMES M. PEREL
DR. GEORGE A. PERERA*
DR. ELI PERLMAN
DR. GERTRUDE PERLMANN*
DR. BENVENUTO G. PERNIS
DR. JAMES H. PERT
DR. DEMETRIUS PERTSEMLIDIS
DR. BARRY W. PETERSON
DR. MALCOLM L. PETERSON
DR. RUDOLPH PETERSON
DR. MITCHELL L. PETUSEVSKY
DR. FREDERICK S. PHILIPS
DR. ROBERT A. PHILIPS*

DR. LENNART PHILIPSON
DR. EMANUEL T. PHILLIPS
DR. MILDRED PHILLIPS
DR. JULIA M. PHILLIPS-QUAGLIATA
DR. JOHN G. PIERCE
DR. CYNTHIA H. PIERCE-CHASE
DR. LOU ANN PILKINGTON
DR. JOSEPH B. PINCUS
DR. MATTHEW PINCUS
DR. JOHANNA PINDYCK
DR. KERMIT L. PINES
DR. XAVIER PI-SUNYER
DR. MARGARET PITTMAN*
DR. CHARLES PLANK
DR. CALVIN F. PLIMPTON
DR. CHARLES M. PLOTZ
DR. FRED PLUM
DR. NORMAN H. PLUMMER*
DR. BEATRIZ G. T. POGO
DR. ALAN PAUL POLAND
DR. WILLIAM POLLACK
DR. MARGARET J. POLLEY
DR. MARCEL W. PONS
DR. EDWIN A. POPENOE
DR. J. W. POPPELL
DR. HANS POPPER
DR. KEITH R. PORTER
DR. JEROME G. PORUSH
DR. JEROME B. POSNER
DR. EDWARD L. PRATT
DR. RUDOLF PREISIG
DR. JOHN B. PRICE, JR.
DR. RICHARD W. PRICE
DR. MARSHALL P. PRIMACK
DR. JOHN W. PRINEAS
DR. R. B. PRINGLE
DR. PHILIP H. PROSE
DR. JOHN F. PRUDDEN
DR. LAWRENCE PRUTKIN
DR. CHARLES B. PRYLES
DR. MAYNARD E. PULLMAN
DR. DOMINICK P. PURPURA
DR. FRANCO QUAGLIATA

*Life member.

Dr. Paul G. Quie
Dr. James P. Quigley
Dr. Michel Rabinovitch
Dr. Julian Rachele
Dr. Efraim Racker
Dr. Bertha Radar
Dr. C. A. Ragan, Jr.
Dr. Kanti R. Rai
Dr. Ilene Raisfeld
Dr. Morris L. Rakieten*
Dr. Henry T. Randall
Dr. Helen M. Ranney
Dr. Felix T. Rapaport
Dr. Howard G. Rapaport
Dr. Richard II. Rapkin
Dr. Fred Rapp
Dr. Maurice M. Rapport
Dr. Sarah Ratner*
Dr. Aaron R. Rausen
Dr. Rulon W. Rawson
Dr. Bronson S. Ray*
Dr. Lawrence W. Raymond
Dr. Stanley E. Read
Dr. George G. Reader
Dr. Kutumba K. Reddi
Dr. Walter Redisch
Dr. Colvin Manuel Redman
Dr. S. Frank Redo
Dr. George Reed
Dr. George N. Reeke, Jr.
Dr. Gabrielle H. Reem
Dr. Carl Reich
Dr. Edward Reich
Dr. Lee Reichman
Dr. Marcus M. Reidenberg
Dr. Christine Reilly
Dr. Joseph F. Reilly
Dr. Leopold Reiner
Dr. Donald J. Reis
Dr. Charlotte Ressler
Dr. Paul Reznikoff*
Dr. Goetz W. Richter
Dr. Maurice N. Richter*

Dr. Ronald F. Rieder
Dr. Harold Rifkin
Dr. Richard A. Rifkind
Dr. Robert R. Riggio
Dr. Walter F. Riker, Jr.
Dr. Conrad M. Riley
Dr. Vernon Riley
Dr. David Allen Ringle
Dr. Harris Ripps
Dr. Richard S. Rivlin
Dr. Carleton W. Roberts
Dr. Jay Roberts
Dr. Kathleen E. Roberts
Dr. Richard B. Roberts
Dr. Alan G. Robinson
Dr. William G. Robinson
Dr. Dudley F. Rochester
Dr. Olga M. Rochovansky
Dr. Morris Rockstein
Dr. William M. Rogers*
Dr. Bernard Rogoff
Dr. Ida Pauline Rolf*
Dr. Paul Rosahn*
Dr. Marie C. Rosati
Dr. Harry M. Rose*
Dr. Herbert G. Rose
Dr. Gerald Rosen
Dr. John F. Rosen
Dr. Ora Rosen
Dr. Murray D. Rosenberg
Dr. Philip Rosenberg
Dr. Richard E. Rosenfeld
Dr. Isadore Rosenfeld
Dr. Herbert S. Rosenkranz
Dr. Arthur F. Rosenthal
Dr. William S. Rosenthal
Dr. William Rosner
Dr. Herbert Ross
Dr. Pedro Rosso
Dr. Eugene F. Roth
Dr. Alan B. Rothballer
Dr. Sidney Rothbard*
Dr. Edmund O. Rothschild

*Life member.

Dr. Ewald Selkurt*
Dr. Fabio Sereni
Dr. Aura E. Severinghaus*
Dr. David Schafritz
Dr. Robert E. Shank
Dr. James A. Shannon*
Dr. Harvey C. Shapiro
Dr. Herman S. Shapiro
Dr. L. L. Shapiro*
Dr. Lucille Shapiro
Dr. William R. Shapiro
Dr. Lewis Inman Sharp*
Dr. Aaron Shatkin
Dr. Elliott Shaw
Dr. David Shemin*
Dr. Paul Sherlock
Dr. Raymond Lionel Sherman
Dr. Sol Sherry
Dr. Maurice E. Shils
Dr. Bong-Sop Shim
Dr. W. C. Shoemaker
Dr. Charles D. Siegel
Dr. George Siegel
Dr. Morris Siegel*
Dr. Philip Siekevitz
Dr Raymond F. Siemankowski
Dr. Ernest B. Sigg
Dr. Selma Silagi
Dr. Robert Silber
Dr. Maxmillian Silbermann*
Dr. Lous E. Siltzbach
Dr. Lawrence Silver
Dr. Richard T. Silver
Dr. Morris Silverman
Dr. Philip Silverman
Dr. William A. Silverman
Dr. Emanuel Silverstein
Dr. Martin E. Silverstein
Dr. Samuel C. Silverstein
Dr. Saul Silverstein
Dr. Michael Simberkoff
Dr. Eric J. Simon
Dr. Norman Simon

Dr. Joe L. Simpson
Dr. Melvin V. Simpson
Dr. Inder J. Singh
Dr. Gregory Siskind
Dr. William R. Sistrom
Dr. Anneliese L. Sitarz
Dr. Mark T. Skarstedt
Dr. Vladimir P. Skipski
Dr. Lawrence E. Skogerson
Dr. Robert J. Slater
Dr. Daniel N. Slatkin
Dr. George K. Smelser*
Dr. Frank Rees Smith
Dr. James P. Smith
Dr. M. De Forest Smith*
Dr. Elizabeth M. Smithwick
Dr. Edna Sobel
Dr. Louis Soffer*
Dr. Richard Luber Soffer
Dr. John A. Sogn
Dr. Arthur Sohval
Dr. Leon Sokoloff
Dr. Samuel Solomon
Dr. Alex C. Solowey
Dr. Martin Sonenberg
Dr. Sun K. Song
Dr. Joseph A. Sonnabend
Dr. Carol F. Soroki
Dr. Hamilton Southworth*
Dr. Paul Spear
Dr. Abraham Spector
Dr. Francis Speer*
Dr. Robert Sisson Spiers
Dr. Frank C. Spencer
Dr. Gabriel Spergel
Dr. Morton Spivack
Dr. David Sprinson
Dr. Norton Spritz
Dr. Katherine Sprunt
Dr. P. R. Srinivasan
Dr. John M. Steele, Jr.
Dr. Neal H. Steigbigel
Dr. Richard M. Stein

*Life member.

Dr. Carmine T. Vicale
Dr. Herman Villarreal, Jr.
Dr. F. Stephen Vogel
Dr. Henry J. Vogel
Dr. Mögens Volkert
Dr. William C. Von Glahn
Dr. Salome G. Waelsch
Dr. Bernard M. Wagner
Dr. Bonnie A. Wallace
Dr. Lila A. Wallis
Dr. Roderich Walter
Dr. John L. Wang
Dr. S. C. Wang
Dr. Lewis W. Wannamaker
Dr. George E. Wantz
Dr. Bettina Warburg*
Dr. Robert C. Warner
Dr. Louis R. Wasserman*
Dr. Norbert H. Wasserman
Dr. Alice M. Waterhouse*
Dr. Robert F. Watson*
Dr. Samuel Waxman
Dr. Annemarie Weber
Dr. Bruce Webster*
Dr. Richard P. Weeden
Dr. Rene Wegria
Dr. Richard Weil, III
Dr. Virginia L. Weimar
Dr. Leo Weiner
Dr. Herbert Weinfeld
Dr. I. Bernard Weinstein
Dr. Leonard H. Weinstein
Dr. Stephen W. Weinstein
Dr. Irwin M. Weinstock
Dr. John M. Weir
Dr. Gerson Weiss
Dr. Harvey J. Weiss
Dr. Paul A. Weiss
Dr. Herbert Weissbach
Dr. Bernard Weissman
Dr. Gerald Weissmann
Dr. Francis M. Weld
Dr. Daniel Wellner

Dr. Gerhardt Werner
Dr. Sidney C. Werner*
Dr. Arthur R. Wertheim
Dr. W. Clarke Wescoe
Dr. C. D. West
Prof. Otto Westphal
Dr. Joseph P. Whalen
Dr. Abraham White
Dr. Abraham G. White
Dr. John C. Whitsell, II
Dr. Edkhart Wiedeman
Dr. Stanley Wiener
Dr. Norman Wikler
Dr. Herbert B. Wilcox, Jr.*
Dr. David L. Williams
Dr. M. Henry Williams
Dr. John Wilson
Dr. Victor J. Wilson
Dr. Sidney J. Winawer
Dr. Erich E. Windhager
Dr. Myron Winick
Dr. Asher Winkelstein
Dr. Robert M. Winters
Dr. Jonathan Wittenberg
Dr. Herbert Wohl
Dr. Abner Wolf*
Dr. George A. Wolf
Dr. Julius Wolf
Dr. Stewart G. Wolf, Jr.
Dr. James A. Wolff
Dr. Harvey Wolinsky
Dr. Sandra R. Wolman
Dr. Henry N. Wood
Dr. John A. Wood
Dr. John L. Wood*
Dr. James M. Woodruff
Dr. Kenneth R. Woods
Dr. Melvin H. Worth, Jr.
Dr. Walter D. Wosilait
Dr. Irving S. Wright*
Dr. Melvin D. Yahr
Dr. Martin L. Yarmush
Dr. Sehchi Yasumura

*Life member.

DR. CHESTER L. YNTEMA*
DR. BRUCE YOUNG
DR. STUART H. YOUNG
DR. FULI YU
DR. TASAI-FAN YU
DR. JOHN B. ZABRISKIE
DR. RALPH ZALUSKY
DR. ESMAIL D. ZANJANI
DR. ITALO ZANZI

DR. CHARLES G. ZAROULIS
DR. VRATISLAV ZBUZEK
DR. JAMES E. ZIEGLER, JR.*
DR. NORTON ZINDER
DR. BURTON L. ZOHMAN
DR. JOSEPH ZUBIN*
DR. MARJORIE B. ZUCKER
DR. DOROTHEA ZUCKER-FRANKLIN
DR. BENJAMIN W. ZWEIFACH

*Life member.

DECEASED MEMBERS, FORMERLY ACTIVE AND ASSOCIATE

T. J. ABBOTT
ISIDOR ABRAHAMSON
HAROLD ABRAMSON
MARK H. ADAMS
ISAAC ADLER
DAVID ADELERSBERG
ANDREW J. AKELAITUS
F. H. ALBEE
BENJAMIN ALEXANDER
HARRY L. ALEXANDER
SAMUEL ALEXANDER
F. M. ALLEN
AARON A. ALTER
ALF S. ALVING
H. L. AMOSS
DOROTHY H. ANDERSON
RUPERT S. ANDERSON
W. B. ANDERTON
WM. DEWITT ANDRUS
HERMAN ANFANGER
W. PARKER ANSLOW, JR.
WILLIAM ANTOPOL
VIRGINIA APGAR
R. T. ATKINS
JOSEPH C. AUB
HUGH AUCHINCLOSS
JOHN AUER
J. HAROLD AUSTIN
O. T. AVERY
HALSEY BAGG
C. V. BAILEY
HAROLD C. BAILEY
PEARCE BAILEY
ELEANOR DeF. BALDWIN
CLARENCE G. BANDLER
BOLTON BANGS
W. HALSEY BARKER
HERBERT J. BARTELSTONE
F. H. BARTLETT
LOUIS BAUMAN

W. W. BEATTIE
CARL BECK
WILLIAM H. BECKMAN
EDWIN BEER
JEANETTE A. BEHRE
SAM M. BEISER
RHODA W. BENHAM
A. A. BERG
MAX BERGMANN
CHARLES M. BERRY
SOLOMON A. BERSON
CHARLES H. BEST
HERMANN M. BIGGS
ROBERT M. BIRD
FRANCIS G. BLAKE
N. R. BLATHERWICK
HUBERT BLOCH
SIDNEY BLUMENTHAL
ERNEST P. BOAS
AARON BODANSKY
VICTOR BOKISCH
CHARLES F. BOLDUAN
RICHARD WALKER BOLLING
A. BOOKMAN
RALPH H. BOOTS
J. B. BORDEN
DAVID BOVAIRD
MAX BOVARNICK
SAMUEL BRADBURY
ERWIN BRAND
A. BRASLAU
S. M. BRICKNER
NATHAN E. BRILL
J. J. BRONFENBRENNER
DETLEV BRONK
HARLOW BROOKS
F. TILDEN BROWN
SAMUEL A. BROWN
WADE H. BROWN
MAURICE BRUGER

247

JOSEPH BRUMLIK
JOSEPH D. BRYANT
SUE BUCKINGHAM
JACOB BUCKSTEIN
LEO BUERGER
HENRY G. BUGBEE
FREDERICK C. BULLOCK
JESSE H. M. BULLOWA
JOSEPH L. BUNIM
CLAUDE A. BURRETT
GLENWORTH R. BUTLER
GEORGE F. CAHILL
W. E. CALDWELL
XENOPHON C. CALLAS
WM. F. CAMPBELL
ALEXIS CARREL
HERBERT S. CARTER
JOHN R. CARTY
L. CASAMAJOR
RUSSELL L. CECIL
WILLIAM H. CHAMBERS
HARRY A. CHARIPPER
JOHN W. CHURCHMAN
W. LeGROS CLARK
HANS T. CLARKE
F. MORRIS CLASS
A. F. COCA
MARTIN COHEN
ALFRED E. COHN
L. G. COLE
RUFUS COLE
CHARLES F. COLLINS
HARVEY S. COLLINS
ROBERT A. COOKE
ALBERT H. COONS
OTIS M. COPE
A. CURTIS CORCORAN
JAMES A. CORSCADEN
POL N. CORYLLOS
FRANK CO-TUI
GEORGE COTZIAS
WALTER P. COVELL
E. V. COWDRY
EDWIN B. CRAGIN
LYMAN C. CRAIG

FLOYD M. CRANDALL
G. W. CRARY
GLENN E. CULLEN
JOHN G. CURTIS
EDWARD CUSSLER
H. D. DAKIN
C. DARLINGTON
WILLIAM DARRACH
LEO W. DAVIDOFF
MARTIN H. DAWSON
RICHARD C. DE BODO
H. J. DEVEL, JR.
SMITH O. DEXTER, JR.
HENRY D. DIAMOND
JOSEPH S. DIAMOND
L. S. DIETRICH
PAUL A. DINEEN
KONRAD DOBRINER
E. A. DOISY
BLAKE F. DONALDSON
EDWIN J. DOTY
HENRY DOUBILET
W. K. DRAPER
ALEXANDER DUANE
E. F. DuBOIS
THEODORE DUNHAM
C. B. DUNLAP
L. C. DUNN
JOHN H. DUNNINGTON
F. DURAN-REYNALS
WALTER H. EDDY
WILHELM E. EHRICH
MAX EINHORN
ROBERT ELMAN
C. A. ELSBERG
W. J. ELSER
A. ELYWYN
HAVEN EMERSON
EARL T. ENGLE
ALBERT A. EPSTEIN
LOWELL ASHTON ERF
SAMUEL M. EVANS
JAMES EWING
GIOACCHINO FAILLA
K. G. FALK

L. W. FAMULENER
MORRIS S. FINE
MAURICE FISHBERG
SIMON FLEXNER
AUSTIN FLINT
ROLFE FLOYD
JOSEPH E. FLYNN
JORDI FOLCH-PI
ELLEN B. FOOT
N. CHANDLER FOOT
JOSEPH FRAENKEL
EDWARD FRANCIS
THOMAS FRANCIS, JR.
ROBERT T. FRANK
VIRGINIA K. FRANTZ
ROWLAND G. FREEMAN
WEBB FREUNDENTHAL
WOLFF FREUNDENTHAL
E. D. FRIEDMAN
LEWIS F. FRISSELL
CLAUDE FROMAGEOT
H. DAWSON FURNISS
JACOB FURTH
NICOLAS F. GANG
C. Z. GARSIDE
HERBERT S. GASSER
F. L. GATES
F. P. GAY
SAMUEL H. GEIST
BERTRAM M. GESNER
H. R. GEYELIN
WILLIAM J. GIES
HERMAN GLADSTONE
J. H. GLOBUS
HARRY GOLD
HENRY P. GOLDBERG
HARRY GOLDBLATT
ROSS GOLDEN
S. GOLDSCHMIDT
S. S. GOLDWATER
KENNETH GOODNER
FREDERICK GOODRIDGE
MALCOLM GOODRIDGE
N. W. GREEN
HARRY S. N. GREENE

ISIDOR GREENWALD
MAGNUS I. GREGERSEN
LOUISE GREGORY
MENAS S. GREGORY
LOUIS GROSS
MILTON M. GROSS
EMIL GRUENING
FREDERICK GUDERNATSCH
H. V. GUILE
ALEXANDER B. GUTMAN
JOHN H. HALL
JOHN W. HALL
ROBERT H. HALSEY
MARY G. HAMILTON
FRANKLIN M. HANGER
LAWRENCE W. HANLON
MEYER M. HARRIS
R. STUART HART
FRANK HARTLEY
ROBERT A. HATCHER
HANS O. HATERIUS
H. A. HAUBOLD
LOUIS HAUSMAN
JAMES A. HAWKINS
SELIG HECHT
R. M. HEGGIE
HENRY O. HEINEMANN
GEORGE HELLER
MILTON HELPERN
CARL M. HERGET
W. W. HERRICK
GEORGE J. HEUER
HOWARD H. HINES
CHARLES L. HOAGLAND
AUGUST HOCH
EUGENE HODENPYL
GEORGE M. HOGEBOOM
ARTHUR L. HOLLAND
FRANKLIN HOLLANDER
A. W. HOLLIS
EMMETT HOLT, JR.
J. G. HOPKINS
HENRY HORN
HERBERT I. HOROWITZ
FRANK HORSFALL, JR.

HUBERT S. HOWE
PAUL S. HOWE
STEPHEN HUDACK
JOHN H. HUDDLESTON
DAVID M. HUME
F. B. HUMPHREYS
H. M. IMBODEN
MOSES L. ISAACS
A. C. IVY
BENJAMIN JABLONS
LEOPOLD JACHES
HOLMES C. JACKSON
ABRAHAM JACOBI
WALTER A. JACOBS
GEORGE W. JACOBY
A. G. JACQUES
JOSEPH JAILER
WALTER B. JAMES
EDWARD G. JANEWAY
H. H. JANEWAY
FRODE JENSEN
JAMES W. JOBLING
SCOTT JOHNSON
WILLIAM C. JOHNSON
NORMAN JOLLIFFE
DON R. JOSEPH
LOUIS JULIANELLE
FREDERICK KAMMERER
DAVID KARNOPSKY
HAIG H. KASABACH
LUDWIG KAST
JACOB KAUFMANN
M. RALPH KAUFMANN
F. L. KEAYS
EDWARD C. KENDALL
FOSTER KENNEDY
I. NEWTON KERGELMASS
LEO KESSEL
BEN WITT KEY
E. L. KEYES
DANIEL V. KIMBERG
GEORGE KING
FRANCIS P. KINNICUTT
D. B. KIRBY
JOHN E. KIRK

STUART F. KITCHEN
HERBERT M. KLEIN
I. S. KLEINER
PAUL KLEMPERER
WALTER C. KLOTZ
ARNOLD KNAPP
HERMANN KNAPP
YALE KNEELAND, JR.
SEYMOUR KORKES
ARTHUR F. KRAETZER
BENJAMIN KRAMER
MILTON LURIE KRAMER
CHARLES KRUMWIEDE
L. O. KUNKEL
ANN G. KUTTNER
RAPHAEL KURZROK
WILLIAM S. LADD
ALBERT R. LAMB
ADRIAN V. S. LAMBERT
ALEXANDER LAMBERT
ROBERT A. LAMBERT
S. W. LAMBERT
ERNEST W. LAMPE
CARNEY LANDIS
GUSTAV LANGMANN
H. CLAIRE LAWLER
BURTON J. LEE
EGBERT LeFEVRA
E. S. L'ESPERANCE
P. A. LEVENE
MICHAEL LEVINE
SAM Z. LEVINE
ROBERT L. LEVY
CHARLES H. LEWIS
JACQUES M. LEWIS
EMANUEL LIBMAN
CHARLES C. LIEB
FRANK L. LIGENZOWSKI
ASA L. LINCOLN
KARL PAUL LINK
WRAY LLOYD
JOHN S. LOCKWOOD
JACQUES LOEB
LEO LOEB
ROBERT O. LOEBEL

LEO LOEWE
ALFONSO A. LOMBARDI
C. N. LONG
PERRIN LONG
WARFIELD T. LONGCOPE
RAY R. LOSEY
ROSE LUBSCHEZ
SIGMUND LUSTGARTEN
F. LYNEN
JOHN D. LYTTLE
W. G. MACCALLUM
DUNCAN A. MACINNES
GEORGE M. MACKENZIE
THOMAS T. MACKIE
COLIN M. MACLEOD
WARD J. MACNEAL
F. B. MALLORY
A. R. MANDEL
JOHN A. MANDEL
F. S. MANDELBAUM
MORRIS MANGES
GEORGE MANNHEIMER
CYRIL C. MARCUS
STEWART L. MARCUS
DAVID MARINE
W. B. MARPLE
KIRBY MARTIN
WALTON MARTIN
HOWARD MASON
JAMES A. L. MATHERS
HUNTER MCALPIN
CHARLES MCBURNEY
GERTRUDE S. MCCANN
W. S. MCCANN
W. ROSS MCCARTY
WALTER S. MCCLELLAN
J. F. MCGRATH
EARL B. MCKINLEY
FRANKLIN C. MCLEAN
PHILIP D. MCMASTER
GEORGE MCNAUGHTON
EDWARD S. MCSWEENY
FRANK S. MEARA
W. J. MEEK
VICTOR MELTZER

WALTER MENAKER
ADOLF MEYER
ALFRED MEYER
K. F. MEYER
MICHAEL MICAILOVSKY
HENRY MILCH
EDGAR G. MILLER
GEORGE N. MILLER
SAMUEL CHARLES MILLER
ALFRED E. MIRSKY
H. C. MOLOY
CARL MOORE
ROBERT A. MOORE
ROBERT MORISON
C. V. MORRILL
A. V. MOSCHCOWITZ
ELI MOSCHCOWITZ
ELI MOSCHCOWITZ
ABRAHAM MOSS
JOHN H. MULHOLLAND
JOHN P. MUNN
EQUINN W. MUNNELL
EDWARD MUNTWYLER
J. R. MURLIN
JAMES B. MURPHY
CLAY RAY MURRAY
V. C. MYERS
JAMES F. NAGLE
JAMES NEILL
CARL NEUBERG
SELIAN NEUHOF
ISAAC NEUWIRTH
WALTER L. NILES
CHARLES V. NOBACK
JOSE F. NONIDEZ
VAN HORNE NORRIE
CHARLES NORRIS
NATHANIEL READ NORTON
FRANCIS W. O'CONNOR
CHARLES T. OLCOTT
PETER K. OLITSKY
EUGENE L. OPIE
B. S. OPPENHEIMER
HANS OPPENHEIMER
KERMIT E. OSSERMAN

Sadao Otani
John Overman
Ralph S. Overman
George H. Paff
Beryl H. Paige
Arthur Palmer
Walter W. Palmer
George W. Papanicolaou
A. M. Pappenheimer
William H. Park
Gary Aiken Parks
Stewart Paton
John M. Pearce
Louise Pearce
Charles H. Peck
James Pedersen
E. J. Pellini
Wilder Penfield
David Perla
E. Cooper Person
Mary Locke Petermann
J. P. Peters
Frederick Peterson
Robert A. Phillips
Godfrey R. Pisek
Robert F. Pitts
Harry Plotz
Milton Plotz
G. R. Pogue
Albert Policard
William M. Polk
Abou D. Pollack
F. L. Pollack
Sigmund Pollitzer
Nathaniel B. Potter
Thomas D. Price
T. M. Prudden
Edward Quintard
Francis M. Rackemann
Geoffrey W. Rake
C. C. Ransom
Bret Ratner
George B. Ray
R. G. Reese
Jules Redish

Birdsey Renshaw
C. P. Rhoads
A. N. Richards
D. W. Richards
Henry B. Richardson
Oscar Riddle
Austen Fox Riggs
John L. Riker
Seymour Rinzler
David Rittenberg
Thomas M. Rivers
William J. Robbins
Kathleen Roberts
Andrew R. Robinson
Frank H. Robinson
William M. Rogers
W. Stanton Root
Theodore Rosebury
Martin Rosenthal
Nathan Rosenthal
M. A. Rothschild
F. J. W. Roughton
Peyton Rous
Wilfred F. Ruggiero
F. J. Ryan
George H. Ryder
Florence R. Sabin
Bernard Sachs
F. B. St. John
Wm. P. St. Lawrence
Stanley W. Sajdera
William A. Salant
T. W. Salmon
Benjamin Salzer
E. F. Sampson
Harold E. Santee
Wilbur A. Sawyer
Reginald H. Sayre
Herbert W. Schmitz
Rudolph Schoenheimer
Louis C. Schroeder
Herman Von W. Schulte
E. L. Scott
John Scudder
David Seegal

H. Shapiro
Harry H. Shapiro
George Y. Shinowara
Ephraim Shorr
Harold Shorr
William K. Simpson
M. J. Sittenfield
J. E. Smadel
A. Alexander Smith
Carl H. Smith
Homer W. Smith
R. Garfield Snyder
Harry Sobotka
F. P. Solley
Earl W. Sutherland, Jr.
H. J. Spencer
J. Bentley Squier, Jr.
W. C. Stadie
Norbert Stadtmüller
Henricus J. Stander
Daniel Stats
J. Murray Steele
Richard Stein
Antonio Stella
J. W. Stephenson
Kurt G. Stern
Chandler Stetson
George D. Stewart
H. A. Stewart
Harold J. Stewart
E. G. Stillman
Ralph G. Stillman
L. A. Stimson
C. R. Stockard
Herbert C. Stoerk
George H. Stueck, Jr.
Arthur M. Sutherland
John E. Sutton
Paul C. Swenson
Homer F. Swift
W. W. Swingle
Sam Switzer
Jerome T. Syverton
L. James Talbot
E. L. Tatum

Sterling P. Taylor, Jr.
Oscar Teague
J. de Castro Teixeira
Edward E. Terrell
John S. Thacher
Allen M. Thomas
Giles W. Thomas
W. Hanna Thompson
Karl J. Thompson
William S. Tillett
Edgar W. Todd
Wisner R. Townsend
Theodore T. Tsaltas
James D. Trask, Jr.
H. F. Traut
Norman Treves
Raymond C. Truex, Sr.
Folke Tudvad
Joseph C. Turner
Kenneth B. Turner
Robert A. Turner
Cornelius J. Tyson
Edward Uhlenhuth
F. T. Van Beuren, Jr.
Philip Van Ingen
R. Van Santvoord
Donald D. Van Slyke
H. N. Vermilye
Wolf Vishniac
Karl Vogel
Alfred Vogl
Augustus Wadsworth
Heinrich B. Waelsch
I. H. Wagman
H. F. Walker
George B. Wallace
Wilbur Ward
James S. Waterman
Janet Watson
Hans Weber
Jerome T. Webster
Leslie T. Webster
R. W. Webster
Webb W. Weeks
Richard Weil

Louis Weisfuse
Julia T. Weld
Sara Welt
John R. West
Randolph West
George W. Wheeler
John M. Wheeler
J. S. Wheelwright
Daniel Widelock
Carl J. Wiggers
Herbert B. Wilcox
H. B. Williams
Armine T. Wilson
Margaret B. Wilson
Philip D. Wilson
Joseph E. Winters

Dan H. Witt
Harold G. Wolff
R. B. Woodward
I. Ogden Woodruff
D. Wayne Woolley
Herman Wortis
S. Bernard Wortis
Arthur M. Wright
Jonathan Wright
Walter H. Wright
John H. Wyckoff
L. Zechmeister
Frederick D. Zeman
H. F. L. Ziegel
Hans Zinsser